Yesterday's Shopping

Yesterday's Shopping

Gamages General Catalogue 1914

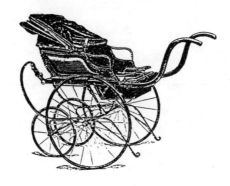

Wordsworth Editions

This edition published 1994 by Wordsworth Editions Ltd,
Cumberland House, Crib Street, Ware, Hertfordshire, SG12 9ET.

Copyright © Wordsworth Editions Ltd 1994.

Reprinted 1994
Reprinted 1995

ISBN 1-85326-832-1

Printed and bound in Great Britain by
Mackays of Chatham PLC, Chatham, Kent

Contents

Publisher's Foreword

GAMAGES General Catalogue for 1914 marked the end of a period of astonishing material progress, stability and confidence in the future. However, there had been a terrible portent when the 'unsinkable' *Titanic*, flagship of the White Star Line, had sunk on the night of 14th/15th April 1912 after striking an iceberg on the North Atlantic, thus deeply shaking the certainties of the Edwardian era. As the Gamages Catalogue was being sent out to the store's customers around the world, it was to be only a few months before the Serbian nationalist assassin's shots were to end the lives of Archduke Ferdinand of Austria and his wife in Sarajevo on 28th June 1914, and before German light cavalry was to cross the Belgian frontier at Gemmenich on the morning of Tuesday 4th August 1914 and the most terrible of all wars - the First World War - was to begin. In the next four years and three months an estimated 10 million people were to die and double that number were to sustain injuries. Nothing would ever be the same again.

However, it is in the world before the First World War that the Gamages General Catalogue for 1914 is based. From their stores, Messrs. Gamages of Holborn and Benetfinks of Cheapside in London, the General Catalogue and elaborate Departmental catalogues were dispatched post free to any part of the world. Among the categories specially catered for were Furniture and Household Requisites, Sports and Games, Magic, Cycling, Motoring, Horticulture, Medicines, Fishing, Foreign and Colonial Outfits, Babies, Luggage, Hampers, Scientific Instruments, Bee-keeping, Guns and Rifles, and Photography. The stores themselves were open from 8.30am to 7.00pm Monday to Friday and from 8.30am to 1.30pm on Saturday and customers ordering from the catalogues could do so by mail, cable, telegraph or telephone, the latter being recommended for speed and despatch. Standards of customer care were rigorous, with guarantees being given on price levels, refunds for defective goods, and how complaints might be made direct to the Managing Director. Bargain catalogues were also issued twice a year.

The Gamages General Catalogue was a cornucopia of essential and not so essential items required for everyday life, from Acetylene Lamps to Zither Banjos by way of Arbocu ('The New Indoor Game'), Blanc Mange Powder, Cabin Trunks, Euphoniums, Moirette Underskirts, Ruc Sacks, and Wedding Rings. The modern day reader will be enthralled by the tantalising glimpse of a bygone age revealed in the pages of this delightful catalogue.

GAMAGES

THE LARGE YEARLY INCREASE in the sales since the commencement of business, justifies the policy adopted at that time. We will, therefore, continue to market only goods of high quality at universally low prices for cash, and to treat our customers with fairness and liberality.

CASH SELLING—LOW PRICES.

Our methods of doing business are economical, as we employ no travellers, carry no time accounts and have no collectors to pay. All these methods are costly and must be added to the selling price of goods, and the buyer pays it. We have no such expense and in consequence sell goods at prices below competition. We give our customers the benefit of our saving, and solicit business on a cash basis only.

DEFECTIVE GOODS.

If you submit to us any goods, the manufacture of which we control, claiming that they are faulty in material or construction or not quite as they should be, you are assured that you will receive fair and liberal treatment at our hands. We try to avoid making mistakes, but never to avoid righting them.

BARGAIN SALES.

Twice a year we issue Special Sale Catalogues to our customers giving Special Prices on Clearing Lines, Job Goods and Bankrupt Stocks, secured much below the market value. The full benefit of such purchases are given to our patrons. If you would like to be put on this list please acknowledge receipt of this catalogue, and write "I WANT YOUR BARGAIN SALE CATALOGUE."

COMPLAINTS (IF ANY).

The Management respectfully request that in any case of discourtesy or seeming want of attention by any member of the Staff, immediate notice be given in an envelope, marked PRIVATE, to the Managing Director, who will personally investigate same.

ORDERS BY TELEPHONE.

Immediate attention is given to orders received by telephone and we advise our customers to avail themselves of this speedy method of shopping.
GOODS ORDERED BY PHONE ARE AT ONCE DESPATCHED.

PHONE 2700 HOLBORN.

A. W. GAMAGE, Ltd., HOLBORN, LONDON, E.C.   BENETFINK & Co., Ltd., CHEAPSIDE, LONDON, E.C.

MAIL ORDER DEPARTMENT. POINTS TO REMEMBER WHEN ORDERING BY POST.

A WELL ORGANIZED DEPARTMENT.

We have a well-organized department for Mail Orders, and give them special care. We make immediate despatch of all goods in our Catalogue and will gladly secure for our customers any article not listed herein, which will be charged at the lowest market rate, but is Not Returnable.

TERMS CASH.

To avoid the multiplication of accounts and loss from bad debts, the Proprietors find it absolutely necessary to make it a rule that all orders be accompanied with cash sufficient to cover the price of goods desired, and, if they are to be sent by post, an extra amount added for postage (but if over 10'-, for the United Kingdom, post free), EXCEPT WHERE OTHERWISE STATED. Any surplus will be returned or placed to your credit on the books of the establishment. Strict compliance with the above rules is absolutely necessary, as profits would be wiped out by book-keeping and the collecting of accounts.

HOW TO ORDER.

In ordering please give full description of goods wanted; leave nothing to be guessed. Don't order: "Just like the last," but send full particulars with every order.

Address your letters carefully.

Write your name in full, and be careful to give name of street, city or town.

The rank or conditions of the writer should be added to the signature of the writer.

TELEGRAPHIC ORDERS.

TELEGRAMS.—The only address needed for telegrams (inland and foreign) sent to the Company is "GAMAGE, HOLBORN, LONDON." For the Cheapside Branch, "BENETFINK, LONDON."

Orders by telegram can only be executed for customers having a Deposit Account (to which reference should be made), or where the money is remitted by telegram.

When money is remitted by Telegraphic Money Order customers must inform the Company of the fact by telegram, as no intimation is given to the payee by the Post Office authorities. Money should be telegraphed to P.O., Hatton Garden.

HOW TO REMIT.

Avoid enclosing coin in letters as it is liable to drop out, and double registration fees are enforced. English Postage stamps for small amounts will be accepted. THE SAFEST PLAN IS BY POST OFFICE OR POSTAL ORDER. Fill in the name "A. W. GAMAGE, Limited, payable at Hatton Garden," and cross same, "Lloyd's Bank." Take the number of the Orders for in case of loss the money can be claimed from the postal authorities, if not previously paid.

Responsibility for money sent through the Post and lost in transit cannot be acknowledged. If the loss is occasioned by our employee we will be responsible.

Customers abroad can remit by Bankers' Draft, Post Office Orders, or through a Commission House in England. Foreign Stamps cannot be accepted in payment.

DEPOSIT ACCOUNTS.

To save the trouble and expense of sending money through the Post, Deposit Accounts may be opened with the Company for sums of not less than £2. The Deposit Account will be debited with the amount of each order and balanced half-yearly, but on application to the Secretary it will be balanced at any time, and the amount due, if any, returned within a week. Deposit Accounts cannot be overdrawn. Orders to be paid for out of Deposit Account should be so marked.

At the close of each half-year interest will be credited at the rate of 5 per cent. per annum on the minimum balance for each month during which it has not fallen below £1. No interest will be allowed for fractions of a pound, or for a less period than a complete month.

GOODS BY LETTER POST.

We cannot be responsible for goods sent by Letter Post. We strongly advise our patrons to order by Parcel Post:—the lowest rate is 3d., but in case of loss the value can be recovered, and we will be responsible; and any article that may not be approved of will be readily exchanged or cash returned (less amount of carriage), except goods made to order.

ORDER FORMS.

Purchasers are requested to use the printed Order Forms, and to obviate crowding and inconvenience to make out their Orders, when practicable, at home. Order Forms will be supplied on application.

LETTERS OF ENQUIRY.

Letters enquiring for orders delayed, or goods not received, *should always mention the date of order, the description of goods, and the Department concerned,* and also state whether the order was given personally or by post, and whether on Deposit Order Account or not. Letters referring to goods already received should be accompanied by the invoice. **When replying to letters received from the Firm the reference number on the Company's letter or invoice should be quoted.**

Customers are specially requested, when telegraphing respecting orders, to quote name of Department concerned, and the nature of goods referred to, as, owing to the omission of these, it is often impossible to trace the transaction. It is of the greatest importance that in sending telegrams or giving telephone messages, customers should quote the reference number of the order referred to.

HOW TO BE FORWARDED.

Please state how goods are to be despatched, whether by Passenger or Lug. Rail, Parcel Post or by Letter Post. (If by Mail include Postage.)

If sent by Rail, minimum Carriage on Fireworks is 5/-; Rubber Solution, 8d.; Calcium Carbide, 1/-.

Calcium Carbide can only be sent by rail, and not by steamer.

GOODS RETURNED.

If through any fault of ours a mistake has been made in goods sent you, please notify us first, and we will give instructions to have them returned at our expense. If the fault is yours return to us with invoice and full particulars ENCLOSED IN THE PARCEL, all charges prepaid, and we will exchange or credit you with amount. Goods which we do not Catalogue, but procure to your special order from others, are not returnable.

GOODS FOR REPAIR.

Goods left with the Company for Repair, Alteration or otherwise.

Every care is taken of such articles, but the Company will not hold itself responsible for any damage done to very fragile goods, provided due care has been taken in the repair; or for any damage or loss to articles left for repair, alteration or otherwise, if not taken away within three months.

ALL PREVIOUS LISTS CANCELLED. PRICES SUBJECT TO FLUCTUATIONS OF THE MARKET.

Chief Depot:	City Depot:
A. W. GAMAGE, Ltd., HOLBORN, LONDON, E.C.	BENETFINK & Co., Ltd., CHEAPSIDE, LONDON, E.C.

GAMAGES

INSTRUCTIONS
AND TERMS FOR
THE DELIVERY OF GOODS & PARCELS
ALSO PARTICULARS OF OUR
FREE DELIVERY SYSTEM.

¶ THE CONSISTENT LOWNESS of price and the general excellence of the goods supplied, has made GAMAGES what it is to-day.

This, combined with the fact that our Delivery Charges are the lowest possible, to say nothing of our Free Delivery in London, places our Establishment as a buying centre second to none in the world.

LONDON AND DISTRICT.	Within the Radius of our Express Motor Van Service, orders of any amount and description of goods Delivered Free, except goods sent direct from Growers or Manufacturers.
COUNTRY ORDERS.	Orders of 10/- and over (unless otherwise stated), sent Carriage Paid to any Goods Station in England and Wales. Goods value £2 and over, are sent Carriage Paid to any Goods Station in Scotland, Ireland, or Channel Islands, unless otherwise stated. Should customers elect to have goods sent by Fast or Passenger Trains, the difference in Carriage will be chargeable.
PARCEL POST.	Postage paid on goods of the value of 10/- and over to any part of England, Scotland, Wales, Ireland and the Channel Islands, not exceeding 11 lbs. in weight. Liquids, Ammunition, Calcium Carbide, Rubber Solution, Fireworks or any Explosives, cannot be sent by post.
PACKING ARRANGEMENTS.	We strongly recommend that when toys or goods of a fragile and breakable nature, are ordered to be sent by rail or boat, they should be packed in strong returnable crates or cases, full amount (paid) allowed when returned. When returning, reverse label and advise by post. Please add 6d., 1/- or larger amount according to the size of the article ordered.
EXPORT ORDERS.	We give special attention to this Branch of our business, all orders received being executed with the utmost despatch. We carry large stocks of goods suitable for the export trade, and every care is taken in the fulfilment of customers' commands. Orders should be accompanied with a remittance sufficient to cover the cost of the goods together with the expenses of special cases, shipping charges, insurance, etc. Orders of £2 and over delivered free to any of the London, Southampton, Hull, Liverpool or Glasgow Docks.
EXPORT PARCEL POST.	Customers are specially requested to enquire at their Post Office for rates, as the Inland English Postal Rates do not apply to the Colonies or British Dominions beyond the seas, or to foreign countries. To assist customers as to weight of articles listed, the English Inland Postage Rate is :— 3d. the first 1b., 2 lbs. 4d., 3 lbs. 5d., 5 lbs. 6d., 7 lbs. 7d., 8 lbs. 8d., 9 lbs. 9d., 10 lbs. 10d., 11 lbs. 11d. Customers will please bear in mind that they must add the cost of a lb. or lbs. to their remittance, but when small articles are ordered, several will go to the lb. weight.

REMITTANCES may be made by Banker's Draft, Post Office Orders, or through a Commission House in England. Foreign stamps cannot be accepted in payment.

THE ABOVE CANCELS ALL PREVIOUS INFORMATION.

RATES OF POSTAGE.

These Rates are subject to alterations.

COLONY OR COUNTRY.	3 lbs.	7 lbs.	11 lbs.
Abyssinia	4/6	4/6	4/6
Aden, including Perim	1/-	2/-	3/-
Algeria	1/4	1/8	2/-
Argentine Republic	2/-	3/-	4/-
Ascension	1/-	2/-	3/-
Austria-Hungary	1/4	1/8	2/-
Australia (Commonwealth, *i.e.*, States of New South Wales, Queensland, South Australia, Tasmania, Victoria, and Western Australia), Papua (British New Guinea) and Norfolk Island, not over 1 lb.	1/-	—	—
For each additional lb., up to 11 lbs.	6d.		
Azores	1/4	1/8	2/-
Bahamas	1/-	2/-	3/-
Barbadoes	1/-	2/-	3/-
Bechuanaland Protectorate	1/-		
Belgian Congo	1/7	2/3	2/7
Belgium	1/-	1/4	1/9
Benadir	2/9	3/1	3/5
Bermuda	1/-	2/-	3/-
Bolivia	3/6 per parcel of 7 lbs.		
Borneo and Sarawak	1/-	2/-	3/-
Brazil, limit of weight 6½ lbs.	3/6	4/-	—
British East Africa and Uganda	1/-	2/-	3/-
British Guiana	1/-	2/-	3/-
British Honduras	1/-	2/-	3/-
British Somaliland	1/-	2/-	3/-
Bulgaria	2/4	2/8	3/-
Cameroons	2/2	2/6	2/10
Canada	1/-	2/-	3/-
Cape Verde	2/2	2/6	2/10
Caroline Islands	2/2	3/3	3/7
Ceylon	1/-	2/-	3/-
Chili	2/-	3/-	4/-
China—British Agencies	1/-	2/-	3/-
Chinese Agencies	2/-	3/-	4/-
German Agencies	2/2	3/3	3/7
Russian Agencies, 5/- any weight up to 11 lbs.			
Japan Agencies	2/-	3/-	4/-
Colombia Republic	2/-	3/-	4/-
Corsica	1/4	1/8	2/-
Costa Rica	2/-	3/-	4/-
Crete	1/11	2/3	2/7
Cuba	2/2	2/11	3/3
Cyprus	1/-	2/-	3/-
Danish West Indies	2/-	3/-	4/-
Dahomey	2/2	2/6	2/10
Denmark, including Greenland	1/-	1/4	1/7
Dominican Republic	3/-	4/-	5/-
Dutch East Indies	2/6	3/3	4/-
Dutch Guiana	2/-	3/-	4/-
Dutch West Indies	2/6	3/2	3/10
Ecuador	2/-	3/-	4/-
Egypt, including Soudan	1/-	1/9	2/6
Via Italy	2/-	2/6	3/-
Falkland Islands	1/-	2/-	3/-
Fiji Islands	1/8	3/4	5/-
France and Corsica	1/-	1/4	1/7
Gambia	1/-	2/-	3/-
Germany	1/-	1/4	1/7
Gibraltar	1/-	2/-	3/-
Gold Coast	1/-	2/-	3/-
Greece	2/4	2/8	3/-
Holland	10d.	1/2	1/6
Hong Kong	1/-	2/-	3/-
India, including the Andaman Islands and Burma; also the following places on the Persian Gulf and in Turkish Arabia:— Bagdad, Bahrain, Bandar Abas, Bushia, Busrah, Guadur, Jask, Linga, Mohammerah and Muscat	1/-	2/-	3/-
Via France	1/8	2/8	3/8
Italy	1/6	1/10	2/2
Jamaica, including Cayman Island	1/-	2/-	3/-
Japan, including Formosa and Corea	2/-	3/-	4/-
Leeward Islands, including Antigua, Nevis, St. Kitts, Tortola, Montserrat	1/-	2/-	3/-

COLONY OR COUNTRY.	3 lbs.	7 lbs.	11 lbs.
Montenegro	2/2	2/6	2/10
Madagacar	2/2	2/11	3/3
Madeira	1/4	1/8	2/-
Malay States, including Negri Sembilan, Pehang, Perak, Selangor and Johore	1/-	2/-	3/-
Malta	1/-	2/-	3/-
Mauritius	1/-	2/-	3/-
Mexico	1/-	2/6	3/6
Morocco, including Casablanca, Mazagan, Mogador, Larache, Rabat, Saffi, Tangier, and Tetuan	1/-	2/-	3/-
Newfoundland and Labrador	1/-	2/-	3/-
New Zealand, including Fanning Island, Cook Islands, Danger, Pukapuka Manahiki, Palmerston, Rakaanga, Avarua, Penrhyn, Tongareva, Savage (Niue) and Suwarrow Islands, for parcels not exceeding 4 feet in length and girth combined	1/-	2/-	3/-
For parcels over 4 feet and not exceeding 6 feet in length and girth combined	2/-	3/-	4/-
Nigeria, including Southern and Northern Lagos	1/-	2/-	3/-
Norway	1/-	1/4	1/7
Nyasaland	3/-	4/-	5/-
Persia, North	3/9	4/1	4/5
Persia, South	2/-	3/-	4/-
Peru	2/-	3/-	4/-
Portugal	1/4	1/8	2/-
Rhodesia, via Cape Town, 1/9 per lb. up to 11 lbs.			
Rhodesia, via Beira	3/6	5/-	7/6
Rhodesia, via France and Aden	4/6	6/-	8/6
Roumania	1/11	2/3	2/7
Russia, including Finland	1/11	2/3	2/7
Russia in Asia	2/11	3/3	3/7
Siam	2/-	3/3	4/6
Sierra Leone	1/-	2/-	3/-
South African Union— Cape Colony, Natal, Orange Free State, Transvaal and Swaziland, 9d. per lb. to 11 lbs.			
Servia	1/9	2/1	2/5
Spain	1/6	1/10	2/2
Straits Settlements— Labuan, Malacca, Penang, Prince, Wellesley and Singapore	1/-	2/-	3/-
Via France	1/8	2/8	3/8
Sweden	1/2	1/10	2/6
Switzerland	1/4	1/8	2/-
Turkey—British Agency or Austrian Agency should form part of the address. Ottoman Post Offices in Europe—Poste Ottoman should form part of the address.			
Beyrout	1/-	2/-	3/-
Constantinople and Smyrna	1/-	1/4	1/8
Austrian Agency	1/11	2/3	2/7
Ottoman Agency	2/4	2/8	3/-
Offices in Europe and Asia	2/6	2/10	3/2
United States of America Official Service, including Philippine Islands, Porto Rica, Alaska, Panama	1/3	2/3	3/3
Semi-official Service, all places except New York City	3/6	4/6	5/6
Brooklyn, Jersey City or Hoboken	2/6	3/6	4/6
Parcels addressed to New York State are subject to higher rate.			
Uruguay— Canelones, Durazzo, Florida, Fray Bentos, Mercedes, Minas, Monte Video, Paysandu, Salto, San José	2/-	3/-	4/-
Venezuela	2/6	3/3	4/-
West Indies (British), Trinidad), St. Vincent, St. Lucia	1/-	2/-	3/-
Zanzibar	1/-	2/-	3/-
Via France	1/8	2/8	3/8

Please note Ammunition or Explosives cannot be forwarded by post.

THE WAY TO REACH GAMAGE'S BY TRAIN OR BUS.

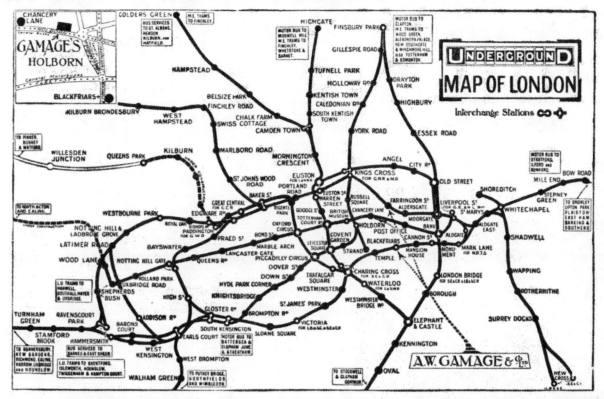

DISTRICT.	Enter Service as below.	Change Omnibuses at	Enter Service as below, and alight at GAMAGE'S.	DISTRICT.	Enter Service as below.	Change Omnibuses at	Enter Service as below, and alight at GAMAGE'S
Acton	17 or 23	Direct to	—	Holloway	5 or 14	King's Cross	18 or 45
Bank	7, 8, 17, 22, 23, 23A, 25, 26	Do.	—	Hornsey Rise	14	Do.	11 or 45
				Ilford	25	Direct to	—
Barnes	9 or 33,	Piccadilly Circus	22	Islington	19	Gray's Inn Road	18
Ditto	74	Holland Park Avenue	17, 23, 23A, 50	Kensington	9 or 33	Piccadilly Circus	22
Barnsbury	5 or 14	King's Cross	18 or 45	Kensington (South)	5 or 14	Oxford Street	7, 8, 17, 22, 23, 23A, 25
Battersea	19	Oxford Street	7, 8, 17, 22, etc.	Kensal Green	18	Direct to	—
Ditto	57	Blackfriars	45	Kentish Town	41	Do.	—
Bayswater	17, 23, 23A, 50	Direct to	—	Kew	27	Notting Hill Gate	17, 23, 23A, 50
Brixton	45	Do.	—	Kilburn	8	Direct to	—
Brompton	5 or 14	Oxford Street	7, 8, 17. 22, etc.	King's Cross	18 or 45	Do.	—
Brondesbury	8	Direct to	—	Leyton	35	Liverpool Street	7, 22, 26
Ditto	1, 16, 58	Marble Arch	17, 23, 24A, 50	Leytonstone	10, 10A, 51	Stratford	25
Camberwell	45	Direct to	—	Liverpool Street Station	7, 22, 26	Direct to	—
Camden Town	3, 24, 29	Oxford Street	7, 8, 17, 22, 25, 50	London Bridge Station	17 or 18	Do.	—
Canonbury	19	Gray's Inn Road	18 or 45	Maida Vale	8	Do.	—
Charing Cross Station	1, 24, 29	Oxford Street	7, 8, 17, 22, etc.	Marylebone Station	18	Do.	—
Chelsea	22	Direct to	—	Mortlake	9	Piccadilly Circus	22
Child's Hill	2 or 13	Oxford Street	7, 8, 17, 23, 23A, 50	Muswell Hill	43	Bank	7, 8, 17, 22, etc.
Chiswick	20	Oxford Circus	7, 8, 17, 23, 23A, 25, 26	Norwood, West.	2	Brixton	45
Clapham Common	45	Direct to	—	Notting Hill Gate	17, 23, 23A, 50	Direct to	—
Clapham Junction	19	Oxford Street	7, 8, 17, 22, etc.	Paddington Station	7	Do.	—
Ditto	19	King's Road (Chelsea)	22	Peckham Rye	12	Camberwell	45
Cricklewood	16, 46, 58	Marble Arch	7, 8, 17, 23, 23A, 50	Ditto	43A	Bank	7, 8, 17, 22, 23, 23A, 25, 26, 50
Dalston	22	Direct to	—				
Dulwich (West)	20	Piccadilly Circus	22	Piccadilly Circus	22	Direct to	—
Ditto	68 or 68A	Camberwell Green	45	Putney	22	Do.	—
Ealing	17	Direct to	—	Richmond	37 or 37A	Putney	22
Earl's Court	30 or 54	Hyde Park Corner	25	Seven Kings	25	Direct to	—
East Ham	23 or 23A	Direct to	—	Shepherd's Bush	17, 23, 50	Do.	—
East Sheen	33	Piccadilly Circus	22	St. John's Wood	2 or 13	Oxford Street	7, 8, 17, 23, 23A, 50
Ditto	37 or 37A	Putney	22	St. Pancras Station	18	Direct to	—
Elephant	45	Direct to	—	Stoke Newington	65	King's Cross	18
Ditto	34	Bank	7, 8, 17, 23, 23A, 25, 26, 50	Stratford	25	Direct to	—
				Stroud Green	5	King's Cross	18
Euston Station	18	Direct to	—	Tulse Hill	20	Brixton	45
Forest Gate	25	Do.	—	Ditto	(better) 68	Camberwell Green	45
Fulham	22	Do.	—	Turnham Green	20	Oxford Circus	7, 8, 17, 23, 23A, 26
Golders Green	13	Oxford Circus	7, 8, 17, 23, 23A, etc.	Victoria Station	25	Direct to	—
Hackney	6, 22, 26	Direct to	—	Ditto	76 (quicker)	Blackfriars	45
Hammersmith	9 or 33	Piccadilly Circus	22	Walham Green	5 or 14	Oxford Street	7, 8, 17, 22, 23, 23A, 26, 50
Hampstead (South)	2 or 13	Oxford Street	7, 8, 17, 23				
Harringay	29	Holloway	See Holloway	Walthamstow	35	Liverpool Street	6, 8, 22, 26
Ditto	21 or 21A	Bank	7, 8, 17, 23, 23A, 25, 26, 50	Waterloo Station	68 or 68A	Oxford Street	7, 8, 17, 22, etc.
				Ditto	98	Blackfriars	45
Hendon	13	Oxford Circus	7, 8, 17, 23 23A, 50,	Willesden	8 or 18	Direct to	—
Herne Hill	68	Brixton	45	Wood Green	29, 29A, 29B	Oxford Street	7, 8, 17, 22, etc.
Highbury	19	Gray's Inn Road	18 or 45	Wormwood Scrubs	7	Direct to	—
Highgate	43 or 43A	Bank	7, 8, 17, 22, 23, 23A, 50				

These Services are liable to alteration from time to time.

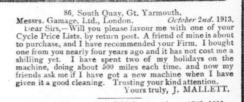

THE GAMAGE CYCLES for 1914.

Everything which goes to make up a high-grade machine is in the "Gamage," only the price is different.

"GAMAGE" Gent's Roadster Model.

FRAMES AND TUBING.

The frames of all "Gamage" Cycles are made up from the finest cold-drawn Weldless English Steel Tubing.

This is a point of much importance, and should be borne in mind when cycle buying.

Price, as Specification - **£5 10 0**   Coaster Hub Model - **£5 10 0**   Three-Speed Model - **£6 10 0**

The "Gamage" is the choice of those riders who prefer a little extra finish and refinement above the previous model. "Dunlop" or any other well-known tyres will be fitted, also an eccentric steering head lock. The frame is tastefully lined gold leaf, and the centres of the plated rims are enamelled and lined to match. If wished, we will fit any kind of Coaster Hub instead of Back Brake, without extra charge to the purchaser. A very complete outfit is also given with the machine. The "Gamage" Model embodies not only perfection of constructional details and finish, but many little refinements to be found only on the most expensive machines; a combination of handsome appearance, ease of running and durability.

The Lady's Model, illustrated below, has a reputation second to none for lightness, elegance of design, and general handsome appearance, but its most appreciated feature is its ease of running—sweetly and silently, a point always remarked upon when an inexperienced cyclist rides a "Gamage" for the first time.

THE "GAMAGE" Lady's Model has been aptly described by a leading lady writer as the "Ideal Bicycle for ladies who require elegance and reliability in their cycles."

"GAMAGE" Lady's Roadster Model.

THE "GAMAGE" Lady's Model is at once elegant and easy running, and is built on most graceful lines.

Price, as Specification, **£5 10 0**   Coaster Hub Model **£5 10 0**   Three-Speed Model, **£6 10 0**

Full Specification of the above Two Models.

FRAME.—Finest English Steel, weldless. Gent's 22, 24 and 26 in.; Lady's 20, 22 and 24 in.; each allowing ample adjustment. The above sizes are standard, others to order. No extra charge.

FRAME.—Best Cold-drawn weldless steel tube.

FORKS.—Symmetrically and scientifically built to absorb all vibration, double butted stem and slotted ends for ease of wheel removal.

FORK CROWN.—Our special sloped-shoulder pattern, bevel-edged. Far neater and twice as strong as the usual sharp-edged square box crown. Heavily plated on copper.

HANDLE-BARS.—Three styles: Upturned, Flat or North Road (dropped) as desired. Nickel-plated.

HANDLES.—Figured Black Celluloid.

STEERING-LOCK.—Neat, eccentric lever.

RIMS.—Plated, with enamelled centres and edges.

SPOKES.—High tension rustless; tangent.

HUBS.—Cut from solid bar steel, heavily plated ball bearing, dust-proof and oil-retaining.

CHAIN.—Genuine "Perry" or "Coventry" hardened steel rollers, ½ in. pitch, ⅛ in. wide.

CHAIN WHEEL.—Williams', Stamped from finest cold steel. All heavily plated.

BEARINGS.—Cups from Teutonic unbreakable finest steel, ground, hardened and polished as smooth as a billiard ball. Steel balls by the Hoffmann Steel Ball Manufacturing Co. (Chelmsford, England); guaranteed true to within one ten thousandth part of an inch—the secret of the sweet, silent easy running.

FREE WHEEL.—Genuine "Perry" frictionless ball-bearing.

CRANKS.—Gent's 7 in. Lady's 6½ in.; tapered down to pedal and bevelled at edges. Plated on copper.

PEDALS.—Genuine Brampton, ball-bearing, oil-retaining and dust-proof. Screw in. Rubber or rat-trap, as preferred.

GEAR.—Gent's 74, Lady's 62; Standard or to order.

GEAR CASE.—Dover transparent chain cover on lady's only.

BRAKES.—Crabbe Back and Front Rim Brakes on new roller lever principle. Coaster hub fitted instead of back brake if desired.

SADDLE.—Genuine Brooks Roadster saddle adjustable, with comfortable coil springs.

TYRES.—Dunlop, or any other well known make.

MUDGUARDS.—Handsome enamelled steel, detachable back and front.

FINISH.—Three coats of best jet black enamel on first coat of **anti-rust** stove-hardened and polished. Tastefully **lined best gold leaf**, and burnished. All usual parts nickel-plated on copper.

FREE OUTFIT.—Celluloid pump, spring pump-clips, tool bag, tools, oilcan and polishing cloth.

Carriage paid.

A SPECIAL FEATURE FOR 1914.

GAMAGE'S *"Featherweight"* CYCLES

WE have been so impressed by the inconsistency of expecting all Cyclists to propel the same weight of machine, irrespective of their own weight or strength, that we have designed a new "FEATHERWEIGHT" Model, in which by means of new and important variations in the detail of Cycle construction, we are enabled to produce a machine of very light weight, yet equally as strong as the ordinary heavy models of other makers. This Bicycle is very largely hand-made by our most skilful mechanics, and so costs more to produce than our "Popular," which is made in large quantities mostly by automatic machinery, and so the "Featherweight" is bound to cost more, but we know that those riders who can afford the extra cost and who appreciate the ease of propulsion of a very light rigid Cycle, will willingly pay the additional price. From our past experience in selling Cycles to every class of Cyclists, we feel sure this model will especially appeal to Ladies, many of whom are physically incapable of propelling the ordinary heavy Cycle, and so the introduction of this model will bring back to our ranks many Lady Cyclists who have had to forego the pleasures of Cycling on account of the weight of the ordinary Cycle sold to-day.

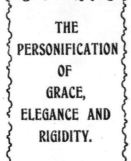

THE PERSONIFICATION OF GRACE, ELEGANCE AND RIGIDITY.

THE BICYCLE FOR THE DISCRIMINATING CYCLIST OF FASTIDIOUS TASTES.

THE GENT'S  *"Featherweight"* **PRICE - £9 9 0**
Carriage Paid.

THE IDEAL BICYCLE FOR MORNING SHOPPING OR VISITING. LIGHT AND GRACEFUL.

In this Machine, QUALITY IS PRE-EMINENT COMBINED WITH A DUE REGARD FOR MODERATION IN PRICE.

THE LADY'S *"Featherweight"* **PRICE - £9 17 6**
Carriage Paid.

SPECIFICATION SPECIAL GAMAGE, "FEATHERWEIGHT" LADY'S AND GENT'S.

FRAMES—Gent's, 22, 24, 26 in. Lady's, 20, 22, 24 in. Best cold drawn Weldless steel tubes, Duplex chain stays. Very light and strong, and designed to prevent the whipping of the frame so usual with light machines.
FORKS.—Stem double butted. FORK CROWN.—Special slope shoulder pattern.
HANDLE BARS.—Raised or any other position required.
WHEELS.—26 by 1⅜ in. RIMS.—Roman Rust'ess.
SPOKES.—Double butted and Rustless.
HUBS.—Turned from solid bar steel, Dustproof and Oil Retaining.
CHAIN.—Hans Renold. CHAIN WHEEL.—Stamped from finest cold steel (Williams)
AXLES.—Turned from solid bar steel, case hardened.
BEARINGS.—Made from finest steel, Hoffmann's balls.
FREE WHEEL.—Hyde. CRANKS.—Gent's 7 in. tapered and bevelled. Lady's 6½ in.

PEDALS.—Aluminium Leaf. GEAR.—Gent's 74 in., Lady's 62 in., or to order.
BRAKES.—Back and front rim brakes, roller levers, concealed bar.
SADDLES.—Brooks' B 75 plated springs.
TYRES.—Dunlop's, Canvas side, non-slipping tread.
MUDGUARD.—Roman detachable extended front.
FINISH.—Three coats of best black enamel on first coat of anti-rust, lined gold leaf and translucent colour.
GEAR CASE.—Combination metal and celluloid on lady's only.
BOTTOM BRACKET.—Patent Cotterless and disc adjusting.
Complete with Pump, Tool Bag, Tools, Oil Can and Selvyt Cleaning Cloth.
WEIGHT.—Men's, 26½ lbs. Ladies', 27½ lbs.

PRICE, as Specification - - £9 17 6 Carriage Paid.

If any variation is required in the Specification, we cannot keep to the weight stated. Three-speed Gear, 20/- extra.
NOTE—The Duplex Chain Stays——Handle Bars with Concealed Brakes——Fixed Pump Clips——Aluminium Pedals.

Variable Gears, etc.

Sturmey Archer 3-speed Hub.

LATEST PATTERN.

With top bar control	**20/-**
Fitted to your Cycle	**25/-**
Plated Wheel, ready for fitting	**25/-**

Armstrong Triplex, same prices.

Sturmey Archer Tricoaster.

With top bar control	**26/6**
Fitted to your Cycle	**31/6**
Plated Wheel, ready for fitting	**31/6**

Handle-bar Control fitted to any of the above gears .. **1/-** extra.

The B.S.A. 3-speed Hub.

With top bar control	**20/-**
Fitted to your Cycle	**25/-**
Plated Wheel, ready for fitting	**25/-**

The Eadie Coaster Hub.

LATEST PATTERN HUB.

Hub with cog	**12/-**
Fitted to Cycle	**16/6**
Plated Wheel, ready for fitting	**16/6**

Particulars Required for 3-Speed Gear.

Make of Cycle ....
Lady's or Gent's ....
Height of Frame ....
Diameter of Handlebar (for Lady's)...........
Ditto Top Tube.....................
Ditto Seat Tube.................
Number of Teeth on Cog ....
Width and Pitch of Teeth...............
Width Between Stays.................
Ditto Outside...................
Chain Line ....
Size of Wheel required ....
If required for Wired or Beaded Tyre ....

The Eadie 2-speed Hub.

With top bar control	**15/-**
Fitted to your Cycle	**19/6**
Plated Wheel, ready for fitting	**19/6**

The "New Departure" Hub.

		List price
Hub with cog	**12/6**	15/-
Fitted to Cycle	**17/-**	18/6
Built up into wheel, with plated rim	**17/-**	18/6

All above Post Free.

Eadie 2-speed Coaster Hub.

With top bar control	**24/-**
Fitted to your Cycle	**28/6**
Plated Wheel, ready for fitting	**28/6**

Villier's 2-speed Gear.

	Gamage's Price.	List Price
With top bar control	**16/6**	17/6
Fitted to your Cycle	**19/6**	21/-
Plated Wheel, ready for fitting	**19/6**	21/-

Jelly's Oil Bath Free Wheel.

Sizes 18 by ½ by ⅛ or ₁/₁₆
20 by ½ by ⅛ only

Price **1/4**   Postage 4d.

FREE WHEELS.

The Gamage Ball Bearing Free Wheel.

Guaranteed. This clutch is made from steel stampings throughout. The back of clutch and driven part, or centre, is all in one stamping. The ratchet teeth are wider and deeper than usual in free wheel clutches, thus giving a more positive drive and longer life to the ratchet and pawl.

Price .. **1/11**   Postage 3d.
Special size bore made to order. **3/6**

The B.S.A Free Wheel.

Price .. **2/3**   Postage 3d.

Hyde Free Wheel. **2/9**

Bluemel's Free Wheel Covers.

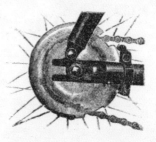

Keeps out mud and dust from the mechanism of free wheel. Transparent celluloid.

Price .. .. **2/-** each.

"Ever-ready" Electric Bicycle Lamps (Best London Manufacture)

Fitted with the WONDERFUL NEW BEREC SUPERIOR ("B.S.")

EXTRA LONG-LIFE DRY BATTERIES AND NEWEST TYPE OF METALLIC FILAMENT BULB.

No. 1550.

PRICE - **6/6** COMPLETE.

If fitted with Bull's-eye Lens, 7/6

Refills, B.S. Type, **1/-**   Ordinary Type, **9**d.

Spare Bulbs, **1/6** each.

Weight, 11 ozs.   Heigh', 3½ in.

No. Cy. 1550.

No. Cy. 1500.

A VERY HANDY LAMP.

Fitted with a Berec Superior dry battery and metallic filament bulb.

Giving 18 hours' light.

Weight, 17 ozs.   Height, 4 inches.

PRICE - **8/6** COMPLETE.

Refills, B.S. Type, **1/-** Ordinary Type, **9**d.

Spare Bulbs, **1/6** each.

SPECIAL TYPE, fitted with handle for carrying in addition to cycle bracket.

This Lamp is fitted with a prismatic reflector,

GREATLY INCREASING Reflected LIGHT

PRICE - **10/6** COMPLETE.

Weight, 17 ozs. Height 4 inches.

Refills, B.S. Type, **1/-**

Ordinary ,, **9**d.

Spare Bulbs, **1/6** each.

No. Cy. 1500. Special.

Any of the above Lamps supplied in Black Nickel Plate, highly polished, easily cleaned, 1/- extra.

"Ever-ready" Dry Battery Lamp.

The Batteries are contained in solid leather case fitted with straps to fasten to any convenient part of the frame. A thin flexible cord connects battery case with reflector, which is fastened to lamp bracket, same as any ordinary lamp.   No. 28A.

The whole is an article of the very

Highest Grade of superior Construction and Finish.

PRICE - **19/-** COMPLETE.

Refills, B.S. Type .. .. **2/-** each.

Spare Bulbs .. .. .. **1/6** ,,

The "Ever-ready" Accumulator Sets.

No. Cy. 1070.
Self-contained, with unspillable Accumulator.

Note.—Can be easily recharged at any Garage or Electricians.

Reflector fitted with 2-volt Metallic Filament Bulb.

Black solid leather case with best nickel-plated fitings,

COMPLETE, as illustration

21/-

Refill Accumulators, **12/6**
Spare Bulbs .. **1/6**

No. Cy. 1071a.

Consisting of Well-made

Brass or Nickel-plated Lamp.

Fitted with 4-volt Osram Bulb, S.B.C. holder with flexible cord, unspillable 4-volt Accumulator in solid leather case (as illustrated).

Complete with switch.

PRICE **37/-** SET.

No. Cy. 1071. Lamp only *without Bulb* **9/6**

"VOLTALITE"
Self-Generating
MOTOR CYCLE LAMP

"SUBURBIA" ELECTRIC CYCLE LAMP.

Highly finished, all Metal, Electric Cycle Lamp, with splendid efficient reflector and lens, takes standard pocket lamp refil.

Complete with "Volex" Refil and "Osram" Bulb

5/- each.

"VOLEX" GIANT MOTOR CYCLE LAMP
(Dry Battery).

Comprises brass headlight with 4-volt metal filament bulb, twin conducting cord and satchel with straps for fixing, and 4-volt Giant "Volex" Battery giving 60 to 80 hours light in ordinary use. Immensely superior to accumulators. When refil is exhausted, a new one can easily be inserted in satchel. More hours of burning can be obtained by using two batteries alternately.

Complete 22 6

THE FAMOUS (All British)
"VOLTALITE"
Self-Generating Electric Cycle Lamp.

This Model gives twice the brilliancy of light of the previous model, weighs less and is simple to fix. A highly finished article with aluminium sides, made on the principle of a dynamo and is remarkably efficient. When not required it can be easily switched out of use. When in use it gives a brilliant, steady white light at from walking speed to 30 miles per hour. The special metal filament bulb being unaffected by speed and vibration. It is driven by means of a small rubber-tyred wheel, which works on rim of cycle and adapts itself automatically to any unevenness of the rim.

"VOLEX" Fortavox Dry Battery.

11/8

Length of Fortavox Electric Horn, 7¾ in.
Diameter of Horn body ... ... 2¾ in.
Weight ... ... 15 oz.
Dimensions of 6 volt Fortavox Battery, 4¼ by 3 by 1½ inches.
Weight ... ... 1 lb. 4 oz.

Gives a loud, clear commanding sound, most effective for motor and push cycles. The new 1914 Model has the Push Button fitted in to Cycle or Motor Cycle handle bar in a few minutes. In ordinary use the battery supplied will actuate the horn well for about 12 months.

Complete outfit, including Fortavox Electric Horn with Push Button attachment, Twin Conducting Cord, and 6-volt Fortavox "Volex" Battery ready for fixing **11/8**

Introduced after making a long series of tests. Ball bearings and very strong construction to withstand the strain and vibration of a motor cycle. The advantages of this lamp can be calculated by looking at the advantages of the "Voltalite." The lantern has a self-focussing attachment for bulb. It can be adjusted to throw the rays in any desired direction. Brass finish. Complete with two spare bulbs and cord, 52/- Nickel-plated 2/6 extra. Spare rubber pulley rings 4d. each. Spare Metal Filament Bulbs 1/- each.

The "LUXRAY"
Electric Rear Lamp.
(Provisional Patent)
Gives an actual red warning illumination which can be seen at a considerable distance. Fits on cycle back fork in a few moments in similar manner to other rear lights.

Complete with instructions, 3 9

Spare Refils can be kept 12 months without exhaustion, 9d. ea.

Every lamp sent out complete with instructions, ready for fixing, 18 6
The "VOLTALITE" MODEL DE LUXE comprises the same Generator as our usual "Voltalite" but the lantern is of exceptionally handsome appearance, and is fitted with self-focussing bulb holder attachment. The lantern is highly nickel-plated with a parabolic spun copper reflector silver-plated. No. V 3. ... ... 25/-
The "Voltalite" Cycle Lamp and Electric Rear Light Combined gives a brilliant light in front and a red light behind. Can be attached to any cycle in a few moments with the utmost ease. The rear light is a beautifully-finished lantern of special design and is fitted with ruby glass, metal filament bulb and reflector. It is arranged that the light is the same time. The rear light is fitted to the back fork of cycle by means of a screw and a clip and connected up to the "Voltalite" by means of the wire which is provided. The bulb in "Voltalite" Lantern is changed for the one provided with the rear light. No. V 5, Electric Rear Lamp and attachment, with bulb for "Voltalite," and connecting cord... 5/-
No. V 6, The "Voltalite" Cycle Lamp, complete with head and rear lamps, ready for attachment to cycle 24/-

The "TOURIST" CYCLE LAMP SET.

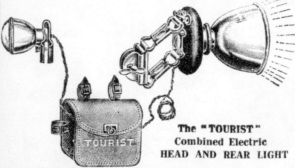

The "TOURIST"
Combined Electric
HEAD AND REAR LIGHT

This excellent combination ensures a bright light at the head lamp, and an actual red light in the rear lamp. The rear lamp having a red glass front with an "Osram" Electric Bulb behind. The Refil Battery is of our "Volex" Tourist Long Life type. Complete outfit—

12/6

Spare Tourist Combination Refil, 3/-   Spare Bulbs, 9d. each.

The "KNIGHTRIDER" or "HOLBORN" Lamp for Cyclists

Most of the dry battery cycle lamps previously sold have such a limited capacity that they are only of use for short rides of 10 to 20 minutes at a time. With the "Knightrider," much longer nightly rides may be taken without the fear of the battery exhausting itself, and if necessary, occasional or 2 hours' lighting may be obtained of an evening, and the battery soon recovers itself. In short with the "Knightrider" using the lamp for say 20 to 30 minutes of a night, about 40 hours' light may be obtained, and using the lamp for 1 hour every night about 25 hours' light can be obtained.

Complete as illustrated, with Special Osram metal filament bulb 7 6
Spare Metal Filament Bulbs, 9d. each.
Spare "Knightrider" Battery Refil, 2 6

We strongly recommend that a spare battery be used by cyclists who are riding regularly at night, so that every week the battery be changed and allowed a week's rest, this increases the useful hours of light from each battery enormously. Specially Recommended for the Colonies.

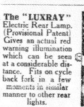

DYNALITE

MODEL 1914-1915

THE DYNALITE

Is a Magneto Lighting Dynamo manufactured in 3 Types for Cyclists, Motor Cyclists and Car Owners, who see a Practical, Foolproof and always Ready Light. Many Toys on the market, adapted from ordinary dynamos are notoriously cumbersome and unreliable, and have small practical value as an illuminant. All parts exposed to weather on the 9 4-1915 Models are Mud, Dust, Rust and Rainproof. The **DYNALITE** gives a distinctive appearance to your Cycle, being **NEAT** and compact, 4½ in. high, 1¾ in. diam. **WEIGHT 14 oz.** (lighter than the average gas or oil lamp). The drive is applied to the wall of tyre, contact being made by a neat plated spring. This form of drive gives the minimum frictional drag, and leaves **ABSOLUTELY NO WEAR ON TYRES.** Speed will not injure either the bulb or Dynalite. Tests in this direction up to 30 miles per hour are conclusive proof, while walking is sufficient to produce a riding light. The milled screw at side forms a simple method for adjusting the contact on tyre and putting dynamo out of use when not required. If you value your riding comfort, remember the **DYNALITE** is the only **BALL BEARING** Cycle Lighting Dynamo on the Market.

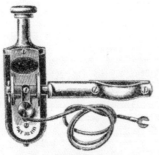

Fig. D 1.
BALL BEARING DYNALITE.
Output 4 to 8 volts, 5 amps.
No Commutator to get out of order.

Front View.
Neat and Compact.
Filled in 2 min.
to any make.

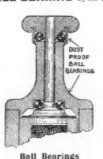

Ball Bearings
All 1814-15 Models are fitted
with TWO 6-Race Ball
Bearings. A Masterpiece.

Fig. D 2.

DYNALITE HEADLAMPS.

NO ACID.   NO CHARGING.   NO BATTERY.   NO BLOWING OUT.   NO CARBIDE.

D 1.	THE DYNALITE on Ball Bearings	... ...	Each **17/6**	Post 4d.
D 2.	" " and Focusing Headlamp	... ...	" **23/6**	" 6d.
D 3.	Ruby Rearlamp, with Bulb and Bracket, ready for use	...	" **4/6**	" 2d.
D 4.	DYNALITE HEADLAMP only, ready for the road...	...	" **6/6**	" 3d.
D 5.	Spare Dynalite Bulbs	... ...	" **9d.**	" 1d.

N.B.—All 1914-15 Models are capable of Head and Rear Lighting.

NOTE—ADJUSTABLE ROAD FOCUS.

NOTE SPECIAL DRIVE.
Clean and compact Behind
Ignition Magneto.
Fitted in 2 minutes.

BALL BEARING M.C. DYNALITE.
6 to 8 volts, ¾ amp.

Showing Attachment and Drive to "Royal Enfield."

DYNALITE A.C.U. HEADLAMP
Adjustable Focus, Hinged Front.
Easy to Clean.

Motor Cyclists as a body anticipate Magneto Electric Lighting as the solution of the Carbide nuisance. The method must be foolproof and as **RELIABLE** as the ordinary ignition Magneto. It must be easily fitted without hours spent in bending and altering the present equipment. Its light must give equal illuminating results to that of Acetylene, quickly switched on, electrically sound, substantial **BALL BEARINGS**, and of solid mechanical construction to stand against heavy vibration, yet in appearance neat and compact. All these points are embodied in the **MOTOR CYCLE DYNALITE**, and customers will find it a Lighting equipment one can forget yet **ALWAYS READY** and free from the minor worries of Carbide, Accumulators, Water or Oil. **WEIGHT 2½ lbs.** approx. **SIZE** 6½ in. long by 1¾ in. Each supplied with 5 ft. Waterproof Cable, which allows of Front or Rear Attachment. Ideal for Side Car use, for this Dynamo will easily light front and rear lamps on series. The filaments in Bulbs supplied are of drawn Tungsten Wire and will stand against the Roughest Roads. Eminently suitable for Colonial use.

D 9.	MOTOR CYCLE DYNALITE on Ball Bearings	... ...	Each **40/-**	Post 6d.
D 10.	" " and A.C.U. Focusable Headlamp	...	" **60/-**	" 9d.
D 11.	A.C.U. HEADLAMP only	... ...	" **20/-**	" 8d.
D 12.	SPARE BULBS ... **1/4** each, Post 1d.	D 13. Douglas Special Fitting, extra		" **7/6**

CHILD CARRIERS.

The New Babscar.

The fittings are suitable or carrying child on the rear or the front of Cycle. The former method because the child is protected from wind and dust. We recommend the former method because the child is protected from wind and dust. Price **10/6**

The Babscar. No. 3.

Strong and Light.
Fits on the head and down tube of frame.
Price **7 6**

The Babscar or Front Carrier.

One of the leading features of this improved form of Child Carrier is that it can be instantly fixed and detached from the Machine when once the fork clips are in position, and further, by simply removing the Wicker Chair and transferring strap thereon, an exceedingly useful carrier remains and which is capable of carrying 1 cwt. Thus this very useful line will serve a double purpose.
Price **7/6**

The Child Carrier.

Very strong.   Will fit any Machine.
Made of Enamelled Metal with Canvas Seat
and Straps.
Price **5/6 each.**

The Dawson Tandemette

A NEW AND UP-TO-DATE METHOD OF CARRYING CHILDREN, whereby they can pedal, and assist in driving the machine. Can be readily attached or detached, converting Ladies' or Gent's Bicycle into a Tandem, as shown in above illustration. IT IS

SIMPLE SAFE AND EFFICIENT.

SUITABLE FOR BOYS OR GIRLS from 7 to 15 years of age.

Price .. **£1 15 0** complete.

The 'Pet' Child Carrier.

5/6

The "Pet" Clip can be attached to the crossbar of bicycle and any ordinary saddle readily affixed. The child is in the arms, thus complete safety being assured.
The "Pet" Clip, plated, **2 6**
Complete with Juvenile saddle,
Price **5 6** Post free.

A most useful novelty.
"Tom Thumb."
(Patent)
Child's Cycle Saddle.
With adjustable Buckled Stirrup.
Our price **1/6** Postage 3d.

"Progress" Child Carrier.

Open and Closes like a Pair of Scissors.
Most Comfortable and Safe.

The "Progress" Ready for Use.

The "PROGRESS" Folding Child Carrier.
Black Enamelled with Strong Canvas Seat and Straps. Price .. **7/6** each.

ADVANTAGES OF THE "PROGRESS"
PACKS UP SMALL.
WILL FIT ANY MACHINE.

Hooks are adjustable to fit any Handle Bar.

Seat Adjustable in Height, for small, medium and tall children. Absolute Safety of Child, the child cannot come in contact with any part of the Bicycle. Clips holding carrier to fork stays are made secure by screws. Neat appearance.

TRICYCLES AND TRAILERS

THE "GAMAGE" TRICYCLE.

The "Gamage" Tricycle is really wonderful value and, at the price offered, is at once the cheapest and best three-wheeler on the market. It is fitted with patent axle with free-wheel.

The Racing Tricycle, which is based on this model, has been remarkably successful during the past seasons, all the principal Tricycle Road Records having been broken.

£12 12 0

Note—We can supply above Gent's as Racing Tricycle with close-built back and road racing tyres at same price.

Specification.

FRAMES—22 in. and 24 in.
AXLE—Free-wheel, patent.
WHEELS—26 in.
CHAIN—½ in. pitch roller.
HANDLE-BAR—As illustrated.
SADDLE—Lycett L19 plated, 3-coil

BRAKES—Front Rim Brake and Internal Expansion Hub Brake.
CHAIN COVER — To Lady's only. Metal, with plated disc.
TYRES—Scott, 26 in. by 1⅜ in.
FINISH—Black, lined red and green bright parts plated.

MODEL.	As specified above.	With Patent Bracket Two-speed Gear.
"Standard" Gent's	£12 12 0	£13 12 0
Lady's	13 13 0	14 13 0

THE "GAMAGE SPECIAL" TRICYCLE.

The "Gamage Special" Tricycles are equipped with first-grade tyres, saddles, etc. The differential axle is of special manufacture, and includes free-wheel and double internal expansion brakes, either foot or hand applied, as desired.

Specification.

FRAMES—22 in. and 24 in.
AXLE—Free-wheel, patent.
WHEELS—26 in. equal, black centres, red lined.
CHAIN—½ in. pitch roller.
HANDLE-BAR—As illustrated.
BRAKES—Front Rim and Band Brakes on rear axle.

SADDLE—Lycett L19 plated, 3-coil.
GEAR-CASE—On Lady's Model only. Metal, registered pattern.
TYRES Dunlop or Palmer, 26 in. by 1⅜ in.
FINISH—Black, lined green and gold, axle plated.

£15 15 0

MODEL.	As specified above.	With Patent Bracket Two-speed Gear.
"Royal" Gent's	£15 15 0	£16 15 0
Lady's	16 16 0	17 16 0

THE "GAMAGE" PASSENGER TRAILER.

Although the addition of a passenger in a Trailer may be so much dead weight, yet the act of trailing does not call for so much work on the part of the rider as would appear at the first blush—provided, of course, that one has a well-made, easy running Trailer such as shown here, which is simply and quickly attached to the seat pillar of any cycle.

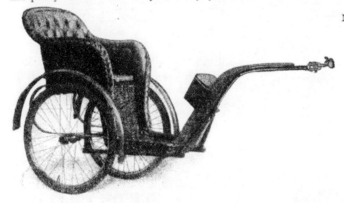

No. Cy. 1.	Juvenile Trailer, wicker body, pneumatic tyres	£4 9 6
" " 2.	Ditto, wicker body, C springs, pneumatic tyres	5 10 6
" " 3.	Adult Trailer, wicker body, double C springs, pneumatic tyres, (special value)	5 19 9
" " 4.	Ditto, with telescopic adjustment, rims heavily plated on copper, with wide mud uards, pneumatic tyres, including lunch and umbrella baskets	8 8 0
" — " 5.	Adult Trailer, in artistic cane work, Sheffield steel carriage springs, plated rims, detachable mudguards, patent Universal joint clip, with safety lock and any pneumatic tyres, including lunch and umbrella baskets	9 19 6
" " 6.	Motor Cycle Trailer, finished as Model 5, but extra strong and with 2 in. special Dunlop Tyres	10 10 0
" " 7.	Ditto, with double body in cane or wood, upholstered in cloth, tyres and finish as No. 6.	15 15 0

Carriage extra.

SOMETHING QUITE NEW!

THE TRADESMEN'S SIDE-CAR.

PRICE:

£3 10 0

WITH

Extra Strong Tyre.

PRICE:

£3 10 0

WITH

Extra Strong Tyre.

¶ Can be attached to any Bicycle in a few minutes.   ¶ Should be used in conjunction with every Carrier Cycle.

STRONG——LIGHT——EASY RUNNING——AND

THE BICYCLE STANDS ALONE.

A USEFUL NOVELTY!

THE CHILD'S SIDE-CAR.

PRICE:

£4 0 0

PRICE:

£4 0 0

Easily attached to or detached from any ordinary Cycle in a few minutes.

LIGHT——STRONG——EASY RUNNING.

THE ONLY SAFE METHOD OF CARRYING A CHILD ON YOUR CYCLE.

CARRIAGE PAID.

GAMAGES

DURABLE AND EFFICIENT MOTOR CYCLE

 THE RENOWNED "GAMAGE" LIGHT WEIGHT MOTOR CYCLE
IS JUST OF THAT RELIABLE QUALITY WHICH MAKES
MOTOR CYCLING A DELIGHT.

THE
"Gamage" Light Weight Motor Cycle

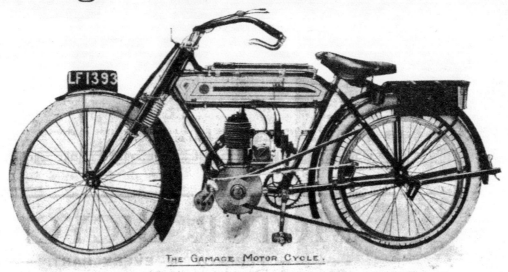

THE GAMAGE MOTOR CYCLE.

An ideal solo mount. Capable of a good turn of speed and a splendid hill climber. After exhaustive tests it has proved itself to be thoroughly satisfactory in every way; it is capable of accomplishing performances which many machines of higher power cannot equal.

£29. 10s. IF FITTED WITH STURMEY-ARCHER 3-SPEED HUB AND FREE ENGINE £38. 10s.

SPECIFICATIONS.

Engine.	2¾ h.p. single cylinder, adjustable tappets, ball-bearing main shaft, adjustable pulley, 70 by 76 bore and stroke.	**Stand.**	Fixed on chain stays, and when not in use clipped up to end of rear mudguard and operated from back stay by tension spring.
Frame.	Specially strong, elegant design, giving very low riding position.	**Carburetter.**	Brown & Barlow, with handle-bar control and variable jet.
Brakes.	Front rim actuated by inverted lever; back brake acting on belt drum, and operated from foot-rests.	**Ignition.**	Bosch magneto (Z.A.I. ball-bearing) enclosed waterproof type requiring no cover. Gear driven.
Forks.	The famous Druid patent spring.	**Tank.**	Petrol capacity one gallon, sufficient for about 125 miles, fitted with large filler caps, glass top to petrol cap, drain tap. Oil capacity one quart, internal oil pump.
Wheels.	Extra strong 26 by 2 in., beaded edge rims, heavily plated, with black, centres and black hubs.		
Tyres.	Hutchinson 26 by 2 in. beaded edge, rubber studded.		
Saddle.	Lycett's La Grande, No. 110.	**Transmission.**	Dunlop rubber belt, ⅞ in. V section. 7 ft. 3 in. long.
Mudguards.	Extra strong, 3 in. wide, front extension and extra side flaps.	**Finish.**	Best black enamel, usual part heavily plated, except handle-bars and hubs, which are black celluloid covered. Aluminium tank with blue panels.
Handle-bar.	Raised, with slightly dropped ends, giving excellent riding position, BLACK CELLULOID FINISH, WATERPROOF.	**Guarantee.**	All parts with the exception of tyres and magneto are guaranteed against any fault in material or workmanship for a period of six months from date of purchase.
Carrier.	Tubular, very strong and light.		

A 3

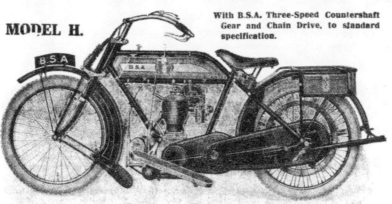

"Standard"
Model

£16. 16.

(Made at Autowheels
Ltd.,
Farnham Factory

"Modele
de Luxe"

£18. 18.

Made by B.S.A. Co.)

Y OU can cycle **without pedalling** over all sorts of roads, uphill and against headwinds **at 16 miles an hour,** by fitting to your cycle a self-propelling Wall Auto-wheel.

A 1 horse-power motor "makes the wheels go round," while you sit at your ease and steer.

Driving a Wall Auto-wheel is simplicity itself. To start, stop or regulate speed, you merely touch a little lever, the machine does the rest. The 1 horse-power motor wheel can be easily fitted, only weighs a few pounds, runs silently, oils itself and will propel your cycle over 100 miles at a cost of a few pence for petrol.

H.R.H. PRINCE GEORGE OF BATTENBERG and H.R.H. PRINCE HENRY OF PRUSSIA ride and recommend Wall Auto-wheels. Send for Art Catalogue and read what eminent motoring experts and delighted users say in praise of the novel labour-saving speed increasing device.

B.S.A. ROADSTER BICYCLE
—SPECIALLY DESIGNED TO SUIT THE AUTO-WHEEL—

W ITH the growing popularity of the Auto-wheel a demand has arisen for a machine giving a fairly low and comfortable seat position, hence the introduction of this special model. The frame is designed with slightly longer wheel-base than usual, and gives ample clearance for 1¾ in. tyres. The Eadie Coaster Hub is particularly recommended, as it provides a perfect free wheel, and a powerful back-pedalling brake, which are essential to this combination.

SPECIFICATION.

FRAME.—Sizes: Gent's—20 in., 21 in., 22 in., 23 in., and 24 in. Lady's—20 in., 21 in., and 22 in. WHEELS.—26 in., equal. Rims highly polished and heavily nickel-plated, edges and centres enamelled and lined. TYRES.—Dunlop or Palmer 1¾ in., with wired or beaded edges. BACK HUB.—Eadie Coaster. CHAIN—B.S.A. ⅝ in. pitch, tested to a strain of 2, 00 lb. GEAR.—74, or to order. PEDALS.—B.S.A. rat-trap or rubber; size to order. SADDLE.—Brooks' latest design, Gent's B 90/3; Lady's B 85, with enamelled springs. FINISH.—Four coats of brilliant best black enamel on one coat of rustproof prepara on; neatly lined out with green. Equipped with 15 in. celluloid inflator, plated clips, complete with tool-bag, oiler, and the necessary B.S.A. spanners to fit all nuts, cones and cups.

PRICES.

GENT'S—

Model No. 15.—As per Specification.

Net Cash .. **£9 5 0**

Or **£1** deposit, and 12 monthly payments of **15/4**

Can also be supplied in 'All-black' finish if required.

PRICES.

LADY'S—

Model No. 16. As per Specification, but with oil-bath gear case.

Net Cash - **£9 17 6**

Or **£1** deposit, and 12 monthly payments of **16/6**

Can also be supplied in 'All-black' finish if required.

CARRIERS, &c.

The "Gamage" Tricarrier.

Specification of Tricarrier, above illustrated.

FRAME—Built of best quality, extra strong, weldless steel tubes.

WHEELS—Size 28 in. by 26 in., tangent spokes, extra large ball bearings, and large lubricator.

RIMS—Westwood Motor Rim, with triangular corners specially designed to protect the tyre when drawn up thoughtlessly against the kerbstone.

GEAR—50 or to order, 7 in. cranks, closed ends, 6 in. treads.

BRAKE—Patent powerful band brake, acting on both front hubs.

TYRES—Size 1½ in. Clincher "A Won" Tandem.

BOX The box is thoroughly well made from well-seasoned timber.

MUDGUARDS—To all wheels. Extra wide. Steel. Motor strength.

PEDALS—Brampton's solid centre motor pedals, with best rubber. 4½ in. wide, screwed into cranks with right and left-hand B.S.A. threads.

CHAIN—Hans Renold block chain, 1 in. pitch by ⅜ in. wide.

DIMENSIONS—Seat stem 21 in. Extreme width over dust caps 3 ft. Length 6 ft. 7 in. Height 3 ft. 8 in.

ACCESSORIES—Pump, spanner, oilcan, and wrench for dust caps.

Price **£18 18 0**

No. Cy. 2. Similar to above, but not so expensively finished, with best solid tyre **11 10 0**

The "Gamage" Carrier Cycle.

A strongly constructed machine, which will stand the roughest wear. Of good appearance (makes an effective advertisement); easy running; very suitable for special deliveries by **Butchers, Fishmongers, Provision Merchants**; will take quite heavy loads; and, if wished, a back carrier can be fixed in addition to the existing front basket carrier.

SPECIFICATION as the "Popular Roadster," on page 3 & 4, except that this machine has several parts strengthened, and has Special Tandem Tyres.

A HIGH GRADE COVENTRY MACHINE.
SPECIALLY STRENGTHENED.   SPECIAL TANDEM TYRES.

Advertising Plate.   Front Carrier and Basket.

Price, fitted complete, as illustrated **£6 10 0**

The "NEW" Carrier Bicycle.

Adult and Invalid Side-car.

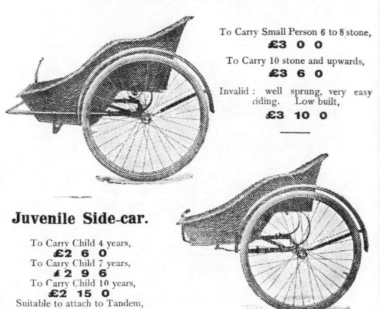

To Carry Small Person 6 to 8 stone,
£3 0 0

To Carry 10 stone and upwards,
£3 6 0

Invalid : well sprung, very easy riding.   Low built,
£3 10 0

Juvenile Side-car.

To Carry Child 4 years,
£2 6 0
To Carry Child 7 years,
£2 9 6
To Carry Child 10 years,
£2 15 0
Suitable to attach to Tandem,
£3 0 0

— SPECIFICATION. —

FRAMES—Patent Open Fork Carrier Pattern, 22 in. and 24 in.

WHEELS 28 in. by 1½ in., plated and enamelled rims.

GEAR—61 in.

FREE WHEEL—James.

BRAKES—Two Rim Brakes.

SADDLE—Lycett, L19 enamelled three-coil.

TYRES—Special "Mirco" Heavy Roadster Carrier Tyres, 28 by 1½ in.

FINISH—Black enamel all over.

NAME-PLATE—Metal detachable, sign writing in colours, 1/- per doz. Letters.

BASKET 18 by 12 by 9 in.

Carrier, as specified above **£7 15**   ::   Coloured Enamel, 5/- extra.

The Sidecars are Light and Strong, easily propelled.   Adjustable Clips can remain on Cycle.   Sidecars can be attached or detached in two minutes.

SPECIAL POINTS OF THE "NEW" CARRIER.

The Splayed Open Forks.—A feature quite our own providing a substantial base upon which the carrier platform is built.   They are stronger than the ordinary cycle fork sides, and from the fact of their being splayed, they are incapable of being buckled by any force.

The Hubs.—Specially designed with wide flanges large bearings, and made to stand the hard wear and strenuous use to which such machines are subjected.

The Basket Platform.—Note the substantial way this is built on to the fork sides. The weight of the load is taken directly by this platform not distributed cant lever fashion upon the frame tubes.

The Patented Fork Crown.—Another exclusive feature of these machines.   It is made of solid drawn weldless steel tube manipulated to form lock joints to receive the fork sides, and heavily butted fork stem tube.

The Mudguards are well stayed by double wires, with an additional tie at the front extension which keeps the load from dirt and mud.

The Basket Rail is made of solid cold forged bright steel.   It is strong and light and cannot be bent or broken.

The Front Wheel is specially strengthened to effectively withstand severe strains.   It is built with heavy spokes and rims.

The Handle-Bars.—Another unique point.   The strain of the steering is taken up the whole length of the bar.   It is therefore impossible for it to slip or twist and cause the steering to become unmanageable.

GOODS AND PARCEL TRUCKS.

THESE HANDSOME HAND VANS

Are strongly constructed and made in First-class style.

They are beautifully COACH painted and lined any colour to order. The rubber-tyred Wheels are built SPECIALLY STRONG, the Tyres being full 1¼ ins. in thickness.

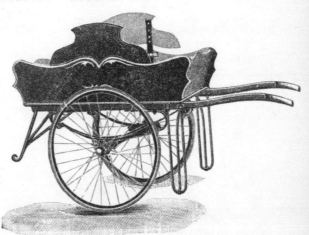

SPECIFICATION.

Wicker covered top, with half lid, as illustrated. Back leg rest only.

List Nos.	Wooden Wheels.	PLAIN Bearing Rubber Tyred Wheels.	BALL Bearing Rubber Tyred Wheels.	Length of Body.	Width of Body.	Depth of Body.	Width over Caps.	Size of Wood'n Wheels.	Size of Rubber Tyred Wheels.
				Inches.	Inches.	Inches.	Inches.	Inches.	Inches.
Cy. 156	—	73/-	—	35	25	12 by 16	37	—	28 by ⅞
157	—	82/6	92/6	38	27	12 by 18	39	—	28 by 1

Front leg rest .. 4/- extra. Parcel rail on top .. 5/- extra.

SPECIFICATION.

Smart and useful for general purposes. Well made, strong wheels, front and back leg rests. Painted and lined to order.

List Nos	Wooden Wheels with Brass Caps.	PLAIN Bearing Rubber Tyred Wheels.	BALL Bearing Rubber Tyred Wheels.	Length of Body.	Width of Body.	Depth of Body.	Width over Caps.	Size of Wood'n Wheels.	Size of Rubber Tyred Wheels.
				Inches.	Inches.	Inches.	Inches.	Inches.	Inches.
Cy. 165	102/6	107/6	112/6	44	25	10	37	32	30 by 1¼
166	112/6	117/6	122/6	48	27	12	39	34	30 by 1¼

Two movable name boards at side, 12/- extra. Hinged tail board, 3/6 extra.

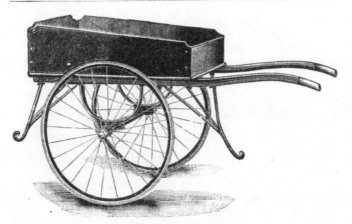

SPECIFICATION.

Useful light Truck, with wired-on rubber tyres, and back leg rest only.

List Nos.	Wooden Wheels.	PLAIN Bearing Rubber Tyred Wheels.	BALL Bearing Rubber Tyred Wheels.	Length of Body.	Width of Body.	Depth of Body.	Width over Caps.	Size of Wood'n Wheels.	Size of Rubber Tyred Wheels.
				Inches.	Inches.	Inches.	Inches.	Inches.	Inches.
Cy. 180	—	58/-	—	33	21	10 by 5	31	—	25 by
181	—	70/-	80/-	36	24	10 by 5	34	—	28 by 1

Front leg rest .. .. 4/- extra.

SPECIFICATION.

The wooden top is covered with canvas and painted, making it waterproof. Narrower at the bottom than the top to reduce the over-all width.

List Nos.	Wooden Wheels with Brass Caps.	PLAIN Bearing Rubber Tyred Wheels.	BALL Bearing Rubber Tyred Wheels.	Length of Body.	Width of Body.	Depth of Body.	Width over Caps.	Size of Wood'n Wheels.	Size of Rubber Tyred Wheels.
				Inches.	Inches.	Inches.	Inches.	Inches.	Inches.
Cy. 115	124/-	126/-	131/-	34	20 top 16 btm.	21	31	30	28 by 1¼
116	134/-	136/-	141/-	39	24 top 20 btm.	24	35	30	28 by 1¼

Carriage paid.

Clockwork & Steam Torpedo Boats & Destroyers.

Exact models, superfine grey or all black japanning.

Ty. 1. CLOCKWORK TORPEDO BOAT,   Post
12¾ in. long, 2 funnels, 3 cannons, 2 torpedo tubes, **4 9**   4d.

Ty. 2. CLOCKWORK DESTROYER,
17 in. long, 4 funnels, 4 cannons, 2 torpedo tubes, **7/6**   6d.

Ty. 3. CLOCKWORK DESTROYER,
22¾ in. long, 4 funnels, 4 cannons, 3 torpedo tubes, **9 11**   8d.

With superior Clockwork movement, 23½ in. long
with torpedo tube and lifeboats ..   ..   ..**15/6**   9d.

Driven by steam, 23½ in. long with torpedo tube and
lifeboats ..   ..**16/6**   9d.

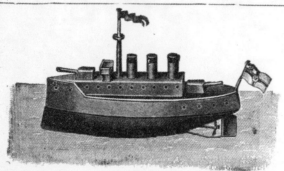

New Range of Gun Boats with best Clockwork Movements.

Gun Boat, finely japanned, with 2 funnels, 2 guns, 7½ in. long, **1/-**   Post 3d.
  ,,   ,,   ,,   ,, 3 ,, 2 ,, 8¾ ,, ,, **2/-**   ,, 3d.
  ,,   ,,   ,,   ,, 3 ,, 2 ,, 10½ ,, ,, **3/-**   ,, 4d.

Model Dreadnought, with strong reliable Clockwork Movements.
finely japanned.   Price **5/11**   Postage 4d.
Dreadnought, with strong reliable Clockwork Movements, finely japanned, correct
naval grey, 11¾ in. long   Price ...   ... **3/11**   Postage 4d.

Automatically Firing Gun Boats.

After winding up the clockwork, put boat on
the water. It will go straight ahead for some distance,
then, as if intending to attack an enemy, it will
suddenly fire a shot. After this, the boats (size 1 and
2), will sail on in a circle, whilst boat size 3 will turn
round and steer back to its original starting place.

Finely finished and beautifully japanned, with best
quality clockwork and with automatic steering gear.

Ty. 1. With 1 gun, 12 in. long .. **5/9** Post 5d.
 ,, 2. ,, 1 ,, 15¾ ,,   .. **8/11** ,, 7d.
 ,, 3. ,, 2 guns, firing 2 shots at
       intervals, 19¼ in lon . **13 9** ,, 9d.

LARGE DESTROYER. Finely japanned, typical, narrow shape, with very strong superior Clockwork, torpedo tubes, lifeboats
and 2 anchors, 39¼ in long, **39/6** each. Post free.   Ditto   ditto   ditto   27½ in long ..   .. **23 6** each   Post free.
Ditto   ditto   steam propelled .. **39/6**   Ditto   ditto   ditto   **steam propelled** .. **22 6** ,,   ..

L1

Superior Motor Cars and Lorries.

Clockwork Motor Bus in fine polychrome japanning, with strong clockwork. 12¾ in. long. 6½ in. wide, with driver.
Price .. **2/11** Post 3d.

Extraordinary Value. A complete Motor Garage with doors to open and 2 clockwork Motor Cars, exactly as illustration .. **1/-** Post 3d.

Limousine Motor Car. Strong clockwork movement, will run forward and backwards, also stop by lever in cab, can run straight or circular Length 12 in. Height 4½ in. Wide 5¼ in. Price **13 6** Post 6d.

New Model Broughams. Torpedo bodies, strong clockwork movement, rubber tyres, doors to open, fitted with brake, Bevel Glass Windows, front axle adjustable to straight or circular run.
No. 3. 16 in. long, 6½ in. wide .. price, **25/-**
" 4. 18¼ " 7 " .. .. " **35/-**

New Model Open Touring Car. Torpedo bodies, superior quality best hand-painted, strong, powerful clockwork movement, nicely regulated, rubber tyres. correct pattern seat, with brake, front axe adjustable for straight or circular run. No. 1, 12½ in. long, 5½ in. wide ... **11/9** Post 6d.
No. 2. 15¼ in. long 6¼ wide **21/-**

New Model Broughams. Torpedo bodies, superior quality strong clockwork movement with brake and rubber tyres, doors to open Bevel Glass windows, front axle adjustable for straight or circular run.
No. 1. 10½ in. long, 4½ in. wide, price **8/11** Post 4d.
" 2. 13 " 5¼ " .. **14 6** " 5d.

Motor Lorry with Tip-Up Body. Can be tilted as illustration. Superior quality and finish, strong clockwork movement, rubber tyres, front axle adjustable to allow either straight or circular run. 11¾ in. long, 3½ in. wide .. **5/11** Post 4d.

Motor Lorry. Loaded with sacks, and covered with tarpaulin. Very realistic. Strong clockwork movement.
8¼ in. long, 3½ in. wide .. .. price **2/11** Post 3d.

Spears, Bows & Arrows, Tomahawks, etc., extra

GENUINE IMPORTED
American Indian
Warrior Suits.

GENUINE IMPORTED
American Indian
Wigwams.

Style 1010. Indian Chief Outfit Made of khaki drill, and consists of a coat with coloured front, trimmed with coloured fringes and yellow edging throughout; trousers same trimming. Bonnet of similar material, in cap style, trimmed tapes and fringes, and 4 coloured feathers, **3/11** Post 4d.

Cheaper qualities, **3/11 4/11 5/11** Post 4d.

Style S O 2. Outfit consists of coat made of khaki drill with blue facings piped yellow braid and trimmed red fringe; trousers of khaki with khaki felt trimmings and red fringe. Bonnet of Sioux style with 26 coloured feathers. Exceedingly well made - **22/6** Ditto, with less trimmings and feathers, **17/6**

Style 1375. Indian Chief Outfit. Fine grade of khaki, consists of coat with genuine leather inserts on front, fully beaded; trimmed throughout with woven non-curling fringes; trousers have coloured genuine leather inserts on each side, fully beaded, trimmed with woven non-curling fringes. Bonnet has a full crown of coloured felt, wide front band of genuine coloured leather, fully beaded. and 24 large tipped (two colour) feathers, taped at bottom with coloured cloth. **16/6** Post 6d.

Style 1142. Indian Chief Outfit, in khaki drill, consists of a coat with coloured front, trimmed throughout with double colour non-curling felt fringes and yellow edging; trousers similarly trimmed. Bonnet made in Sioux style, khaki front trimmed with coloured fringes and tapes, and with 20 coloured feathers. Price ... **5/11** Post 6d.

Style 3035. Outfit consists of coat made of red drill, with non-curling felt fringe, green felt piping on coat; and trousers with leather fringe. Bonnet made in Sioux style with leather front and felt band, containing 29 coloured feathers, with bells and red and khaki ribbons. **13/6**

Style 1091. Indian Chief Outfit in khaki drill, consists of a coat with double colour felt non-curling fringes, 2 pockets similarly trimmed; trousers same trimming down sides. Bonnet of similar material trimmed coloured fringes and tapes and with 12 coloured feathers. Price ... **4/11** Post 4d.

Style 3041. Coat made of khaki drill with green felt stripes and yellow fringe, red collar. Skirt of khaki drill piped with green and red felt with yellow fringe. Bonnet of red felt and 9 coloured feathers. Price **10/6** Post 6d.

Indian Wigwams.

No.		Height.		Price.
1	Unbleached Sheeting,	5 ft.,	3 poles	6/11
13	Khaki Drill ..	.. 5 ,,	3 ,,	8/11
2	White Drill ..	.. 6 ,,	3 ,,	8/11
3	White Drill ..	.. 6 ,,	5 ,,	15/-
4	White Duck..	.. 6 ,,	5 ,,	18/6
5	Waterproof Khaki ..	6 ,,	5 ,,	25/-
6	Waterproof Khaki ..	8 ,,	5 ,,	37/6
8	Khaki Drill ..	.. 6 ,,	5 ,,	18/6
9	Khaki Drill ..	.. 5 ,,	5 ,,	15/-
10	Waterproof Khaki ..	5 ,,	5 ,,	18/6

Style 3033. Outfit made of khaki drill and consists of coat with red front and yellow and green non-curling felt fringe with Sioux style bonnet with leather front and 30 coloured feathers. Price **10/6**

Style 1163. Indian Chief Outfit, in khaki drill, consists of a coat elaborately trimmed with wide coloured felt bands, fully decorated double colour non-curling felt fringes; trousers with similar fringes; bonnet with full crown of coloured felt, wide felt front band trimmed with beads, and 20 coloured feathers taped at bottom with coloured cloth. Price **8/11** Post 6d.

Style 1182. Indian Chief Outfit, made of khaki drill, consists of a coat with coloured cloth inserts on front, trimmed with felt non-curling fringes and yellow tapes. Trousers have felt non-curling fringes and yellow tapes. Bonnet in Sioux style, khaki front trimmed with coloured fringes and tapes, and 20 coloured feathers. **7/11** Post 6d.

Style 3034. This Outfit is made of khaki drill with red front and green-and-yellow trimming and fringe; trousers green felt stripe and red non-curling fringe. Bonnet made Sioux style with leather front and 24 coloured feathers. Price ... **10/6**

Harmless Pistols and Cannons.

Toy Cap Guns, 1/4½ 1/10½ Post 4d. **2/6 3/6**
Post 6d. Bayonet and Belt, **3/6** Post 5d.

Toy Cap Pop Guns, 10½d. **1/4½**
Post 4d.   Post 4d.

GUN. Field-piece with spring stretching. Nicely burnished gun of metal, breech and mouth of nickelled brass, metal carriage, iron wheels, japanned by hand. Adjustable range finder, with trigger. To fire with peas, rubber balls, &c.

Size 6¾ by by 3½ in.

Price **1/6**

Post 2d.

The Gun of the Royal Horse Artillery (Patented).
Price **10½d.**   Postage 2d.

Metal Field Gun.

Strongly made.   Enamelled only.

To fire peas or small leaden bullets.

Price .. **6d.**   Post 2d.

Amorces (Caps) cannot be sent by post.

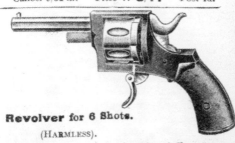

Field-Howitzer to Fire Amorces and Rubber-Shells.

(HARMLESS.)

Solid construction with detachable breech and striking-pin. Barrel with two chambers for double charge of amorces. Burnished barrel of solid brass with adjustments. Metal carriage finely enamelled.

Length 6 in.   Calibre ½ in.   Length of barrel 3 in.

Complete with 4 rubber-shells, wire and sponge.

Price .. **5/11**   Postage 5d.

Harmless Modern Coast Cannon

For double charge to fire amorces and rubber-shells. Armoured carriage with ingenious mechanism for revolving to any direction. Massive barrel of burnished brass, with striking pin and 2 chambers for double charging with amorces and adjustable for sighting. Carriage mounted with crane, enamelled iron plate, brass mounted. Accessories—1 box of amorces and rubber-shells. Length 7 in. Height 6½ in. Length of barrel 3½ in. Calibre ⅛ in. Price **9/6** Post 4d.
Ty. 2. For double charge with amorces and rubber-shells. Amoured carriage with ingenious mechanism for revolving to any direction. Massive barrel of burnished brass, with striking pin and two chambers for double charging with amorces, adjustable for sighting Carriage mounted with crane, enamelled iron-plate, brass mounted. Length 10 in. Height 8½ in. Length of the barrel, 5 in. Caliber, ½ in. With 4 rubber-shells and 1 box of amorces.   Price **16/6** Postage

Cannon, FIELD PIECE (HARMLESS). Breech loader with powder, caps and RUBBER SHELLS. Shells to be pressed into the muzzle. Solid construction—Gun metal barrel, steel blue burnished, cast iron wheels, metal carriage, grey colour. New handy loading and firing mechanism, detachable breech bolt with bayonet closure, fixed chamber, trigger with spiral spring
Length of barrel 2½ in., total length 5½ in.
Caliber 7/32 in.   Price .. **2/6**   Post 3d.
Length of barrel 3½ in., total length 7½ in.
Caliber 9/32 in.   Price .. **3/11**   Post 4d.

Breech-Loader Pistol.

With interchangeable cartridges to fire Amorces Caps and rubber-shells.
Stock of iron with embossed nickel cheeks. Rifle barrel of nickelled brass, with sights.
Accessories—Sponge, 1 box of amorces caps, 10 rubber-shells.
Length 10 in.   Calibre 5/16 in.   Price .. **3/11**   Post 4d.
Extra rubber shells, **6d.** per doz. Post 4d.

Toy Sentry Box.

Size 2 by 2 by 3½ in.

Price 6½d.   Post 2d.

Revolver for 6 Shots.

(HARMLESS).

Ammunition : Amorces and rubber-shells. Original design, automatic revolving, detachable breech part, holding both the amorces caps and shells. Wooden stock, iron frame, nickelled and rifled barrel of massive brass.   Length 6½ in.   Calibre 7/32 in.
Size of card-board box, 8 by 3¾ by 1½ in.
Accessories : 20 rubber-shells, 1 box of amorces 1 sponge, and 1 wire.   Price **8/11**   Post 5d.

Harmless Muzzle-Loader Rifle with Cartridges.

With automatic cocking mechanism.
Beech wood stock, burnished steel plate barrel.
On fine cardboard with target.
Caliber ¼ in.
Complete with 10 rubber shells.
Price .. .. .. **5/11**   Post 6d.

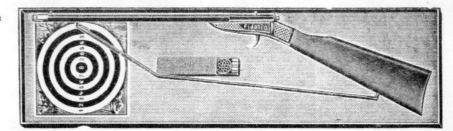

Drums. Bagpipes. Pianos.

Metal Head Drum.

as illustration **6½d.** Post 3d.
Ditto, 10 in **1/-** Post 4d.

Drums with Metal Rims, vellum heads and tightening screws, 9½ in.
1- Post 4d.

Ditto 12 in. **2/6** Post 4d.

Side Drum.

as illustration with vellum heads.
Price **2 11** Post.

Organ Chimes.

When the Toy is twirled round it gives off sounds similar to that of an organ. Price **6d.** Post 2d.

Bagpipes.

Best Rubber Bags and turned painted pipes and Drones
No. 1 Pipe without Drone Price **6d.** Post 1d.
No. 2   „   with two Drones **10½d.** „ 1½d.
No. 3   „   „   three „ as illus. **2/-** „ 2d.
No. 4   „   „   three „ extra large as illustration
3/6 Post 3d.

Strongly made Nickel Drum.

Tightening Screws
Vellum Heads

As illustration, 10½ in. diam.

2/6 Post 5d.

Model Pianos with Metal Notes.

Superior finish.

8 Notes .. **4/11** Post 6d.
10 „ .. **5/11** „ 7d.
12 „ .. **7/6** „ 9d.

Drum Major's Baton.

With metal head, 34 in. long .. **10½d.** Post 3d.
Ditto, with brass head, 34 in. long .. **1/9** , 3d.

Novelty Drum

Mechanical part inside drum. Drum fitted with handle, which, when turned, produces sounds equal to an expert Drummer.

Metal Rims, Brass Body.
8 in. Head **2/6** Post 4d.

Drums with Wooden Rims solid brass body, vellum heads, belt hook and knee rest, 10½ in.
Price .. **4/11** Post 6d.
Do., do., 11 in. .. .. **5/11** Post 6d.
Do., do., 10½ in., extra strong **7/11** „ 8d.
Do., do., 11½ in. „ „ **8/11** „ 9d.
„ „ 13 in. „ „ **11/9** .. 10d.

Bass Drum.

as illustration with Vellum heads
3/11 Post 5d.

Smart Toy Piano.

WIRE STRUNG. CAN BE TUNED.

No. 1. With 8 Notes .. **8/11** Post and packing, 7d.
„ 2. „ 10 Notes .. **10/9** „ „ 8d.
„ 3. „ 14 Notes .. **13/6** „ „ 8d.
„ 4. „ 16 Notes .. **15/6** „ „ 9d.
„ 5. „ 18 Notes .. **18 9** „ „ 1/-
„ 6. „ 20 Notes .. **23/9** „ „ 1/-

New Model Piano with Metal Notes,

With 6 Notes .. .. .. **1/9** Post 4d.
„ 8 „ .. .. .. **2/3** „ 6d.
„ 10 „ .. .. .. **2/11** „ 6d.
„ 12 „ .. .. .. **3/11** „ 6d.

FINE MODEL Overstrung Baby Grand Piano,

with Playable Sharps on Raised Keys.

Style D. As illustration.
Height 8½ in. Length 20½ in.
Width 15½ in.
Height, with lid up, 18 in.
25 notes .. **35/-**

Style B. Without sharps.
Height 7½ in. Length 20½ in.
Width 12½ in.
Height, with lid up, 14 in.
15 notes .. **21/-**

L 3

TOY MUSICAL INSTRUMENTS.

Real Horn Horns.

Price .. **1/10½**   Postage **3d.**

Sword Pop Gun.

Price .. .. **6d.**   Postage **2d.**

Guitar.

With 4 strings,
Price .. **6½d.**
Post **2d.**

Ditto, larger.
With 8 strings, as
Illustration.
Price .. **1/-**
Post **3d.**

Autoharp.

with 12 strings.

Price .. **1/-**
Post **3d.**

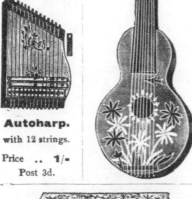

Accordeons.

With 6 Notes.
Price .. **1/-**   Post **3d.**
Smaller size. Price .. **6d.** Post **2d.**

Solid Brass Cornets.
Superior make. 4 Notes.
3/6   4/6   4/11 Post **4d.**

Double Pop Gun. 6d. Post **2d**

Pop Whistle, as Illustration. **4½d.** Post **2d.**

Cornet. With 8 notes. Nickel **1/-** Post **3d.** With 4 notes.
Enamelled, **6½d.** Post **2d.**
Brass Cornets. 4 notes **1/10½**   6 notes **2/4½**   notes **2/11**

Wood Trumpet

As illustration. **4½d.** Post **2d.**   **6d.** Post **3d.**

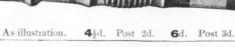

Painted Trombone .. **1/-**   Post **3d.**
Ditto   Brass   **2/-**   ,,   **3d.**
Ditto   (larger) .. .. **2/11**   ,,   **3d.**

Tubephones, superior quality, price **10½d., 1/6,
2/4½, 3/6, 4/6, 5/11, 10/6** Postage extra.

Ariston Musical Box. As illustration. With 18 notes
and Moveable Pictures.   Price .. **1/-**   Post **3d.**

MUSICAL VARIETY SHOW.

As illustration With Six Notes and changeable pictures.

Price .. .. **6d.** Post **2d.**

Metal Trumpets.

3d. ... Post **2d.**
6d. ... ,,
1/- ... Post **3d.**
1/4½ ...
1/10½ ..

Musical Boxes.

Price .. **4½ d.**
Post **2d.**

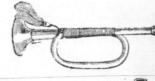

Police Rattles

As illustration.
Price **2d.** Post **2d.**
  ,, **4d.**   ,, **2d.**

Musical Bottle.

Price .. **4½d.**
Postage **2d.**

Mandoline

As illustration.
Price .. .. **6d.**
Post **2d.**

Concertinas.

Price, **6d.** and **1/-**
Post **2d.** and **3d.**
  Extra large,
Price **2/-** Post **4d.**

PAINTED WOODEN HORN.
Price **4½d.**
Postage **2d.**

Zithers.

With 8 Strings.
Price .. **6½d.**
Postage **3d.**

Clown Pop Gun.

6d. Post **2d.**

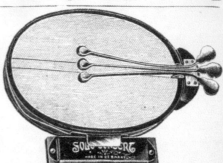

Drum Mouth Organ. As illustration. Price **1/-**
Postage **3d.**

MIRTH MAKERS.

ONE DOZEN RUBBER Blow-out "Dying" Novelties.

Eight different kinds — Horse, Bear, Swan, Donkey, Elephant, Cockerel, Humpty-Dumpty & Monkey .. **1/-** Post 1½d

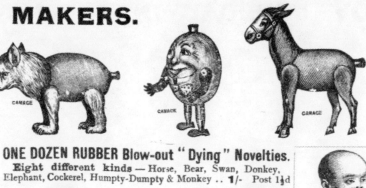

The "Dying" Baby.
Extra stout rubber. Composition head.
Price **5½**d. Post 1d.

Harry Lauder
Amusing 'dying' toy.
Price **5½**d. Post 2d.

The Wonderful Air Torpedo
Makes a report like a Gun. No Smoke. No Explosive. No Danger.

Simply place a piece of paper inside lid, fasten down, then strike any object with the round end (which is flexible and cannot cause any damage). Try hitting your friend on the shoulder unawares! The greatest Boy's Toy invented for years. A ripper for Carnivals. Price **10½**d. Post 3d.

The Whistling Nigger.
Exceedingly clever. By pressing the ball, the Nigger-Hustler puts out his tongue, whistles and rolls his eyes.
Price **1/-** Post 2d.

The Piping Bullfinch.
This is an exceedingly clever and entertaining singing **Toy**. The results which can be obtained after a few minutes' practice being really extraordinary To operate remove cap on pipe, partly fill with water and blow gently down tube.
Price **8**d.
Postage 2d.

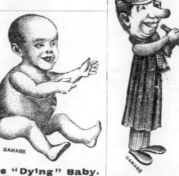

The Vocophone.
An Evening's Entertainment in your Waistcoat Pocket.
Try this simple MUSICAL NOVELTY. It will strengthen your Voice, and develop true sounds.
You can imitate all Brass Instruments, rendering good Solos.
The effect of harmonizing is good.
It is a companion to the Cyclist and Scout. The Vocophone will do anything you wish it to do, as regards intensifying vocal sounds. By removing the cap and speaking through the tube, it will increase the sound given forth, and will answer the purpose of a **Pocket Megaphone.**
Price, with instructions. **6**d. Post 1d.

Singing Tie Pin
This novelty will cause great wonderment if fitted in the tie and worked by the small ball which is concealed in the waistcoat pocket. When singing, the bird moves its beak in a most realistic manner. Price ... **1/-** Postage 1d.

Where is that Dog?
The "Yapper" Dog Barker will produce endless fun for the person possessing one, with a "Yapper" in your pocket, you are a person to be reckoned with at parties, carnivals, etc.
Price .. **6**d.
Postage 2d.
Ditto, larger, **10½**d. Post 2d.

Plate Lifters.
UP-TO-DATE SPIRITUALISM.
DISHES AND PLATES WILL DANCE!
Plate Lifters are made of thin rubber tubing with small rubber ball at one end, which is inflated by squeezing the ball fixed at the other end of tube. When placed under the plates of your guests at supper (under cloth, so that the tube is out of sight), endless fun is caused as the plate is made to jump up and down at will.
Price **3**d. each. Extra long, **4½**d. Postage 1½d.
New Winged Plated Lifter, lifts two articles at once .. **5½**d. Postage 1½d.

Surprise Water Camera.   As illustration.
AN AMUSING NOVELTY.   Price .. **1/-** Post 3d.
Cheaper quality, without View-finder, **6**d. Post 2d.

KINDERGARTEN TOYS.

The Liliputian Writing Companion.

Price **10½d.** 3/6
Post 2d. 3d.

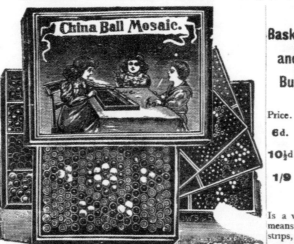

CHINA BALL MOSAIC.

A most interesting pastime for young children, who can make up pretty designs with the differently coloured balls. Price **6**d. Post 2d.

Basket Work and Stick Building.

Price.	Post.
6d. ..	2d.
10½d. ..	3d.
1/9 ..	3d.

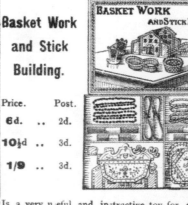

Is a very useful and instructive toy for children. By means of the cut-out pieces, the wooden sticks, paper strips, etc., etc., the children can make all sorts of different objects, as houses, baskets, etc.

Character Dolls.

Price .. .. .. **10½**d.

Post 2d.

Wood Mosaic.

By means of the 108 highly varnished and differently colored wooden pieces of various shapes, children can make up hundreds of different designs. Provides hours of amusements for children.
Price **6**d. **10½**d. **1**/**10½** Post 2d. 3d. 3.

DOLLY'S WARDROBE.

The favourite of our girls consists of a wardrobe made of thick cardboard and decorated in modern style. The Wardrobe contains 2 cardboard dolls, 8 hats and bonnets, 8 dresses (latest fashions, also umbrella, muff, boa, school bag, tennis racket, etc. The dresses are fastened in the wardrobe on metal hooks, and the hats, etc., are kept in the drawer. Each wardrobe is packed in leatherette box with gold lettering. The dolls as well as the dresses, etc., are printed in full colours on stout cardboard and are nicely embossed.
Undoubtedly one of the best presents for our Girls.
Smaller, **6**d. Post 2d. As illustration, **2/6** Post 3d

The Mosaic Designer.

An ingenious arrangement of cups and coloured balls for forming various designs.

Price	..	..	..	**10½**d.	**1/9**	**2 6**
Post	..	..	..	3d.	3d.	4d

Pricking and Sewing.

As illustration.

Price .. .. **10½**d.

Post 3d.

WEAVING AND PAPER PLAITING

The pretty designs into which our little ones have to work the paper strips will not fail to arouse their interest.

Price	..	..	**6**d.	**10½**d.	**1/4½**	**1/10½**
Post	..	..	2d.	3d.	3d.	3d.

KINDERGARTEN TOYS.

Flower Making at Home.
Complete Outfit for Flower Making.

Price	10½d.	1/4½	1/10½	2/4½	3/6	4/11	5/11
Post	2d.	3d.	3d.	3d.	4d.	4d.	5d.

Price **6/11** **9/6**   Post 6d. 8d.

Toy Village, as illustration.
Complete with Cottages, Flowers, Trees, etc.

Price	..	..	10½d.	1/10½	3/6
Postage	..	..	2d.	3d.	4d.

Models for Embroidery
Containing 12 perforated coloured designed cards
for embroidery according to Froebels principles
Price **2/11** Post 3d.

Threadwork Pictures.
Containing coloured pencils, coloured thread,
needles, model, and designed perforated cards for
colouring, cutting out and erecting.
Price .. **2/-** Post 3d.

Artistic Pea and Bean Work.
Containing 6 different coloured lots of Peas and Beans
rubber stalk tubing, elastic fasteners and wire also,
model making an amusing occupation for girls.
Price .. **2/-** Post 4d.

Little Canvas Embroiderer
Containing 16 canvas sheets, model with skeins
of thread, needles and designs.
2/6 smaller **6d. 1/0** Post 2d. 3d.

The Little Architect.
Containing cardboard stands, steel knife, tube of
liquid glue, 4 different lots of coloured sticks, with
diagrams showing how to build houses, churches, etc
Price .. **2/11** Post 3d.

Mosaic Cubes
Beautifully enamelled in colours.
Price **1/-** Post 3d.

Bread Basket Worker
Containing sticks, 3 coloured strings of Beads, and cardboard material for
Basket making. Price **1/0, 3/6, 4/6.** Post 2d. 4d. 4d.

ZILLOGRAPH or SHADOW THEATRE.
Price ... **6**d. and **10½**d.   Post 2d. and 3d.

SHADOW PICTURES, containing shadow sheet & various figures for fitting on to finger tips, forming an amusing Punch and Judy Show ... **2/-** Post 3d.

British Made.
CLOCK MAKING MADE EASY.
Every part is numbered and can easily be fitted together by a boy of 8. Guaranteed to keep good time. Complete and clear instructions given. All parts for making a complete 30-hour clock with wood case, brass wheels, escapement and and metal back.
Price ... **5/6**   Post 6d

THEATRE, WITH FOOTLIGHTS.
The best Miniature Toy Theatre in the market. Strongly made and fitted with properly working curtain, English pattern, footlights to burn oil, beautifully lithographed characters, mounted on cardboard and cut ready for use. These Theatres have complete set of characters, etc., as per book.

No.	2a	3a	5a	6a
	7/11	13/9	18/6	37/6

Postage 6d   under 20/- in value

THE INDIAN'S CAMP. A marvelusly clever idea. Contains 22 Jointed Figures of Indians, Cowboys, Cowgirls, Horses, &c., all being painted in bright colours on heavy cardboard and securely riveted at the joints. Also contains a large staled wooden board, with grooves, size 24 by 12 by 2 in.. on which

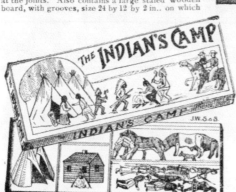

these figures can be made to stand up in hundreds of different positions. There is also a Folding Tent and a Blockhouse with it. The game is most artistically got up in a large showy box ... **4/11** Post 6d.

NEW PUNCH AND JUDY SHOW.
No toy has ever yet captivated the heart of a child of any age quite as much as a Punch and Judy Show. These Punch and Judy Shows are strongly made and nicely ornamented. Supplied complete with life-like figures The figures for the 2 largest sizes are specially made of solid wood, beautifully painted and of large size. Made in the following sizes:
No. 1. 25½ by 12 in. with 6 figures: **5 6** Carriage 6d,
No. 2. 28 by 14 in. ditto, **7 11**   Carriage 8d.
No. 3. 38 by 18 in. ditto, **10 6**   Carriage 10d.
No. 4. 43½ by 20¾ in. ditto, **14 6**   Carriage 1/-
No. 5. 49½ by 23 in. ditto, **20/-**   Carriage 1/3
No. 6. 65 by 29½ in. with 6 wooden figures **35/-**   Carriage 1/6

PET PLAYS. Box containing Theatre, Stage Front, Scenery and the Figures.   Price   **6**d.   Post 2d.

TINY TOWN ZOO, as illustration, complete set in cardboard figures, animals, houses, &c.
Price ..   ..   **7/11**   Carriage 10d.

No. 7.   78 by 34½ in, with 6 wooden figures ..   ..   **45/-**   Carriage 2/-
The comicalities of the game brings forth refreshing laughter and real enjoyment to both young and old.

DOLLS MANSIONS.

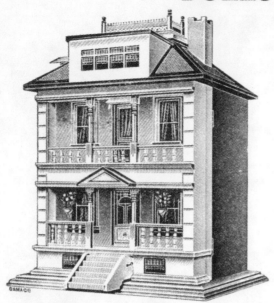

Handsome Dolls House.   As illustration.

With 4 rooms, windows fitted with curtains, balcony on first floor
Beautifully enamelled and finished, imitation tile roof and brick walls.

30 in. High.   25 in. Wide.   20 in. Deep.

Price   ..   **42/-**

Handsome Villa.   As illustration.

With 4 rooms and staircase, imitation electric door bell to ring, all windows
fitted with curtains, doors to open, imitation tile roof and brick walls

Beautifully finished.   31½ in. High.   30½ in. Wide.   20 in. Deep.

Price   ..   **59/6**

Doll House.   As illustration.

Beautifully enamelled and finished

With 5 rooms and staircase, all doors to open, fitted with imitation electric door
bell to ring.   All windows fitted with curtains, imitation tile roof

38 in. High   35 Wide.   26 in. Deep.

Price   ..   **97/6**

Superior Model Dolls House.

With 5 rooms, windows fitted with curtains, 1 window at rear of house
imitation tile roof and brick walls.

Strongly   made   and   well   finished.

36 in. High   29 in. Wide.   19 in. Deep.

Price   ..   **49 6**

Carriage extra on all Dolls' Houses outside London Carrier Radius.

Old Style Rocking Horses.

Saddle Panniers and Straps.
No. 2,
11/6 extra.
No. 3,
13/9 extra.

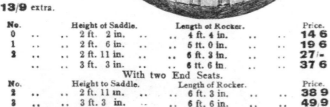

No.	Height of Saddle.	Length of Rocker.	Price.
0	2 ft. 2 in.	4 ft. 4 in.	14 6
1	2 ft. 6 in.	5 ft. 0 in.	19 6
2	2 ft. 11 in.	6 ft. 3 in.	27/-
3	3 ft. 3 in.	6 ft. 6 in.	37 6

With two End Seats.

No.	Height to Saddle.	Length of Rocker.	Price.
2	2 ft. 11 in.	6 ft. 3 in.	38 9
3	3 ft. 3 in.	6 ft. 6 in.	49 9

Gamage's GEE SWING

The latest Novelty for the Nursery and Gymnasium, very strongly made and finished in best style with adjustable hemp ropes. One size only suitable for children up to 10 years of age. Price **42/-**

THE SCOTS' GREYS ROCKING HORSE.

Real Detachable Cavalry Harness, with Shoe Cases, Valise, Holsters, Martingale, Saddle Cloth, Military Bridle, etc.

Plated Metal-work on Stand.

Special Finish Horse and Stand. Harness as above.

No.	Height to Saddle.	Length to Stand.	Price
2	2 ft. 7½ in.	3 ft. 8 in.	55/-
3	3 ft. 0½ in.	4 ft. 4 in.	75/-
4	3 ft. 4½ in.	4 ft. 9½ in.	95/-

Special Clothing for these Horses in Royal Blue and Red with Braided edges, etc.

No. 2, 3/6 each; No. 3, 4/6 each; No. 4, 5/6 each,

Gamage's Celebrated Hobby Horses.
Very strongly made and finished in best style.
Quite safe and practically unbreakable. Painted in various colours.

No.	About height to saddle.	Length of stand.	Price.
Ty. 1	2 ft. 3½ in.	3 ft. 0½ in.	19/6
Ty. 2	2 ft. 7½ in.	3 ft. 8 in.	28/-
Ty. 3	3 ft. 0 in.	4 in. 4 in.	41/-
Ty. 4	3 ft. 4½ in.	4 ft. 9½ in.	49/-

Improved Hobby Horse.

With two end Chair Seats for Children.

Very strongly made in best quality only.
Ty. 2. **46/6**
Ty. 3. **65/6**
A good horse for families, schools, nurseries, etc.
When fixed to the floor, three children can rock it as hard as they like with perfect safety.

Carriage and Packing extra on all above goods outside London Carrier Radius.

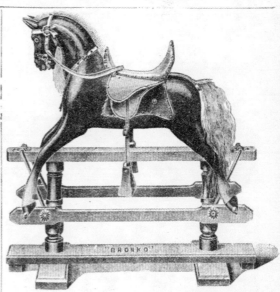

Gamage's "Bronk" Safety Hobby Horse.
Registered No. Ty. 467,670. This horse is specially constructed our own designs. Fitted with cowboy saddle and stirrups, which not only give it an elegant appearance, but render it a much safer horse for a child than the old style. Made in four sizes.

	No. B	No. C	No. D	No. E
	34/6	42/6	63/-	75/-
Hei. to saddle,	27½ in.	31½ in.	36½ in.	40½ in.
Len. of stand,	36½ in.	44 in.	52 in.	57½ in.

Wood Engines, Trams, etc.

Double Deck Electric Tram.
Hardwood, nicely varnished. 19 in. Price, **4/11**

The Rapid Motor Bus as illustrated.
Is a very strong and attractive toy.
Solid construction and splendid finish.
More lettering than on illustrations.
Length 23 inches.
Price on cast iron gilt Wheels .. **6/11**

Strong wooden Tram with iron wheels. Price **10/-**

Motor Lorry (loaded).
This is a large strong Toy, and is loaded as shown in illustration. Nice painted and lined.
Length 25 in.
Price, on Polished Milo Wood Wheels .. **6/6**

Motor Mail Van.
A good Model of the real article. Round top, back doors open. Well painted and lined.
Length 24 in.
Price, on Polished Milo Wood Wheels, **5/11**

Steam Roller.
Strong Toy, painted bright red, solid wood rollers, imitation brake, brass fittings. Price **6/6**

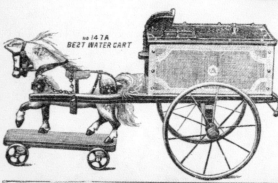

Water Cart and Horse.
These are proper working Models. Tin Lined. Brass Valves and Brass Sprays. Rubber Wheels. Splendidly painted and finished Cart Horse.

As illustrated,
21/- each.

Organ Cart,
No. 1.
A new cheap Organ and Cart, one Tune.
A splendid line, similar to illustration, but with One Tune Organ.
9/11

The Nipper Lawn Mower.
Registered.

This captivating Little Toy is a certain seller.

The Knives revolve in exactly the same way as a big Mower, and it is quite easy to push. A polished Handle is fitted, and the Metal work is finished in Blue, Green, Red and Black Enamel; the Knives in Aluminium Paint. The whole is neatly cardboard boxed. It is not intended to cut much grass, but it snips off some, so may be truly said to cut grass.

Price with detached Grass Box, each **6/3**
Without Grass Box, each **4/11**

Horse Rocking Chair.
As Illustration.
Built of Polished Hardwood .. **13/6**

Gamage's Famous American 'Daisy Waggon.

Substantially built of hardwood, well varnished. Size of body 30 by 14 in., wheels 12 in. and 18 in. with heavy ½ in. welded tyres, shaved spokes and hub caps. **17/6** Carriage forward. These waggons have locked corner bodies, steel axles and boxes, iron and tongued draw, with improved pressed steel rocker plates.

Gamage's Famous Express Waggons.

Soundly constructed of good strong hardwood, well varnished These waggons have frame bottoms with hardwood sills and body braces, locked corners, square steel axles with turned bearings, morticed hubs, shaved spokes, heavy welded tyres and hub caps, as illustration, and with seat. **27/6** Carriage forward.

Hand Carts with Racks

These are specially roomy, light and strong; has folding prop under front, which is easily adjusted with a touch of the foot. Square axles with turned bearings. Wheels have shaved spokes, welded tyres, and steel hub boxes. Bodies set on steel springs. Cut shows top rack on, which can be easily detached when not required. Varnished on the wood. Size 24 by 16 in. body, 18 in. wheels ... **17/6** Carriage extra

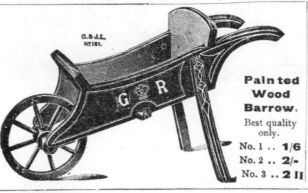

C.S J.L. No 161.

With locked corner bodies, steel axles and boxes, iron tongue draw, and improved steel rocker plates. Body 26 by 13 in. of sound hardwood well varnished. Wheels 10 in. and 15 in., with rivetted tyres, **8/6** Carr. forwd. Similar to illustration, but without splashboard, No. 38, Larger, **13/6**

Painted Wood Barrow.

Best quality only.

No. 1 .. **1/6**
No. 2 .. **2/-**
No. 3 .. **2 11**

Birch Barrow.

Beautifully finished and well varnished.

No. 1 ... **4/6** No. 4, **9/11**
„ 2 **5/11** „ 5, **15/6**
„ 3 **7/11**

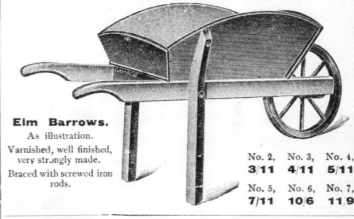

Playcart.

A handsome, easy riding Playcart. The shafts can be used for pushing or drawing. Price **21/-** Carr. extra.

DIMENSIONS.—Length of body, 24 in.; width of body, 13 in.; width of seat, 12 in.; depth of seat, 10 in.; height of seat from floor, 5 in.; height of seat back, 8 in.. The wheels are 14 in. in diam., rubber-tyred, nutless, with brass hub caps.

The Elm Sandow Express

The Strongest Pole Cart made. Registered design.

Size O, **5/11** Size A, Size of Body, 23 by 15 in., upholstered seat, **8/6**

Elm Barrows.

As illustration.

Varnished, well finished, very strongly made.

Braced with screwed iron rods.

No. 2,	No. 3,	No. 4,
3/11	**4/11**	**5/11**
No. 5,	No. 6,	No. 7,
7/11	**10/6**	**11 9**

All goods on this page CARRIAGE PAID within our London Carrier radius: outside, extra.

Price .. **13/9**
Carriage extra.

This cart is modelled on much the same lines as the Playcart, but is not fitted with convertible handle.

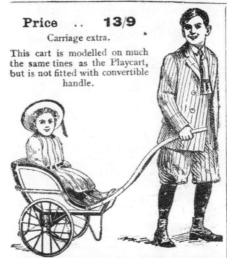

The axles are set in a wooden bolster and bolted through the body. It has both front and back safety stops, as shown in the illustration.

Strongly made Hardwood **Waggons.** As illustration. Large enough for two big children.
Price **20/-** Carriage extra.
Ditto, similar to illustration. Upper length 26 in., width 17½ in.. diam. of wheels 12 by 16 in., **16/6**

Gamages' New Pole Carts.

Strongly made of American Birch and varnished.

1.	16½ by 9 in.	.. **3/11**	3.	30 by 11½ in.	.. **6/11**
2.	18½ by 11 in.	.. **5/11**	4.	22½ by 13½ in.	.. **7/11**

With ⅜ in. iron wheels.

AEROPLANES.

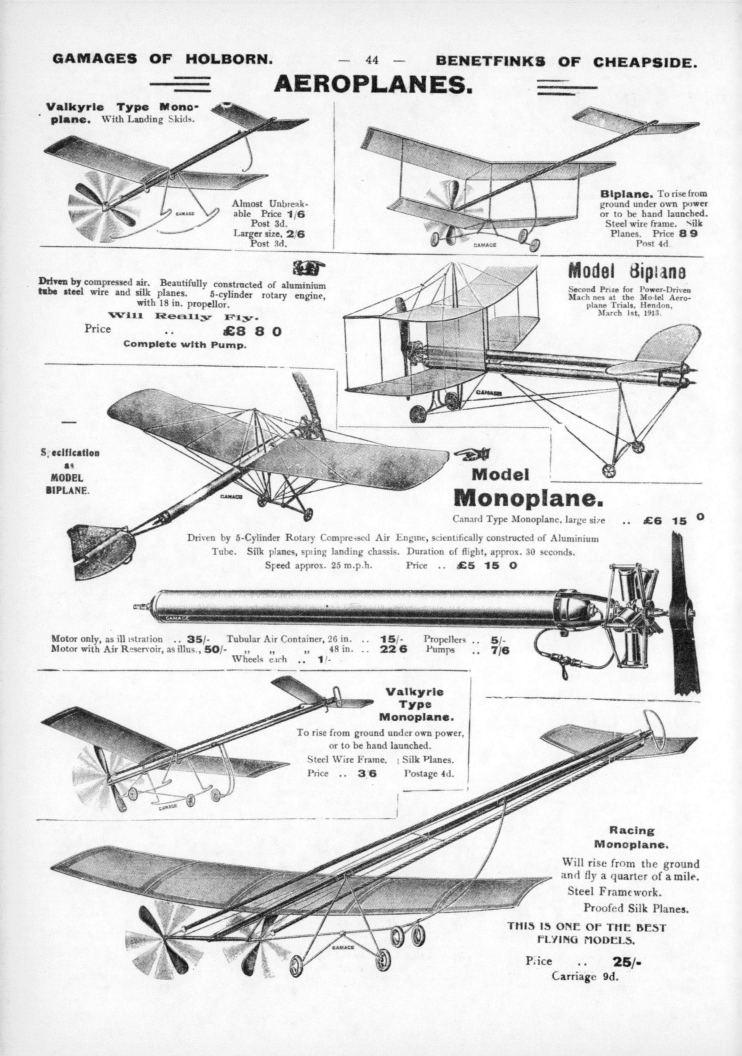

Valkyrie Type Mono-plane. With Landing Skids.

Almost Unbreak-able Price **1/6**
Post 3d.
Larger size, **2/6**
Post 3d.

Biplane. To rise from ground under own power or to be hand launched. Steel wire frame. Silk Planes. Price **8 9**
Post 4d.

Driven by compressed air. Beautifully constructed of aluminium **tube** steel wire and silk planes. 5-cylinder rotary engine, with 18 in. propellor.

Will Really Fly.

Price .. **£8 8 0**

Complete with Pump.

Model Biplane

Second Prize for Power-Driven Mach nes at the Model Aero-plane Trials, Hendon, March 1st, 1913.

Specification as MODEL BIPLANE.

Model Monoplane.

Canard Type Monoplane, large size .. **£6 15 0**

Driven by 5-Cylinder Rotary Compressed Air Engine, scientifically constructed of Aluminium Tube. Silk planes, spring landing chassis. Duration of flight, approx. 30 seconds. Speed approx. 25 m.p.h. Price .. **£5 15 0**

Motor only, as illustration .. **35/-**	Tubular Air Container, 26 in. .. **15/-**	Propellers .. **5/-**
Motor with Air Reservoir, as illus., **50/-**	" " 48 in. .. **22 6**	Pumps .. **7/6**
	Wheels each .. **1/-**	

Valkyrie Type Monoplane.

To rise from ground under own power, or to be hand launched.
Steel Wire Frame. Silk Planes.
Price .. **3 6** Postage 4d.

Racing Monoplane.

Will rise from the ground and fly a quarter of a mile.
Steel Framework.
Proofed Silk Planes.

THIS IS ONE OF THE BEST FLYING MODELS.

Price .. **25/-**
Carriage 9d.

Fine Model Hydroplane.

Rises off water and flies about 100 yds.

Strongly made of ash with cambered silk planes, carved propellers.

Can be steered.

Price **19/6**   Postage 6d.

Complete set of materials with full size drawings to build this machine.

Price **12/9**   Postage 6d.

Deperdussin Tractor Monoplane.

Rises from the ground and flies about 100 yards.
Double surfaced built up planes.
Carved propeller, spring landing chassis.

Price **25/-**

Rises from ground and flies about 100 yards.

Strongly made of ash with cambered silk planes, carved propeller, spring landing chassis.

Packs into small box.

Price **21/-**   Postage 6d.

Sopwith Tractor Biplane.

New Waterplane.

Fine new model of a Modern Waterplane.
Frame of indestructible steel spring wire.
Planes of waterproofed best quality silk.
Floats of very thin sheets of aluminium.
Motor of best India rubber.
Propeller of best nickelled steel.
Perfectly designed and well built.
Strictly reliable.
Will fly from the surface of the water or will also fly from the hand.
Explicit and detailed instructions with each.

24 in. long, 17 in. across.

Price **10/9**   Postage 6d.

Children's Toy Motor Cars

To Pedal.

For Children 3 to 6 years old.

Order Style A. This pedal driven motor car is finished in Dark Green with fine lines only. Specification includes 12 in. rubber-tyred wheels, wings and steps, speedometer and motor clock .. .. Price **25/9**

For Children 4 to 8 years old.

Order Style B. The exclusive model shown above is up to date in all respects. It has the fashionable round-fronted radiator and is fitted with motor headlight, horn, machine cut chain wheels. Finished in Dark Green or Dark Blue with fine lines.

Price **35/-**

For Children 4 to 8 years old.

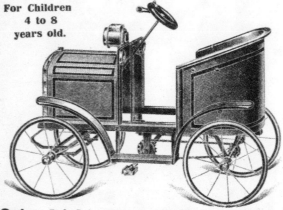

Order Style C. Style C. is complete with mud-guards and step-boards round-fronted radiator, motor lamp and horn, speedometer and motor clock. Machine cut chain wheels, cycle type chain, knuckle-jointed steering gear, stove enamelled ironwork. Adjustable upholstered seat, finished Dark Green or Dark Blue .. Price **42/-**

For Children 4 8 years old.

Order Style D. A handsome model with realistic artillery type wheels fitted with solid rubber wired-on tyres. Very nicely finished in Bright Red or Dark Green. Adjustable upholstered seat, speedometer, motor clock, motor lamp and horn, new round-fronted radiator .. .. Price **52/6**

For Children 6 to 10 years old.

Order Style E. The Model E. Motor is a reproduction of the torpedo shape touring body now so popular on large cars. It includes the new round-fronted radiator, side door, wind screen, two motor lamps, horn, adjustable seat, extra wide mud-guards and steps, speedometer and clock, and upholstered back. Finished in Motor Fawn or Dark Green .. .. .. Price **59/6**

For Children 6 to 10 years old.

Order Style F. This car is a marvel of value, being fitted with good pneumatic tyred tangent-spoke wheels, wind-screen, motor clock, speedometer, two motor lamps, horn, and round-fronted radiator included. Upholstered adjustable seat, finished in Fawn or Dark Green .. Price **97/6**

Carriage extra on all above Cars outside our London Carrier radius.

Children's Toy Motor Cars

To Pedal.

For Children 6 to 10 years old.

Order Style G. A luxurious car, finished specially throughout. Ball-bearing pedals, wheels, and bottom bracket. Fitted wind-screen, adjustable seat, two plated lamps and twisted horn, $\frac{5}{8}$ in. wired-on tyres, tangent spokes, ball-bearing wheels. Beautifully upholstered and painted dark green, dark blue, suede, grey. Speedometer, brake, motor clock and free wheel included. **£6 15 6**

For Children 6 to 10 years old.

Order Style H. THE LAST WORD IN CHILDREN'S AUTOMOBILES It is mounted on tangent spoke wheels with pneumatic tyres, and includes all fittings shown as well as a pump for tyres. Finished in suede grey, French grey, dark green, or dark blue. Price .. **£7 10 0**

For Children 6 to 12 years old.

Order Style I. This commercial motor is modelled on the **B** type 'bus chassis, and has a tipping body operated in a very simple manner. Band brake, speedometer, clock, etc., included. Finished in bright red, black, and grey decoration. Price .. **£2 7 6**

For Children 6 to 12 years old.

Order Style K. A superior town carriage, nicely upholstered and finished coach style, Cape hood, wind-screen, two plated lamps, horn, tangent spoke wheels, $\frac{5}{8}$ tyres wired on, speedometer and clock; ball-bearing pedals and bottom bracket, adjustable seat. Finished dark green-carmine with striped panels. Price **£4 19 6**

Order No. 25.

Tandem Toy Automobile.

The flush-sided body is a really good model of the latest practice. Curvated panels with $\frac{1}{2}$-round beading. Specially well painted, lined and varnished and upholstered in sanitary leather. The chassis is fitted with ball bearings throughout, and is cycle made. Front axle will be appreciated by motorists. Fittings include speedometer, motor clock, two plated lamps and horn, wind-screen, adjustable seat, side doors, band brake, starting handle, finished any colour.

THE LAST WORD IN TOY AUTOS.

Ball-bearing pedals.

Pneumatic tyred wheels. Price **£11 9 6**

Carriage extra on all above motors outside our London Carrier radius

"Handsmobiles" and Hand Propelled Cycle Cars.

The Safety "Scooter."

This is a perfectly safe Toy but at the same time, one from which plenty of excitement, and healthy exercise can be obtained. One foot is placed on the platform while the other is used to strike out skating fashion, and when sufficient speed is attained the operator can put both feet on the platform or sit on the seat. Price as illust., **10/6**

Without seat and pillar, **7/11**

Cycle Car No. 1.

This is the simplest type of hand propelled Cycle Car with rubber tyred wheels working on the crank principle.

It runs easily and can be used by quite young children without the slightest danger.

Very strongly built.

Price **17/6**

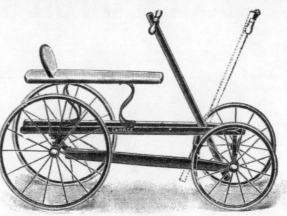

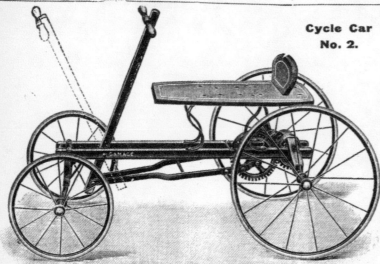

Cycle Car No. 2.

This is a very popular Car operating with steel cranks and cogwheels. Very strongly built with adjustable seat mounted on steel springs, and best quality rubber-tyred wheels. For children of all ages. Price **25/-**

The Nipper Handsmobile.

This is a grand little hand propelled Car working on the crank system Strong and perfectly safe. Splendid value. Price **8/9**

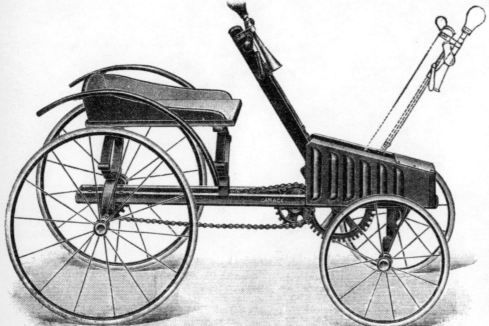

Cycle Car No. 3.

This is the finest Car produced, and is propelled by means of cogwheels operating a cycle chain.

It has a free wheel attachment and can be propelled backwards and forwards.

The seat is padded and mounted on steel springs

Motor type Bonnet rubber-tyred wheels and mudguards.

Price .. **42/-**

Carriage extra on all goods on this page outside London Carrier Radius.

Gamage's "AERIUS FELT" Hats.

THE NEW
Soft Aerius Felt Hat.
Wide band, raw edge.   In brown,
grey, fawn.
Price **4/6**

Aerius Felt, **A.W.G. I.** Jet Black Bowler.
Good medium brim in roll and flat curls.

The Aerius Felt **A.W.G. II,** Jet Black,
Fast Dye Felt Hat.   Full shape.   Angelsea curls.
Price **4/6**

The Shackleton Soft Felt Hat.
Positively waterproof.   Various colours.
Wide galleon
band, greys,
heathers,
browns and
greens.

The Connemara & Mayo.
Stitched Tweed Hat.
Made in all colourings, gray & heather.
Silk lined.   Soft and comfortable.
Price .. **4/6**

The Aerius.
Pure Fur Felt.
The lightest weight hat on earth.   In all colours.
Price .. **4/6**   Post free

The new Aerius Felt with stitched curl brim.
All fur, in slate, brown and stone colour **4/6**

The Derby.   Full Shape, Flat
Set Brim.   Very smart. **4/6** Post free.

The Richmond.
Bound and unbound edges.   In black, slate,
Drab, and Cuba brown.   A good medium
shaped felt. **4/6** Post free.

PANAMAS
For Town and Country.
LOWEST PRICES.

PANAMAS
For Home and Abroad.
MAXIMUM VALUE, MINIMUM PRICES.

The Alpine, 21/- 25/-

SPECIAL VALUE.

The Warwick 7/9

The Vienna 8/9

A LUXURY TO WEAR.
The Holborn, 10/6 Our specialité

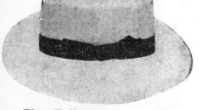

The Alpine .. 21/- 25/-

The Dual .. 35/- 40/- 45/- 50/-

The Eclipse 15/-

ALL
HATS
10/- AND
OVER
SENT
POST
FREE IN
U.K

ALL
SIZES.
—
FINE
PLAITS.

THE FOLDED PANAMA.

The New Golf .. 21/- 25/-

The Palmerston 18/6

The Kensington .. 10/6 12/6

The Beaufort .. 15/-

PACKED IN SPECIAL CARTONS.

The Kempton 18/6

The Mascot 15/-

The Largest Stock of
:: PANAMAS ::
IN THE WORLD.

A. W. GAMAGE Ltd., Holborn, London, E.C.

LADIES' PANAMA HATS

Perfect Summer Headwear.   Charming Shapes.

The Beatrice

Shape P. 163.
Silk Lined, with wide silk ribbon trimming.
7/11   12/6   15/6   21/-

THE PAULINE.

Shape P. 191.
Trimmed, Black Galloon Band and White Silk Lined.
12/6

The Olivette

Shape P. 153.
New Style, Silk Lined, Trimmed Black Moire Ribbon.
8/6   15/6   21/-

The Cranmere

Shape P. 176.
Trimmed with Silk Galloon Banding.
A Very Smart Shape,
6/11   8/11   10/11   21/-   25/-

PANAMA HATS
FOR HOME AND
FOREIGN WEAR.

The Eunice

Shape P. 161
White Silk Lined, with Blade Galloon Trimming.
Very fine quality. Beautiful Plaits.
18/6   21/-   25/-   30/-   40/-

These Shapes only represent a few of the New Styles.

Any Shape can be procured.

———

Panama Hats cannot be sent on approbation.

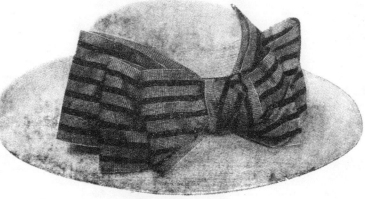

THE MENTONE.
Trimmed with Wide Silk Ribbon, and rich silk lined .. **18/6   25/-   30/-**

ALL HATS
securely packed
and
sent by return
of Post.

All Hats 10/- and over sent post free in United Kingdom.

A. W. GAMAGE, Ltd., Holborn, London, E.C.

SILK HATS.

SILK HATS.

A PERFECT FIT ENSURED

By the Use of

THE CONFORMATEUR.

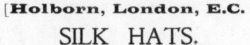

Re-lined, Re-blocked and made equal to New in Three Days.
Price .. **3/6**

ALL SILK HATS
Packed in Box
and CARRIAGE PAID.

The Portland.
Our Speciality, 10/6

The Clumber.
18/6 and 21/-
The Finest Qualities.

The Hurlingham.
Finest quality, smart Silk
Hat. Will sure to suit, 21/-

The Radnor.
Brightest Silk Plushes.
Finest possible make. 21/

Ladies' Riuing Hats.
New shape, with quilted lining and
fittings ... **10/6 12/6**

Opera Hats.
10/6   12/6   15/-
Corded Silk Opera Hats,
15/6   18/6

Livery Hats.
10/6 and 12/6
Cockades .. 1/6

The Ascot.
Full shape. For big men.
18/6

The Westminster.
The Latest in Silk Hats.
Beautiful quality. The middle-
age man's Hat. 15/-

The West End.
Best Plushes.
The Best 10/6 Silk Hat
in London.

The Mall. Correct Felt Hat.. A smart Hat
always in fashion. **8/6 10/6**

The St. James. Full Shape.
An important-looking Hat. Exclusive
Shape, finest quality. **8/6 and 10/6**

The Roxburghe.
A Full-brimmed Hat. Full shape.
Best Black Felt. 6/6 and 7/6

SECTION OF HAT SHOWING
←ELASTIC FOR ADJUSTING
AND SPACE BETWEEN LEATHER
AND HAT FOR VENTILATION.

No. 1 Bon Ton (Small shape).
The finest invention for comfort in Hats
yet brought out. 5/6

The No. 2 Bon Ton (Medium)
The Hat with the Bon Ton Fitting.
Perfect Ventilation and Comfort in Wear. 5/6

The Travellers Hat Iron, 1/3

The Park. Newest Shape. Up-to-date man's Hat.
Finest quality. Patent head-fitting. 7/6

Rotary Hat Iron, indestructible, 3/6

00

"GAMAGE" BRITISH-MADE FOOTWEAR.
EVERY PAIR GUARANTEED.
THREE POPULAR CITY BOOTS.

Black Box.
8/11

Made in Narrow, Medium or Round Toes.

In half-sizes and ⅛ fittings

When ordering, please quote—
A.W.G. Popular Boot

Made in—
TAN or BLACK Leathers.

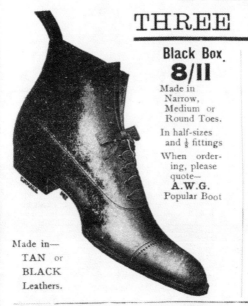

ALL ONE PRICE 8/11

SPLENDID VALUE.

Really High-class Boots.

Up-to-date Stylish Models.

Any Foot accurately Fitted.

TAN WILLOW
8/11

TAN WILLOW **8/11**

Glace Kid.
8/11

Oak Bark Tanned Soles.

square Waists.

EASE AND COMFORT ASSURED.

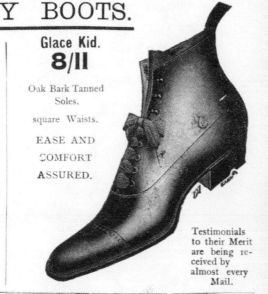

Testimonials to their Merit are being received by almost every Mail.

The "Curzon" Model.
12/6

In tan willow, glacé or box calf.

Marvellous Value. Made in Half Sizes and ⅛ Fittings.

In Narrow, Medium and Round Toes.

Better qualities.

**14 6   16/6   18 6
21 -**

The "Beresford" Model
15/6

Made in Fine quality Black Glacé Kid, in Half sizes and Fittings.

Highly recommended.

The A.W.G. "Tourist" Boot.

MADE IN FINE TAN, WILLOW CALF, and ⅜ STOUT

WATER-PROOF SOLES
15/6

Absolutely Trustworthy. Every pair "Goodyear" welted

The "Continental."
15/6

Made in Black Glacé. Goloshed, with tan willow calf legs.

Also in black glacé kid and Box Calf.

Immaculate Design.

HIGH CLASS FOOTWEAR.

The "Crichton" as illustration.
10/9

A Smart Model.

Made in Black Glace Kid upper.

Patent leather toe caps

A neat walking Boot

Every pair guaranteed

British-made

The "Elgin" Model
18/6

Fine willow calf, ⅜ stout soles.

A very fine walking boot.

½ sizes. ⅛ fittings.

Made to measure, 2/- extra.

P4..

Boot Department.—Our Anti-Rheumatic Boots for Tender Feet.

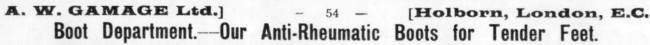

All One Price.

21/-

The Anti-Rheumatic Boot is made in 5 shapes, viz., 1, 2, 3, 4 and 5, ½ sizes, ⅓ fittings Really a High Grade Boot.

Anti-Rheumatic Boots

All One Price.

21/-

Doe Skin Lined throughout. Anti-Rheumatic Boots, once worn, always worn.

All One Price.

21/-

This Boot is worn and recommended by thousands. They are Lined throughout with Doe Skin, are made without Toe Caps, and in 120 different sizes and fittings.

And No More Corns.

Comfort right away A Boot with a great reputation, all one price, **21/-**

The "Arundel."
18/6

Best "C.H." patent golosh glacé legs. Finest workmanship.

When ordering, quote Arundel Model.

Made also in box and willow calf.

14/6   16/6   18/6

The "Promenade" Shoe.

A Special Light Walking Tan Calf Brogue Shoe. Fine quality. "Goodyear" Welted.

12/9

120 different Sizes and Fittings.

The "PORTMAN" Model.

14/6

Made in Tan Willow, Box Calf, and Black Glacé Kid.

½-sizes, ⅓ Fittings.

Solid Oak Black Tanned Soles, Welted throughout.

Smart Models.

Made in Patent Golosh and Grey Antelope Hide Legs. SPECIAL VALUE.

18/6

18/6

HIGH-GRADE FOOTWEAR.

120 Different Sizes and Fittings.

MOTOR FOOTWEAR OUR SPECIALITY.

New Designs

The "Highland"
18/6

Made in Tan Grain, or Black Waterproof Moor Calf. Strong and Durable.

Real Scotch Brogue Shoes.
10/9

In Tan, Willow or Box Calf.

Marvellous value.

Made in Goodyear Welted, **12/6**

In Tan or Black Moor Calf, waterproof throughout, **16/6**

High-class Footwear

Made in Black Glacé Golosh and Grey Antelope Hide Legs.

18/6

18/6

Also made in TAN WILLOW CALF GOLOSH & TAN ANTELOPE HIDE LEGS. **Elegant Designs.**

BOOTS AND SHOES FOR ALL SPORTS.

New Ladies' Shoe Department.

(MAIL ORDERS ONLY.)

The Celebrated 'FOOTHAVEN' Brand.

FIT, STYLE AND DURABILITY GUARANTEED.

The Foothaven No. 835.
13/9

Made in Black Chrome Glace Kid (special quality), Best Bench-made throughout, with either plain Glace or Patent Leather Toe Caps. When ordering please quote above No. **835**

The Foothaven, No. 831.

15/6

Made in Black Glace Golosh, Fancy Grey Calf, Legs and Patent Leather Toe Caps.
Finest Materials and Best Workmanship.

The Foothaven No. 840.
13/9

Made in Fine Quality Black Glace uppers, and Bench made in either Self toe caps or Patent leather caps.
Every pair guaranteed.
Perfect fitting models.

The Foothaven No. 804.

12/6

Made in Black Glace Kid, Patent Leather Toe Caps. Best welted make in Narrow, Medium and Round Toes.

The Foothaven, No. 829.

15/6

Made in Grey Calf Legs, Black Glace Golosh, and Patent **Straight Toe Caps.** Half sizes, ½ Fittings, High Class Stylish Boots.

The Foothaven No. 806.

12/9

Best welted. Fit and style assured. Made in Fine quality Black Box Calf, and Tan Willow Calf

The Foothaven No. 810.

12/6

Made in Black **Glace** (fine quality) Patent Leather Toe Caps. Exceptionally good **wearing shoes** Made in Half-sizes and ½ Fittings.

The Foothaven No. 815

14/9

Made in Patent Golosh. Also in Black Glace Kid, Grey Calf. Inserted top (as illustration). Really Elegant Shoe.

The Foothaven No. 812.

13/9

Made in Fine Quality C.H. Patent Leather, with Dull Kid Inserted Tops. Best Welted. A Neat High-grade Shoe.

The Foothaven No. 800.

16/6

Brogue Pattern
(as illustration).

Made in Black Box Calf, Tan Willow Calf or C.H. Patent Leather.

Best workmanship and Materials throughout.

Correct Corset Models.

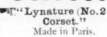

"Lynature (No. 2 Corset."
Made in Paris. NATURE'S FORM CORSET giving just those natural and graceful lines to the figure so very essential to fashionable ladies. Coutille, trimmed embroidery, ribbon and bow. Short above waist, deep below. Suspenders at front and sides.

Price **8/11**
Post free.

"Lynature (No. 1) Corset."
NATURE'S FORM CORSET. Made in Paris. Emphasising the natural and graceful lines of the figure so very essential to fashionable ladies. White Coutille trimmed embroidery, ribbon and bow, very short above waist, extra deep below, suspenders front and sides.
Price **7/6**   Post free.

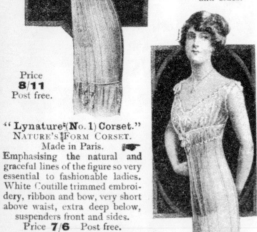

"Beautesia" Corset.
For tall medium to full figures. Coutille, trimmed satin, fancy edging and bow, bias cut, gored, short above waist, extra deep below. Six suspenders. Rustproof.
Price **7/11**   Post free.

"The Ivernia Corset."
For slight to medium figures. White or grey Coutille, trimmed satin ribbon and bow, bias cut. Short above waist, deep below. Suspenders at front and sides. Rustproof.

Price **4/6**

Post free.

The **"Clytie" Corset.**
For medium figures. Coutille, white or grey, trimmed lace and bow, bias cut, gored, short above waist, deep below, suspenders at front and sides. Rustproof.
Price .. **2/11½**
Post free.

The **"Curvator" Corset.**
NATURE'S FORM.
Model C.
RUSTLESS AND UNBREAKABLE.
Retains the beautiful lines of the figure and gives the slight natural curve and necessary support below the waist, without undue accentuation.

White Coutille, trimmed embroidery and ribbon, bias cut, short above waist, deep below, draw strings at bust. Suspenders at front and sides.

Price **7/6**
Post free.

"Maternity" Corset.
White Coutille, finest loom elastic each side of busk, lacing at hips, four suspenders. Modelled on hygienic lines.
Price .. **12/9**
Post free.

NURSING CORSETS.

The **"Wallingford."**
White or grey Coutille, button bust, lacing at hips, short above waist, deep below, suspenders at front and sides. Rustproof.
Price **4/6**   Post free.

The **"Windsor."**
White Coutille, trimmed embroidery and wide ribbon, button bust, lacing at hips, short above waist, deep below, four suspenders.
Price .. **5/11**
Post free.

The **"Bewtifit" Costume.**
A beautiful and fashionable shape, designed with free hip. For tall figures, slim to medium. White Coutille; medium above waist, deep below, suspenders at front and sides. Rustproof.

Price **5/11**
Post free.

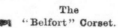

The **"Belfort" Corset.**
For slight to medium figures. Coutille, trimmed fancy ribbon and bow, bias cut, gored, short above waist, deep below, suspenders at front and sides.
Price **4/6**
Post free.

Latest Models in Correct Corset Wear for 1914.

The "Arista" Corset.

A comfortable shape for medium figures. Busk 11 in., depth—front 17 in., back 20 in. White or Dove Coutille, trimmed satin ribbon and bow. Bias cut, gored, short above waist, extra deep below, drawstrings at bust. Suspenders at front and sides .. **6/11** Post free.

The 'Baressa' Corset

Specially designed for full figures. Depth, front 16 in. back 17½ in., Busk 11½ in. White or grey Coutille Trimmed embroidery and ribbon, Bias cut, gored, short above waist, deep below. Suspenders at front & sides. Rustproof. Sizes 21 to 33 inches.. **5/11** Post free.

"Tango" Hip Confiner.

Model B. Coutille with 1 in. elastic Waistband. Suspenders at front and sides **2/3** Post free.

Model C. Coutille with 1 in. Coutille Waist-band and elastic gore at hip. Deeper than Model B. Suspenders at front and sides. **2/11½** Post free.

"Golfette" Corset

For Golf, Riding, Cycling and Athletics. Perfect freedom above waist. No. S.1. Coutille, trimmed bow, wide elastic at bosom, Short above waist, deep below. Four Suspenders. **4/6** Post free. No. S.2. Superior quality Trimmed Embroidery, ribbon and bow, &c., &c. Busk 9 in. Depth, front 14 in. back 15 in. **5/11** Post free.

The "Salento" Corset

For slim to medium figures. Busk 10½ in., depth front 16½ in. back 17½ in. White or dove Coutille, trimmed embroidery and bow. Short above waist, deep below. Suspenders at front. Rustproof. **2/11½** Post free.

The "Curvator" Corset.

NATURE'S FORM.

Models A and B. Model A. Coutille white or grey fanned, trimmed embroidery. Bias cut, short above waist, deep below. Suspenders attached. **4/6** Post free.

Model B. White or grey Coutille, trimmed embroidery and ribbon. Bias cut, short above waist, deep below. Suspenders at front and sides. **5/11** Post free.

The "Curvator" Corset.

Nature's Form. Model D. Rustless and Unbreakable. Scientifically cut to retain the beautiful lines of the figure and give the slight natural curve and necessary support below the waist, without undue accentuation. In white soft Cloth, trimmed Satin ribbon and bow, bias cut, Short above waist, deep below. Suspenders at front and sides **8/11** Post free.

The "Europa" Corset.

An elegant high-class design specially cut for ladies medium to full. White Coutille, trimmed satin, lace and bow, bias cut, gored, very short in front, and under arm above waist, extra deep below, Suspenders at front and sides. Rustproof. **7/6** Post free.

The "Knicker-Skirt" Corset.

For tall, stylish Ladies. Ensures long, graceful lines. In white Coutille, trimmed lace, ribbon and bow, gored bust, short above waist, extra deep below. Elastic lacings below busk, Fastening round leg with elastic loop and button. Six stocking Suspenders **12/9** Post free.

The "Ovaline" Corset.

An elegant Corset for tall, medium figures. In white Coutille, trimmed embroidery, ribbon and bow. Bias cut, short above waist, extra deep below. Suspenders at front and sides.

Rustproof. **8/11** Post free.

Interesting Bargains in Irish Peasantmade Underwear.

Perfect shapes, Excellent Workmanship, Good Quality at Low Prices.

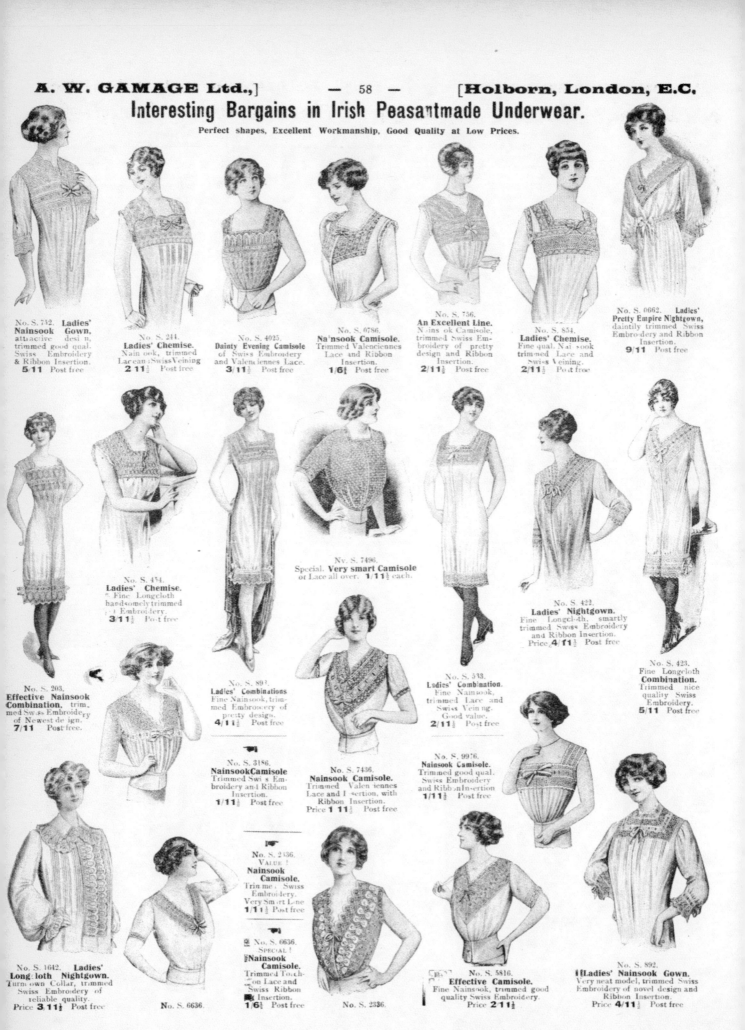

No. S. 752. **Ladies' Nainsook Gown,** attractive design, trimmed good qual. Swiss Embroidery & Ribbon Insertion. **5/11** Post free

No. S. 244. **Ladies' Chemise.** Nainsook, trimmed Lace and Swiss Veining **2/11½** Post free

No. S. 4025. **Dainty Evening Camisole** of Swiss Embroidery and Valenciennes Lace. **3/11½** Post free

No. S. 6786. **Nainsook Camisole.** Trimmed Valenciennes Lace and Ribbon Insertion. **1/6½** Post free

No. S. 756. **An Excellent Line.** Nainsook Camisole, trimmed Swiss Embroidery of pretty design and Ribbon Insertion. **2/11½** Post free

No. S. 854. **Ladies' Chemise.** Fine qual. Nainsook trimmed Lace and Swiss Veining. **2/11½** Post free

No. S. 0662. **Ladies' Pretty Empire Nightgown,** daintily trimmed Swiss Embroidery and Ribbon Insertion. **9/11** Post free

No. S. 454. **Ladies' Chemise.** Fine Longcloth handsomely trimmed Embroidery. **3/11½** Post free

Nv. S. 7496. Special. **Very smart Camisole** of Lace all over. **1/11½** each.

No. S. 422. **Ladies' Nightgown.** Fine Longcloth, smartly trimmed Swiss Embroidery and Ribbon Insertion. Price **4/11½** Post free

No. S. 203. **Effective Nainsook Combination,** trimmed Swiss Veining of Newest design. **7/11** Post free

No. S. 893. **Ladies' Combinations** Fine Nainsook, trimmed Embroidery of pretty design. **4/11½** Post free

No. S. 533. **Ladies' Combination.** Fine Nainsook, trimmed Lace and Swiss Veining. Good value. **2/11½** Post free

No. S. 423. Fine Longcloth **Combination.** Trimmed nice quality Swiss Embroidery. **5/11** Post free

No. S. 3186. **Nainsook Camisole** Trimmed Swiss Embroidery and Ribbon Insertion. **1/11½** Post free

No. S. 7436. **Nainsook Camisole.** Trimmed Valenciennes Lace and Insertion, with Ribbon Insertion. Price **1/11½** Post free

No. S. 9976. **Nainsook Camisole.** Trimmed good qual. Swiss Embroidery and Ribbon Insertion **1/11½** Post free

No. S. 1642. **Ladies' Longcloth Nightgown.** Turn-own Collar, trimmed Swiss Embroidery of reliable quality. Price **3/11½** Post free

No. S. 6636.

No. S. 2436. VALUE! **Nainsook Camisole.** Trimmed Swiss Embroidery. Very Smart Line **1/11½** Post free

No. S. 6636. SPECIAL! **Nainsook Camisole.** Trimmed Torchon Lace and Swiss Ribbon Insertion. **1/6½** Post free

No. S. 2336.

No. S. 5816. **Effective Camisole.** Fine Nainsook, trimmed good quality Swiss Embroidery. Price **2/11½**

No. S. 892. **Ladies' Nainsook Gown.** Very neat model, trimmed Swiss Embroidery of novel design and Ribbon Insertion. Price **4/11½** Post free

New Designs in Ladies' Cami-Skirts, Skirts, Knickers ETC.

S. 123. Dainty Nainsook Skirt. Side opening, trimmed very effective Swiss embroidery.
4 11½ Post free.

S. 387.
Exceptional Value. Nainsook Cami-Skirt, trimmed effective Embroidery & Insertion.
4/11½ Post free.

Peg Top Skirt Knickers

Soft finished Mercerised Sateen with frill.
Colours: White, Sky, Pink, Saxe, Cream, Silver Grey, Helio, Tan, Navy and Black.
2/11½ Post free.

Peg Top Knickers.
JAP SILK KILTED FRILL AND ROSETTE
All Colours
5/11 Post free.

Silk Back Satin Soft-Finish Kilted Frill and Rosette.
Cream, Sky, Pink and Black,
9/11 Post free.

S. 567. Very Smart Model in a Nainsook Cami-Skirt, daintily embroidered.
9 11

S. 687.
Wonderful Value.
Ladies' Nainsook Skirt. Trimmed Handsome design Embroidery.
2/11½ Post free.

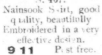

S. 467.
Nainsook Skirt, good quality, beautifully Embroidered in a very effective design.
9 11 Post free.

S. 307. (Post free)
Pretty Nainsook Skirt. Effectively trimmed good quality Embroidery, with veining and ribbon edged Valenciennes Lace. **7/11**

S. 737. Nainsook Skirt. Serviceable quality, trimmed Swiss Embroidery in an effective design.
3/11½ Post free.

S. 926.
Fine Longcloth Skirt. Very Pretty Embroidery Flounce, Pansy Design.
4/11½ Post free.

S. 937.
Princess Cami-Skirt. Effectively trimmed good Swiss Embroidery on fine quality Nainsook.
6/11 Post free.

S. 447.
Princess Cami-Skirt. A unique design, trimmed with a novel Embroidery.
9/11 Post free.

S. 337. Nainsook Skirt. Trimmed Swiss Embroidery of handsome design and splendid quality.
6/11 Post free.

S. 6211. Special Value. Longcloth Knickers, trimmed good quality Embroidery.
1/11½ Post free.

BRASSIERE BUST BODICES.
New V shape Embroidered Yoke **2/3** Post free. Superior style Longcloth, trimmed deep Embroidery in front and over arms **3 3** Post free.
Also ordinary styles, **1/11½** and **2/11½**

S. 6721.
Golt Shape Knickers, (closed). Very serviceable Nainsook, trimmed Swiss Embroidery of good design, and Ribbon Insertion **2/11½** Post free

S. 527.
Very Smart Style Nainsook Skirt, trimmed effective Embroidery of good quality.
6/11 Post free.

Ladies' 'Aeronet' (Cream) Combinations.

A soft and Comfortable Summer Garment. Women's Size, Price **1/11½**

Outsize Women's Size, Price **2/6** Post free.

White Cotton Combinations.

Women's Size. Price **1/6½** Post free.

Ladies'
Ribbed Silk, Wool and Cotton Spencers.

Long Sleeves.
Price **1/11½** Out-size **2/6** Post free.

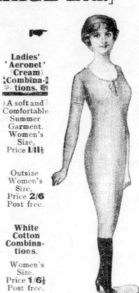

Children's Natural or White Merino Combinations.

High necks and half sleeves.
Sizes 2 3 & 4 5
Prices **1/6½ 1/9½ 1/11½**
  6 7 8
  2/3 2/6 2/11

Also in Pure Natural Wool.
Price **2/9, 2/11, 3/3, 3/6 3/9, 4/3**

Cream Merid an Interlock Fabric.

The Perfect Underwear for Summer Wear and for delicate skins. Very soft and elastic.
Women's Size **3/11**
Out-size Women's Size **4/11½** Post free.

India Gauze Combinations.

White. Women's Size. **2/11½** O.S. Women's Size. **3/6** Post free.

Ladies' Bodices or Spencers.

Cream Meridian Interlock, Fabric.
Warm, Soft Elastic and Durable. High necks and half sleeves.
Women's Size. **1/11½**
Out-size Women's Size, **2/6** Post free.

Ladies' Natural or White Merino Combinations.

High necks and half sleeves.
Women's Size **1/11½** and **2/11**

Out-size Women's Size, **2/6** and **3/6**

Similar Garment in All Wool, summer weight, white or natural. Women's Size. Price **4/11** Post free.
Out-size Women's Size, Price **5/11**

Ladies, "Aeronet" Shape-waist Undervests.

Cream.
Grand Value.
Price **1/0½d.** Post free.
Out-size, Price **1/3** Post free.
Ladies' Silk, Wool and Cotton Vests. Extra Large Size.
Price **1/6½** Post free.

Children's White Silk, Wool and Cotton Undervests.

High Necks and Half Sleeves.
Size 1 2 3 4
Price **1/0½ 1/2½ 1/4½ 1/6½**
  5 6 7 8
1/8½ 1/9½ 1/11 1/11½
Post free.
Ribbed Wool Vests, natural or white.
Size 1 & 2 3, 4 & 5 6, 7 & 8
Price **10½d. 1/0½ 1/3**
Post free.

Ladie's Undervests.

Fancy tops, silk, wool and cotton. Full size.
Price **1/11** Post free.

Also in Cotton, Ribbed, fancy tops.
8½d., 10½d., 1/0½ Post free.

Ladies' White Summer Combinations

Sanitas Elastica. A Perfect Garment. Low or high necks.
Women's Size, **2/11**
Out-size. Women's Size, **3/6** Post free.

Undervests.
to match. Women's Size. **2 3** O.S. Women's Size **2/11**

NEW! CHEMVESTS.

Extra long Swiss Ribbed Vests. Very Smart and Comfortable.
1/0½ 1/3½ 1/11½ Each post free.

Ladies' New Style 'Equestrienne' Knickers.

Perfect Fitting. Colours, cream, black, mole, grey, saxe, and navy.

Price **1/11½** Post free.

Ladies' White Cotton Spencers.

Ribbed Bottoms.
Women's Size, **1/0½**
Out-size Women's Size, **1/3½**
Cheaper Qualities.
8½d. and **10½d.** each.

Ladies' Directoire Knickers.

Colours, cream, white, black, sky, helio, saxe, navy, purple, grey, and mole.
Fine Summer Cotton, elastic, at waist and knee.
Perfect shape.
Price **1/11½** Post free.

Mercerised Cotton.
Price **2/11** Post free.

Fine woven Botany Wool.
Price **4/11** Post free.

Ladies' Golf or Skirt Knickers

Summer Cotton button backs.

Also in Directoire shape

All colours.
Price **1/11½** Post free.

Fleece, summer or heavy weight.
Price **1/11½** Post free.

Striped Zephyr.
Price **1/11½** Post free.

Ladies' Cream or Natural Merino Vests. High necks and half sleeves.
Women's size ... **1/11½**

Out-size Women's Size, **2/6** Post free.

Maids' Tailor-made Costumes to fit young Ladies, ages 14 to 18 yrs.

These Garments can be made to Special Measurements at an extra charge of 3/-

No. S. 8605.
Maid's Sports Coat in
Blanket Serge in all
Fashionable Colours.
Correct Style.
Sizes: 6, 7, 8 and 9.
Price **12/11** Post free

No. S. 728.
**Maids Costume.
Fashionable Tailor-
made** Coat and Skirt.
Made in Saxe, Grey, Tan,
Vieux Rose, etc.
Cheviot Serge.
Coat is lined and Skirt
unbuttons 3 buttons up.
Sizes: 6, 7, 8 and 9.
Price **19/11** Post free

No. S. 868.
**Maid's Costume.
Useful Tailor-made**
Coat and Skirt (Coat lined).
Made in Navy Blue or Black
Coating Serge.
Belt effect at back of Coat.
Sizes: 6, 7, 8 and 9.
Price **12/11** Post free

No. S. 338.
**Maid's Costume.
Smart Tailor-made** Coat
and Skirt (Coat lined) in
durable Cheviot Serge in
Navy Blue, Brown or Grey.
Skirt trimmed Buttons.
Sizes: 6, 7, 8 and 9.
Price **9/11** Post free

No. S. 409.
Maid's Tailor-made
Coating Serge **Costume.**
Colours :
Black and Navy only.
Coat lined Polo.
Collar trimmed Duvetin in
various colourings.
Sizes: 6, 7, 8 and 9.
Price **21/9** Post free

No. S. 708.
**Maid's Tailor-made
Costume** in Fine Serge.
Shades: Saxe, Purple, Grey,
Fawn, Navy and Black.
Sizes: 6, 7, 8 and 9.
Price **15/11** Post free

No. S. 508.
**Maid's Sports
Costume** in all new
bright shades,
including Rose,
Saxe, Emerald, Tan,
&c., &c,
Sizes : 6, 7, 8 and 9.
Price **17/11** Post free

No. S. 808.
Maid's Costume.
Black and White
or
Navy and White
Shepherd's Plaid.
Skirt trimmed buttons.
Coat lined.
Sizes: 6, 7, 8 and 9.
Price **12/9** Post free

No. S. 898.
**Maids Check
Sports Coat.**
Collar trimmed Tango,
Cerise, Emerald,
Purple, or Saxe.
Sizes : 6, 7, 8 and 9.
Price **9/11** Post free

No. S. 348.
Maid's Tailor-made
Art Coloured Serge
Costume.
Coat lined Polo.
Colours: Tan, Saxe,
Grey, Vieux Rose,
Purple and Light Navy,
and Black.
Price **21/9** Post free

No. S. 1845.
Maid's Tailor-made
Coating Serge **Costume**
Coat lined Polo.
Colours :
Navy and Black only.
Collar piped fancy
colourings.
Sizes : 6, 7 8 and 9.
Price **25/9** Post free

LADIES' ECONOMICAL OVERALLS. BOTH BECOMING AND USEFUL.

Model S. 9602.
Ladies' Print Overall.
Dark ground, spot design, high
waist, trimmed striped print
pipings.
Price **1/11½**   Post free.

Model S. 8602.
Ladies' Print Overall.
Striped design.
Trimmed self colour collar,
pocket and pipings.
Price **1/11½**   Post free.

New Artist's Overall.

Model S. 1918.
A Practical Garment
Fastening in front. In good
quality, guaranteed fast washing
colour cloth.   In light, mild and
dark butcher blue. Collar, cuffs
and pocket trimmed fancy cloth
to tone.
Prtce **2/11½**   Post free.

Model S. 1502.
Ladies' Print Overall
White ground, striped design
Trimmed fancy strappings and
self colour yoke.
Price **1/3½**   Post free.

Model S. 8112.
Ladies' Print Overall.
White ground, spot design, trim-
med Paisley design, vest and
self colour pipings.
Price **2/11**   Post free.

Model S. 2602.
**Ladies' Casement Cloth
Overall.**
Plain colours. Trimmed self
colour embroidery.
/9   Post free.

Model S. 3902.
Ladies' Drill Overall.
Light weight cloth, white
ground, striped design.
Trimmed self colour collar and
sleeves, edged border design.
Price **1/11½**   Post free.

Model S. 51,051.
**Long Sleeve Case-
ment Overall.**
In navy, butcher and grey.
Price **1/11½**   Post free.

Model S. 8502.
Ladies' Print Overall.
Dark ground with white spots.
Trimmed handsome border design
and self colour pipings.
Price **1/9½**   Post free.

Model S. 5802.
Ladies' Drill Overall.
Light weight cloth, navy and
butcher blue colours only.
Trimmed dainty border strappings.
Price **1/11½**   Post free.

LATEST DESIGNS IN MUSLIN APRONS. DRAPERY DEPARTMENT.

Our Aprons are well-known for their shape, perfect fitting skirts, and wide and long Strings.

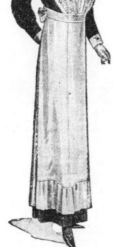

Model S9055.
White Embroidered
Muslin Apron.
Price **1/6½** Post free.

Model S1657.
Dainty Four o'clock White
Muslin Tea Apron.
Price **1/11½** Post free.

Model S9355.
Princess Style White
Embroidered Muslin Apron.
Price **1/11½** Post free.

Model S0365.
Dainty Four o'clock
White Embroidered Muslin
Tea Apron.
Price **2/11½** Post free.

Model S0655.
Princess Style
White Embroidered
Muslin Apron.
Price **1/11½** Post free.

Model S6055.
White Embroidered
Muslin Apron.
Price **1/6½** Post free.

Model S6155.
White Embroidered
Muslin Apron.
Price **1/9½** Post free.

Model S2365.
Dainty Four o'clock
White Embroidered Muslin
Tea Apron.
Price **3/3** Post free.

Model S0055.
White Embroidered
Muslin Apron.
Price **1/3½** Post free.

Model S2955.
White Embroidered
Muslin Apron.
Price **2/11½** Post free.

WARRANTED SHOWERPROOF.
LIGHT IN WEIGHT.

WATERPROOFS

PROOFED BY THE CRAVENETTE CO.
SMART IN APPEARANCE.

The "Bath" (Cravenette proofed). Raincoat as illustration, with inset sleeves, similar style with Raglan sleeves.
Lengths 50, 52, and 54 in.
Price .. **21/9** Post free.

The "Bradford" (Cravenette proofed) Raincoat as illustration, with Belt at back. Inset sleeves, similar style with Raglan sleeves. 48, 50, 52, 54, 56 in.
Price .. **14/11** Post free.

The "Antwerp" Raincoat. (Cravenette proofed). Very smart high-waisted model, with inset sleeves, as illustration.
Sizes: 50, 52, 54, 56 in.
Price .. **21/9** Post free.

The "Epping" Raincoat (Cravenette proofed). Can be worn open at neck, or to button up close in New Style as shown in illustration, Raglan sleeves, or similar style with inset sleeves. Sizes: 50, 52, 54, 56 in.
Price .. **21/9** Post free.

The "Clare" Raincoat (Cravenette proofed). Useful Nurses Cloak, stocked in various qualities, in Navy Blue, Greys, Fawns, &c., as sketch. Lengths 50, 52, 54, 56 in.. **18/11**
Better qualities **21/9 25/9 27/9**

The "Ellesmere" Raincoat. (Craven-proofed). Stylish Coat, with detachable Belt all round, Inset sleeve as illust. In Greys, Greeny-Fawns, Fawn and Navy. Lengths 50, 52, 54, 56 in. Price **21/9** Post free.

The "Grasmere" Raincoat (Cravenette-proofed). A striking model Magyar sleeve and Belted back as illustration. In Greys, Greeny-fawns, Fawns and Navy. 50, 52, 54, 56 in. .. **29/11**
Better qualities **36/9 42/-** Post free.

The "Clacton" Raincoat (Cravenette-proofed). Smart model, with Belt at back and Raglan sleeves, as sketch, or a similar model with inset sleeves.
Sizes: 50, 52, 54, 56 in.
Price .. **15/11** Post free.

Washstands:
Portable Wrought Iron Skeleton Frames. Improved and Original Registered Designs. Fitted with round Earthen, Enamelled Ware, or Japanned Iron Basin, with or without Waste Plug Union and Chain, Metal Filling Cans, Waste Water Receivers, Towel Rails, and Soap Containers. Extra Strong, Reliable Manufacture, Superior Quality.

The "Aldwych" Washstand.
FIXED FRAME.

Complete with earthen basin, 14 in., waste plug union and chain, japanned metal filler, 6 qts., soap dish, towel rail & waste water receiver.

No. Y. 124.
15/6 each.

The "City" Washstand.
Same pattern as above, but lighter, No. Y. 124A .. **10/9** each.
Carriage and packing, 1/6.

"Invigorator" Bath Shower.
A great Sanitary Improvement. It is attached in an instant, and water can be used at any temperature. Pipe is flexible. Supplied in box complete, including Bracket for holding shower when not in use.
9/9 Post 6d. Shampoo Fitting, extra **1/6½**.
When ordering this ideal Spray give size or diam. of Taps and say whether round or oval.

The "Competition" Cabinet Lavatory.

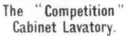

Complete with earthen basin, 14 in., waste plug union and chain, japanned metal filler, waste water receiver, soap and brush dishes, and towel rail attached to each side.
No. Y. 135 .. **33/-** each
Carriage and packing 1/9.

The "Field" Washstand.
FIXED FRAME.

Complete with japanned iron basin, metal filler, and soap dish.

No. Y. 121,
With 14 in. basin, **7/6** ea.

No. Y. 121A.
With 16 in. basin, **9/6** ea.

Carriage and packing 1/6.

Standard Colours
Attractively Finished.

Olive Green,
Marone,
Cerulean Blue,
Hospital White,

prepared to special order.

"Carlton" Washstand.
FIXED FRAME.

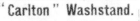
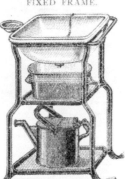

This pattern basin provides ample room for ablution purposes. The frame can be made to telescope for export purposes. Complete with earthen basin, oblong shape, extra deep, waste plug union and chain, japanned metal filler, waste water receiver, soap dish & towel rail. No. Y. 128. With oblong basin:

To 16 by 14	19 by 15½	22 by 16 in.	order only.
36/9	47/6	58/-	

The 'Triangle' Washstand.
FIXED FRAME.

Complete with earthen basin, 14 in., japanned metal filler, 6 qts., soap dish, and towel rail.
No. Y. 126.
Price **9/9** each.

Carriage and packing 1/6

The "Universal."

Consisting of earthen basin, 14 in., brass plug & chain, 6-qt. japanned filler, large japanned receiver and soap dish with earthen lining.

Price **15/-**

Carriage and packing 1/6.

The 'Grafton' Competition Washstand.
Fixed Stand

Complete with japanned iron or enamelled basin, 14 in., japanned metal filler, 4 qts., soap dish and towel rail.
No. Y. 122A. .. **6/9** each.
Carriage and packing 1/6.

Bath Seats.

These Seats are very convenient where baths are fitted. The arms can be adjusted to fit any size bath. The seats are beautifully made of hard seasoned wood with no rough edges, not likely to be warped by steam or hot water. **3/6** Carriage 6d.
Ditto with a ivory white japanned seat to stand hot water, highly finished. **3/9**

Bath Room and Toilet Requisites.

Y. 2. Scullery Tidy, Holds all brushes kept in the scullery, & thoroughly drains them after use, preserving and keeping them in good condition, they will last as long again.
Our price, **1/6½** Post 4d.

Y. 6. Scullery Tidy. This Scullery Tidy holds the brushes upright to drain. It is well finished and japanned dark green.
Fitted with enamelled soap dish.
Our price, **1/0½** Postage 3d.

No. Y. 11. Bath Room Tidy. Japanned green or white. Size, 12 in. by 13 in., at per illustration.
Price ... **5/6** Post 6d.

No. Y. 19. Toilet Roll Holder and Match Holder, japanned green or white.
Price **1/3½** Postage 2d.

No. Y. 31. Sponge & Soap Holder. For the Bath. Strong adjustable hooks to hang on rim of bath. Covered with India-rubber.
Japanned **3/3½**
Nickel-plated on brass **6/6**
Postage 4d.

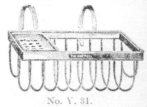

No. Y. 94. Tooth Brush Tidy. Holds 2 brushes. Complete with tumbler, **1/6** Postage 2d.
No. Y. 81. Tooth Brush Rack, to hold 5 brushes, **6½d.**
No. Y. 83. To hold seven brushes, **10½d.** Postage 1½d.

No. Y. 15. Toilet Tidy. Japanned green or white. 7½ in. by 13 in. Holds tooth, shaving & nail brushes sponge and soap
Price **3/9½** Post 4d.

No. Y. 9. 10 by 5 in. Japanned green or white. Holds sponge and soap.
Price **1/10**

No. Y. 10. 12 in. by 7 in. Price **2/5** Postage 3d.

Bath Trays or Tidies. 13½ by 9½ by 30. Fitted with perforated enamelled zinc bottom for sponge, brushes and soap. Whitewood, **1/3** Sycamore, **2/6** Car. 6d.
Gamage's New Design. Fitted with enamelled basin and perforated zinc bottom for brushes, etc.
Sycamore .. 12 in. basin, **3/3** 14 in. basin, **3/6**
Pol. Mahogany .. .. **4/9** **5/9**

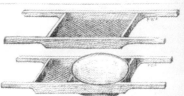

Ironmongery, Turnery and Household Requisites.

BATHS. Our Extra Strong Superior Quality.   Japanned White and Marbled inside.
London Manufacture.   Best Full Moulded Beads.   Oak Outside.   Art Colours at Short Notice.

The unequalled brilliancy of our finish has a character entirely its own and the quality is always reliably good. Cream and Gold decoration is no kept in s ock but can be supplied in a few days' time. It is a handsome decoration and strongly recommended. Sprays of floral decorations to order.

OXFORD HIP BATHS.

Oak and White.

	Y.1	Y.2	Y.3	Y.4
Length	35	38	42	44 in. outside.
	17/11	19/3	23/6	28/9

SPONGE BATHS. VICTORIA.

Splashing is averted by Hollow inside Patent Sanitary Bead.

Y.1	Y.1½	Y.2	Y.3	Y.4
32	34½	36	40	44 in. outside
17/3	19/9	21/3	23/9	30/3

TAPER BATH WITH HIGH BACK.

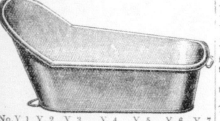

No. Y.1	Y.2	Y.3	Y.4	Y.5	Y.6	Y.7
18/9	21/6	25/-	31/6	36/6	44/6	53/-

Fitting a brass bath waste, plug and union, **5/9** extra.

TAPER BATHS.

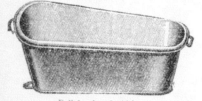

Full depth and width.

No. Y.1	Y.2	Y.3	Y.4	Y.5	Y.6	Y.7	Y.8
34	38	43	46	52	60	64	69	Length, inches outside
13/-	16/9	18/11	25/-	27/9	41/-	43/6	62/6

Fitting Tap to the above Baths to pour off water, **7/9** ex.

NURSERY BATH

with improved white japanned Stand, extra deep seamless enamelled Oval Bath, complete with

Towel Rail, Soap and Sponge Holder.
Size 24 in., **25/-** : Packing extra 1/6

Oak and White.

Y.1	Y.2	Y.3	Y.4
30	33	37	40
14/9	16/9	19/6	23/9

TRAVELLING BATHS.

Oval as illus. with cover, lock key, and best make of strap.

Y.6	Y.7	Y.8	Y.9
Length 26	30	34	38 in.
24/6	28/9	31/6	37/6

TRAVELLING BATHS. Oval, wired edge, with cover, hasp and strap.

No.	in.	Price.
Y.6. Length	25	18/3
Y.7. „	29	19/6
Y.8. „	33	22/3
Y.9. „	37	27/6

WICKER LININGS to fit inside above. Contents may be lifted out intact without disturbance when bath is required for use.

To fit No. Y.6	2/11
„ „ 7	3/3
„ „ 8	3/11
„ „ 9	4/6

WICKER BASKETS for enclosing Travelling Bath. Prevents damage in transit.

For No. Y.6	7/6
„ 7	8/9
„ 8	9/9
„ 9	10/9

CHILDREN'S BATHS.

OVAL

No.	Y.6	Y.7	Y.8	Y.9
Outside	26	33	34	38 in.
Oak and white	11/11	13/6	15/3	18/9

SPONGE BATHS. WIRE EDGE.

Y.0	Y.1	Y.1½	Y.2	Y.3
27	30	33	36	39in. outside
6/9	8/6	9/6	11/3	12/9

THE "HOLBORN" TRAVELLING BATH WITH STAND.

SUITABLE FOR GOLD COAST OR INDIA.

Travelling Bath, iron frame protects it, convertible into a stand when bath is in use.
29 in. .. **30/-**   33 in. .. **32/-**

FOOT BATHS. With cast iron handles.

	No. Y.2	Y.3	Y.4	Y.5
Outside	18	19½	21	24 in.
Oak and white, beaded	6/11	7/8	9/3	10/9

	No. Y.1	Y.2	Y.3	Y.4
Outside	14	16	18	20 in.
Wired edge	4/3	4/9	5/3	6/8

CARRIAGE EXTRA On All Baths.

COMBINATION BATHS.

With seat, combines hip bath, sits bath sponge bath, and child's plunging bath soap dishes in arms as illustrated.

Oak and White	..	31/6
Cream and Gold	..	34/9

SPONGE BATHS. BEADED EDGE.

Y.0	Y.1	Y.1½	Y.2	Y.3	Y.4 [in.
29	32	34½	36	40	44 outside.
13/3	14/9	18/3	19/3	21/6	26/-

No. Y. 805. Child's Bath.
22 in. deep seamless enamelled bath, in strong folding japanned iron frame, with towel holder, soap dish, and sponge bowl.

Our Price .. **14/11**

EQUAL END BATHS.

Best quality. Full depth and width. Length, inches outside

No. Y.0	Y.1	Y.2	Y.3	Y.4	Y.5	Y.6	Y.7	Y.8
In. 28	32	36	42	44	50	58	62	67
11/9	14/3	16/11	18/9	24/6	26/9	38/6	43/6	60/-

Fitting tap to above to pour off the water **7/6** ex.

CHILD'S BATH AND STAND.

No. Y. 34. Enamelled oval bath, sponge bowl, soap dish, and japanned iron frame with towel rail.

21 in.	23 in.	25 in. diam.
15/-	16/6	18/6

All Baths should be carefully crated to prevent damage in transit. A charge of 1/- to 2/6 will be made according to size of bath. Crates are returnable and money refunded.

Bedsteads that Take Up Little Room.

SOFT QUILTED MATTRESS

The "Cabinetta"

No. X. 0/9 Compressible. The Handiest Bed Ever Made.

In solid fumed oak case. Comfortable and strong, well finished, looks well anywhere.

ft. 6 in. by 6 ft. 6 in.	2 ft. 9 in. by 6 ft. 6 in.	3 ft. by 6 ft. 6 in.
32/6	**39/6**	**47/6**

If in Walnut or Mahogany, highest finish **9/-** extra.

Packing 1/- extra.   Carriage paid.

Filled with washed wool in Coloured Sateen to fit above.   2 ft. 6 in. **6/9**   2 ft. 9 in. **7/3**   3 ft. **8/-**

Pillow to match filled with Kapoc **5/-**

Closes up

with bedding
INSIDE.

The "Crusher."

The "Sesame."

No. X. 0/2.   **Cheap and Handy Bed.**   Price .. **17/6**

Most Comfortable and occupies No Room at all.

No. X. 0/3 Has birch top and strong canvas bottom. Size 2 ft. 4 in. by 6 ft. 6 in.   Price .. **17/6**

Soft Quilted Mattress.

Filled with Washed Wool in Coloured Sateen, to fit above. **6/-** each.

(Shuts up so, and has Birch Top when closed).

Similar to above, but made with Solid Fumed Oak Top and best Sailcloth Bottom.   Sizes 2 ft. 6 in. by 6 ft. 6 in., **24/-**   3 ft. by 6 ft. 6 in., **36/-**

Soft Quilted Mattress, fitted with washed wool, 2 ft. 6 in. **6/6**   3 ft., **8/-** each.

No. X. 7.
Collapsible Bedstead.
6 ft. 5 in. by 2 ft. 6 ft.   1 ft. 1 in. Rail.
⅞ in. Filling.
Price   ..   **14/6**
6 ft. 5 in. by 3 ft. Price ... **15/6**
Crates 1/- extra.

COLLAPSED

PATENT

BEDSTEAD LOCKED INTO POSITION FOR USE

Specially adapted for Hospitals Institutions, Barracks, Hotels Boarding Houses, etc.

Complete in one piece, there being no loose parts whatever. It is practically unbreakable, being made of wrought steel throughout. Extremely portable, weighs only 36 lbs., including wire mattress. Can be set up ready for use in 5 seconds, the act of pulling the head and foot rails into position automatically locking them.

No. X. 0c. Cheaper make, Black finish

| ft. by 2 ft. | ... | ... | ... | **8/6** |
| Cushions ... | ... | ... | ... | **9/-** |

No. X. 1c. Heavier make.

6 ft. by 2 ft.	2 ft. 3 in.	2 ft. 6 in.
10/6	**11/6**	**12/6**
Cushions.		
9/-	**10/-**	**11/-**

No. 12c. Reliable and Strong Chair Bedstead, convenient as a chair or bedstead, fitted with brass legs and crossbar.

6 ft. by 2 ft.	2 ft. 3 in.	2 ft. 6 in.
14/9	**16/3**	**17/9**
Cushions **10/-**	**11/3**	**12/6**

No. X. 424.

The "Shut-up" Bedstead.

(Copyright.)

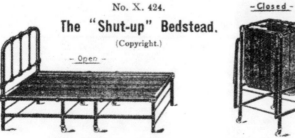

– Open –   – Closed –

Invaluable for Schools, Hotels, etc.

Folds freely and easily with bedding inside, compact and convenient.

USEFUL ANYWHERE.   STRONG AND RIGID.

Fitted with double woven wire spring mattress.

| 6 ft. 6 in. by 6 ft. .. | **24/9** | 3 ft. by 6 ft. .. | **26/3** |
| 3 ft. 6 in. by 6 ft. .. | .. | **28/6** | Packing 1/- |

Owing to the unsettled state of the Metal market, these prices are subject to alteration without notice.

The "Mafeking."

Strong Camp Bedstead ; 1 in. Tube sides fold flat, net weight 30 lbs.

Size, ft. 3 in. **15/6**   2 ft. 6 in. **16/6**   3 ft. **19/11**   Cases extra.

Special Line. No. 911 Similar to the "Mafeking," but single iron frame

ALL STEEL. Price, 2 ft. 3 in. by 6 ft. **10/6**
2 ft. 6 in. by 6 ft. **11/6**

For full Range see Furniture List, Post Free on Application.

RELIABLE BEDSTEADS.

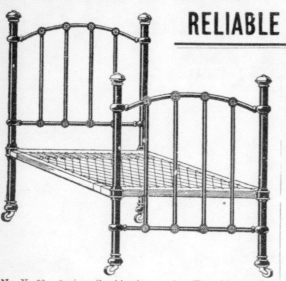

No. X. 63. 3-piece Combination. 1-in. pillars, ⅝-in. panels. Made in 2 ft. 6 in., **21/9** 3 ft., and 3 ft. 6 in. **24/-** only. Price for 3 ft., **22 6** For Art Colours, **2/6** extra.

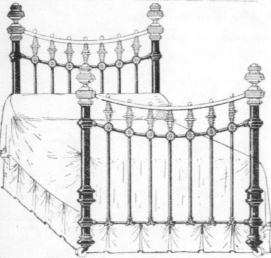

X. 708. 2-in. pillars, ⅝-in. and ½-in. panels, ¾-in. brass rods. Price, 4 ft. 6 in., **43/6**

X. 1208. 1½-in. pillars, ⅝-in. panels, ¾-in. square brass rods. Price, 4 ft. 6 in., **68/6** Art Colours, **3/9** extra.

No. X. 50.
A strong serviceable Bedstead, 1 in. pillars, cast neck vases, ⅝ in. brass rods

4 ft. 6 in.	**23/9**
4 ft.	**22/9**
3 ft. 6 in.	**22/6**

No. X. 202.
A popular Bedstead, with 1¼ in. pillars, ⅜ in. panels, ¾ in. brass swept top rails beautifully finished in art green enamel.

4 ft. 6 in.	**35/6**
4 ft.	**34/9**
3 ft. 6 in.	**34/-**

In black and brass, 4 ft. 6 in., **31/6**
4 ft., 30/9 3 ft. 6 in., **30/-**

No. X. 102.
2 in. pillars, fully mounted, ⅞ in. brass top rail,

4 t. 6 in.	**45/-**
4 ft.	**44/-**
3 ft. 6 in.	**42/6**

Can be had with 1½ in. cast neck vase and brass rail only.

4 ft. 6 in., **28/6**	4 ft., **27/6**
3 ft.	**27/-**

Packing 1/- to 2/- extra.

The LITTLE MARVEL Oak Beadstead.

No. X. 506.
2 in. by 1½ in. pillars with coppered Diamond mesh wire mattress.
Head, 3 ft. 9 in. high. Foot, 3 ft. 3 in. high.
Price— 2 ft. 6 in. **16 11** 3 ft. **17/11**
Packing 1/-

The "Gamage" Adjustable Combination Beadstead.

Fitted with double woven wire mattress.
Exceptional Line. Black Enamelled.

2 ft. 6 in.	3 ft.	3 ft. 6 in.
15/11	**16/11**	**17/11**

Complete.
All brass and better quality wove wire mattress.
2 ft. 6 in. **45/6** 3 ft. **48/6** 3 ft. 6 in. **52/6**
X. 701. Three-piece Combination Beadstead, similar to above, in diamond mesh wire.
2 ft. 6 in. **14/6** 3 ft. **14/11** 3 ft. 6 in. **15/11**

FOR SPECIAL SETS OF BEDDING FOR :: :: ABOVE, SEE PAGE 377. :: ::

The Perfect Settee and Combination Beadstead.

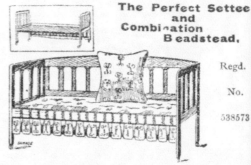

Regd.
No.
538573

Small Illustration shows SETTEE as BEADSTEAD. When not in use can be packed quite flat.
No. X. 141. Useful for any Room.
Size 2ft. 3in. by 6ft. 2in. Solid fumed oak with diamond wire spring bottom, iron frame fitted with dovetails, the back is hinged but can by entirely removed by taking out the pins. Packs quite flat.

Price of Settee only	**40/6**
Sterilized Woollen Flock Squab in cretonne, piped and buttoned	**10/-**
2 Cretonne Piped Pillows filled Kapok, 22 by 22 in.	**6/-**
Canvas Platform with Cretonne Valance attached	**3/-**
Price complete	**59/6**

Packing 1/6 extra. Carriage paid.

For Full Range see
FURNISHING LIST
Post free on application.

All dsteads under 40/- value Carriage Forward.

Garden Tents and Shelters.

The Tokio Garden Shelter

This Shelter is of somewhat similar design to the Tokio Garden House, and will be found a most ornamental as well as useful article.

Price

£3 10 0

Patent applied for.

The "Lowestoft" Bathing Tents.

With patent folding framework, and front curtain.

Can be easily erected single-handed, having patent folding framework.

Walls fitted with flaps for sand or shingle.

Walls 6 ft. 6 in. high.

	Superior Striped Canvas.	Heavy Green Rotproof Canvas
6 ft. square	**£3 5 0**	**£3 17 0**

An extra curtain on rings to divide the tent into two separate compartments for "Mixed" Bathing.

For 6 ft. tent, striped .. **10/6**   Green Rotproof .. **13/-** extra

The "Felixstowe" Bathing Tent.

With Patent **Folding** Corner Post **Framework.**

Size 5 ft. square, Walls, 6 ft. high, provided with flaps for sand or shingle.

In plain Grey Cloth, **31/-**

In striped cloth, **35/6**

In green rotproof canvas, **51/-**

Clothes Hangers, **1/6** each.

The 5 o'clock Lawn Tent or Shelter.

With Patent Folding Wood Framework

Can be easily erected single-handed.

Provided with air space at top of walls, with overhanging eaves.

Size 6 ft. by 6 ft. at base.   Woodwork of Selected Pitch Pine.

Striped Canvas .. **£3 12 0**   Green Rotproof .. **£4 15 0**

The "Ideal" Lawn Tent or Shelter.

For Summer afternoons.

(Patented)

No guy ropes required.

Provided with ventilation at eaves line with overhanging roof.

Easily erected single-handed.

Size 6 ft. by 4 ft. at base.   Woodwork of Selected Pitch Pine

Striped Canvas .. **£2 19 0**   Green Rotproof .. **£3 19 9**

The "TOKIO" Garden House.

Patent applied for.

Size 8 ft. square.   Height to Top Cover, 8 ft. 9 in.

This elegant portable Garden Summer House is constructed of Selected Pitch Pine. The roof or Awning is of Genuine Willesden Rotproof Canvas, and sides or walls are adjustable reed blinds, which give perfect ventilation, while keeping off the sun. The Frame is made on the well-known "X" principle, and while being extremely strong and rigid is of but moderate weight, and folds into a very small compass when not in use.

Price **£6**

All above, Carriage paid London Radius only.

GARDEN AND BATHING TENTS, LAWN PAVILIONS, ETC.

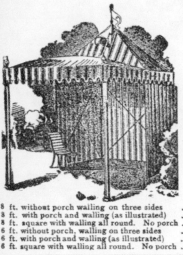

The "Holborn" Tent.

Strongly Recommended.

A portable iron frame folding Garden Tent. Framework of wrought iron, standing firm and rigid. No guy ropes are required. The frame plates, which are hinged and bolted, fold up together in their own height. The porch is constructed dome fashion to throw off moisture. All canvases are of superior quality and durability, and of which we are confident cannot be surpassed. It is the most easily fixed tent in the market.

Portable Folding Bathing Tent.

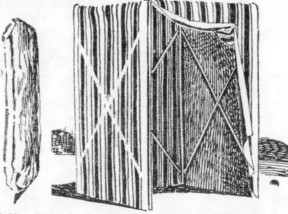

Prices—

In Plain Grey Cloth **22/-**

In Striped Tent Cloth, **25/-**

In Green Rotproof Canvas, **33/-**

Packed in valise complete, with guy ropes for use in very rough weather.

Complete with front Curtain.

	Striped.	Rotproof green.
8 ft. without porch walling on three sides ...	3 15 0	4 15 0
8 ft. with porch and walling (as illustrated) ...	4 12 0	5 17 6
8 ft. square with walling all round. No porch ...	4 5 0	5 10 0
6 ft. without porch, walling on three sides ...	6 0 0	8 6 0
6 ft. with porch and walling (as illustrated) ...	7 5 0	9 17 6
6 ft. square with walling all round. No porch ...	6 15 0	9 6 0

Folded in valise.　　With Front Curtain, 4 ft. square.

Bathing Tent made with Patent corner post, folding wood frame. No centre pole. **Easily** set up or taken down single-handed. Walls fitted with flaps at bottom for sand or shingle. Size 4 ft. square. Walls 6 ft. high.

The "G.B." Sun Awning.

Size, 6 feet square, 6 feet high.

Patent Wood Folding-Frame Lawn Pavilion.

A commodious Tent for many purposes, easily erected and very portable. The roof is carried on strong rafters, the whole of the interior space being quite clear; constructed with patented **corner post, folding frame, easily set up or taken down single handed.** The whole of the woodwork is of selected pitch pine, with strong galvanised fittings.

Guy ropes are supplied for use in exposed positions.

Walls 6 ft. 6 in. high, 9 ft. high to ridge.

12 ft. long by 6 ft. wide, in superior Striped Canvas **79/6**

In heavy Green Rotproof Canvas, Price .. **98/-**

Extra Curtains, 6 ft. by 6 ft.
Striped, **8/6** Green Rotproof, **11/-**

This effective and useful Garden Awning is very strongly made of selected Pitch Pine woodwork and Galvanized Fittings.

The Roof Framework folds into a very small compass, allowing the complete awning to be closely packed.

The Curtain shown in illustration can be attached to either of the four sides, thus giving protection from the sun. Strong canvas is used.

Complete, with Guy Ropes and Pegs (without Curtains)	**23/3**
Side Curtains .. .. **6/9** each extra.	
Made in green Willesden Waterproof	**32/6**
Side Curtains .. .. **11/-** each extra.	
Superior Quality. 9 ft. Square Awning.	
Complete with Guy Ropes and Pegs (without Curtain) in striped canvas	**40/-**
Side Curtains in Striped Canvas .. **13/6** extra.	
Complete with Guy Ropes and Pegs (without curtain) in genuine Willesden Canvas	**50/-**
Side Curtains in Genuine Willesden Canvas	**17/6**

The "G.B." Lawn Tent.

Size 6 ft. square; 6 ft. high extension 6 ft. long

The frame of this tent is of best selected hardwood with galvanized fittings. Woodwork is varnished.

Canvas is of very good quality. The walls of the tent are attached separately and extension is fitted to take a wall on any side for extra protection from sun, or extra walls can be supplied to go all round, forming a tent 12 ft. by 6 ft. Roof of extension is raised by framework similar to roof of tent.

Complete as illustration, striped Cloth, **53/6**; extra Side Curtains, **6/9**

The 'Retreat'

6 ft. across at top, 7 ft. at base.

A six-sided Tent with awning extending 6ft. Brass Jointed Centre Pole and strong Iron Spike.

Suitable for the Garden or Lawn or for Cricket and other field purposes.

Price with Pegs and Tackle.
Plain Cloth **27/9**
Striped Cloth **35/6**

Carriage extra on all the above outside London Carrier Radius.

F 1..

Natural Whole Cane Art Furniture.

No. Z. 427. Ladies' Chair.
Depth of seat 15½ in. Height of back 20 in.
Total height 34 in. Price **15/6**

No, Z. 316 **Ladies' Chair.** Total height 38 in.
Width of seat 19 in. Depth of seat 19 in.
Height of seat from ground 15 in. Price **25/-**

No. Z. 7101. **Gent's Chair.** Height of chair 35 in
Width of seat 19 in. Depth of seat 19 in.
Height of seat from ground 15 in. Price **22 6**

IDEAL CANE WARE.
A Neat Library Chair.
For Hard Wear.
Length of seat 18 in. Width of seat 20 in.
Price .. **25/9**

No. Z. 9001. **Ladies' Chair.** Total height 34 in.
Width of seat 18 in. Depth of seat 18 in.
Height of seat from ground 15 in. Price **25 6**

IDEAL CANE WARE.
A Pretty Drawing Room Desig
Length of seat, 18 in.
Width of seat, 18 in.
Price **22/11**

No. Z. 3101.
Gent's Comfortable Tub Chair
Total height of Chair 35 in.
Width of seat 18 in. Depth of seat 18 in.
Height of seat from ground 15 in. Price **22 6**

No, Z. 4101. **Ladies' or Gent's Chair.**
Height of chair 38 in. Width of seat 19 in., depth 20 in.
Height of seat from ground 14½ in. Price **23 6**

No. Z. 347. **Ladies' or Gent's Easy Chair.**
Total height 38 in. Width of seat 20 in., depth 20 in.
Height of seat from ground 14½ in. Price **29/6**

ALL ABOVE CARRIAGE FORWARD OUTSIDE LONDON RADIUS.

Revolving Shelters and Garden Houses.

The "DAVOS" Revolving Shelter or Sanatorium.

7 ft. by 6 ft., by 7 ft. 6 in. high.

Designed and made on the most up-to-date and approved principles, is highly recommended for invalids, and those who are seeking open air treatment, being sufficiently large to accommodate a small bedstead, table and two small chairs.

It is strongly built on stout framework, the whole being panelled inside and out, felted roof, inside being sized and varnished, outside painted white. The shelter is mounted on a Revolving platform and is so light that a child can move it when required.

Price	**£10 10 0**
If without revolving platform ..	**9 2 6**

Showing Side Ventilators CLOSED.

Showing Side Ventilators OPEN.

RUSTIC SHELTERS.

No. Z. 41.

Weather boarded roof, boarded sides and back, rustic work of fir, and fitted with seat. Sized and varnished 6 ft. 6 in. high in front, 7 ft. 6 in. at ridge.

Size 6 ft. by 4 ft.   Price .. **£4 10 0**

No. Z. 22. **Portable Shelter.**

Strongly made roof, match boarded, and covered outside with felt.   5 ft. by 3 ft.

Price **£2 15 0**

No. Z. 23.   Portable Shelter.

But with sides close boarded instead of lattice work sides, as shown in No. 22.   Size 5 ft. by 3 ft.

Price **£2 8 6**

No. Z. 42. Revolving Shelter.

Strongly framed of deal; weather boarded roof, rustic work of English oak.   Sized and varnished.

Size 7 ft. by 6 ft.   6 ft. 6 in. high to eaves.

Price **£15 5 0**

No. Z. 43. Revolving Shelter.

Strongly framed of deal, weather boarded roof, walls covered with match boarding, roof painted, sides covered with wood-preservative stain outside; inside sized and varnished. Size 7 ft. by 6 ft.   6 ft. 6 in. high at eaves.   Price .. **£11 15 0**

No. Z. 44. Revolving Shelter.

Strong and well made Shelter. Weather boarded roof, rustic work of English oak and fir, walls and roof covered with wood-preservative. Inside sized and varnished.

Size 6 ft. by 4 ft. 6 in.   Size 7 ft. by 6 ft.

Price .. **£10**   **£11 5 0**

The above Prices include delivery to your nearest Railway Station, 50 miles from London, or delivered and fixed up within 15 miles of Charing Cross.

Stair and Oriental Carpets, Rugs and Linoleums.

Genuine Indian Deccan Rugs.

Size approximately about 3 ft. by 5 ft. 6 in. Quiet good wearing colours. Have every appearance of the most expensive Indian Carpets. Some exceptionally fine designs. Price **8/11**

Better quality, also slightly larger, **10/6**

Large variety of Indian and Oriental Rugs.

Mirzapore Rugs and Carpets.

All these are in Art Colours. Special make to suit modern furnishings, of fine quality Red, Green, Blue and Cream Grounds, in various designs.
We can generally match Rugs to the Carpets.

Mirzapore Rugs and Mats.

2 ft. 8 by 1 ft. 4 in., **4/11** 3 ft. by 1 ft. 6, **5/6**
3 ,, 0 ,, 2 ,, 0 ,, **7/6** 4 ,, 2 ,, **10/6**
5 ,, 0 ,, 2 ,, 6 ,, **14/11** 6 ,, 3 ,, **21/-**
7 ,, 0 ,, 4 ,, 0 ,, **35/-**

Mizapore Carpets.

6 by 6 ft., **39/6** 7 by 7 ft., **58/6** 8 by 8 ft., **75/-**
9 ,, 9 ,, **85/-** 8 ,, 5 ,, **45/6** 9 ,, 6 ,, **63/-**
10 ,, 7 ,, **84/-** 10 ,, 8 ,, **93/6** 12 ,, 9 ,, **125/-**
12 by 10½ ft., **£6 19 6** 13 by 10 ft., **£7 10 6**
14 ,, 10 ,, **£7 19 6** 15 ,, 10 ,, **£8 19 6**
15 ,, 12 ,, **£9 19 6**

Mirzapore Corridor Strips.

9 by 3 ft., **29/6** 12 by 3 ft., **39/6**

Mirzapore Billiard Surround.

Set of 4, 12 by 3, to match, **£8 18 6** complete.

Turkey Rugs and Carpets.

Bahana Turkey Rugs, 5 ft. by 2 ft. 6 in... **19/11**
6 by 3 ft., **29/6** 7 by 4 ft., **45/-**

Bahana Turkey Carpets.

9 by 6 ft., **79/6** 9 by 7 ft., **98/6** 10 by 7 ft., **105/-**
11 ,, 8 ,, **139/6** 12 ,, 9 ,, **165/-** 13 ,, 10 ,, **158/6**
14 by 11 ft., **238/6** 15 by 12 ft., **279/6**

Standard Turkey Rugs.

5 by 2 ft. 6 in., **33/6** 6 by 3 ft., **47/6** 7 by 4 ft., **79/6**

Axminster Stair Carpets.

22½ in. wide, per yard **3/11 4/9** 27 in., wiee, **5/6**
Speciality, Turkey Designs and others.

Brussels Stair Carpets.

18 in. wide .. .. .. yard **2/11½**
22½ ,, .. yard **3/4½ 3/6 3/11**

Tapestry Stair Carpets.

18 in. wide .. yard **1/4½ 1/6½ 1/11½ 2/4½**
22½ ,, yard **1/6½ 1/9½ 1/11½ 2/4½ 2/6½**

Special Value in Axminster Hearthrugs

To Match your Carpet.

4 ft. 6 by 2 ft. 3 in. **4/11½ 6/11 9/11 15/11**
5 ,, 6 ,, 2 ,, 6 ,, .. **8/11 15/9 17/11**
6 ,, 0 ,, 3 ,, 0 ,, .. **15/9 18/9 21/9**

Axminster Slip Mats.

Price **1/6½ 1/11½ 2/9 3/11**
In all the best designs and colours.

Mohair Mats.

These Mats, with plain border and cur centre, in a variety of colours form an excellent mat for wear and appearance being all mohair. Price **3/11** each.

Others, all sizes.

Britannia Axminster Rugs.

No. 308. The Britannia is an exquisitely designed Axminster Rug, being both effective and durable. Can be supplied in INDIAN colours with either blue or red predominating, and are made in the following sizes :—

5 ft. 1 in. by 2 ft. 3 in. **8/11**
6 ft. 0 in. by 2 ft. **11/9**
6 ft. 0 in by 3 ft. 0 in. **14/11**

Corridor Rugs—
7 ft. 6 in. by 2 ft. 3 in. **13/9**
9 ft. 0 in. by 2 ft. 3 in. **16/6**
9 ft 0 in. by 2 ft. 8 in **21/-**

No. 4/318. The above illustration is an artistically decorated Rug with self-colour green centre and chintz border Sizes and prices as No. 308.

Linoleums. Patterns on application.

Inlaid Linoleum, an up-to-date selection of designs by the leading makers. Colours right through to the back and can be washed in the ordinary way.

C quality .. .. .. **2/7** square yard.
B ,, ... **3/3** ,,
A ,, .. **3/9** and **4/3** ,,

Printed Linoleum. Patterns on application.

A large selection of the latest designs and colourings.

XX quality .. .. **1/4½** square yard.
X ,, ... **1/6½** ..
E ,, ... **1/9½** .

Bedroom, Kitchen, Hall, Patterns in gre: t v iriety.

Plain Brown Linoleum.

1/4½ 1/6½ 1/9½ 1/11½ 2/6 2/11½ 3/6 sq. yard.
A speciality recommended for offices and shops, or anywhere there is plenty of traffic. Can also be had in various shades of Green.

Sheepskin Rugs.

A Special Line. Very Special Value.
Sizes quoted are actual skin measure. Rugs and Mats when laid down will measure more according to length of wool.

Klondike Sheep Rugs.

Special Cheap Line.

Lined Black. Stock Colours, Black, Brown, Gold, Moss, Ruby, Gold Cinnamon, Fawn, Natural Brown, Natural Grey, Ivory and White Rugs.

Approx. size	Black	Colours, etc
4 ft. 5 by 1 ft. 10 in.	**17/11**	**19/6**
5 ,, 0 ,, 2 ,, 0 ,,	**22/6**	**25/6**
5 ,, 4 ,, 2 ,, 4 ,,	**26/9**	**29/6**
5 ,, 5 ,, 2 ,, 5 ,,	**29/6**	**32/6**
5 ,, 6 ,, 2 ,, 6 ,,	**32/6**	**36/9**
6 ,, 0 ,, 2 ,, 8 ,,	**35/6**	**39/6**
6 ,, 0 ,, 3 ,, 0 ,,	**42/-**	**45/6**

Special sizes **2/6, 2/9** per square foot.

Lincoln Sheep Rugs.

Stock colours, Black, Ruby, Gold, Walnut, Nut Brown, Terra, Bronze, Moss, Gold, Cinnamon, Ivory and White, Skin Measure.

Approx. size		Super quality, Lincoln Sheep. Approx. size	
4 ft. 4 by 1 ft. 9 in.	**27/6**		
4 ,, 6 ,, 1 ,, 11 ,,	**29/11**	5 ft. 0 by 2 ft. 0 in.	**45/-**
4 ,, 9 ,, 1 ,, 11 ,,	**33/6**	5 ,, 4 ,, 2 ,, 3 ,,	**52/6**
5 ,, 0 ,, 2 ,, 0 ,,	**37/6**	5 ,, 5 ,, 2 ,, 5 ,,	**59/6**
5 ,, 4 ,, 2 ,, 3 ,,	**45/-**	5 ,, 6 ,, 2 ,, 6 ,,	**64/6**
5 ,, 6 ,, 2 ,, 6 ,,	**52/6**	5 ,, 9 ,, 2 ,, 7 ,,	**67/6**
5 ,, 9 ,, 2 ,, 7 ,,	**56/9**	6 ,, 0 ,, 2 ,, 8 ,,	**75/6**
6 ,, 0 ,, 2 ,, 8 ,,	**59/6**	6 ,, 0 ,, 3 ,, 0 ,,	**84/-**
6 ,, 0 ,, 3 ,, 0 ,,	**67/6**	All the above felt lined.	

All the above lined Black. Can be had extra long hair **6**d. per square foot extra.

Sheepskin Mats.

Approx. skin measure		Better quality	Super finished
28 by 8½ in.	**3/9**	**5/6**	**5/11**
29 ,, 10 ,,	**4/6**	**6/9**	**7/6**
30 ,, 12 ,,	**5/9**	**8/9**	**9/9**
33 ,, 13 ,,	**6/9**	**10/6**	**11/6**
36 ,, 16 ,,	**8/11**	**10/6**	**14/11**
32 ,, 18 ,,	**11/9**	**13/11**	**19/9**

Special sizes **2/6, 3/9,** and **4/1½** per sq. foot.

All Wool Felts.

50 in. wide. Over 50 different shades of colour. Suitable for Bedrooms, Surrounds, etc.

Price .. **2/11 3/3 3/6 3/11** per yard.
Underfelts, 50 in. wide. **11½**d. **1/3** per yard.
Cedar Paper Underfelt, 50 in. wide, **6½**d. yard.

Chinese Straw Mats.

Various .. .. **1/4½** and **1/6½**

China Matting.

36 in. wide .. **1/3 1/6** and **1/11½** per yard.

All Goods to value of 20/- and over Carriage Paid.

Write for Special Coloured List of Anglo-Orient Reversible Carpets and Rugs. The last word in effect and wear.

Butter and Jam Dishes.

No. F. 885.

Mussel Shell Pattern.

Silver-plated on Nickel Silver. Glass Lined. Complete with Knife Size 6¾ by 3⅜ in. Price **2/6** Post free.

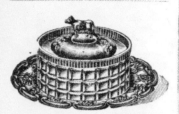

No. F. 14395.

Glass Butter Dish.

Silver-plated on Nickel Silver Stand and Cover. Price **2/6**

No. F. 144.

Shell Butter Dish and Knife complete.

Price **2/9**

No. F. 5038.

Covered Shell Butter Dish and Knife.

Silver-plated on Nickel Silver.

Price **8/9**

No. F. 1024.

Glass Butter Dish.

Silver-plated Mounts. Price **6/11**

No. F. 183. Cut Glass Butter Dish. Silver-plated on Nickel Silver Mounts. Price **6/11**

No. F. 403.

Butter or Preserve Dish.

Bright Pressed Glass. Silver-plated on Nickel Silver Tray. Including Butter Knife or Jam Spoon.

Price **3/6**

No. F. 14084.

Glass Butter Dish.

Silver-plated Frame.

Complete with Knife. Price **6/6**

No. F. 173.

Shell Butter Dish and Knife

Silver-plated on Nickel Silver. Price **5/6**

No. F. 14069. Glass Butter Dish

Silver-plated on Nickel Silver Mounts. Price **8/6**

No. F. 107.

Double-Shell Butter Dish.

Silver-plated on Nickel Silver.

Length 8¼ in. Price **12/6**

No. F. 3. Silver-plated on nickel silver cover for 1lb. size **Marmalade Jar.**

Price **6/6** each.

No. F. 14.

New Pattern **Preserve Dish.**

Silver-plated on nickel silver frame and cover. Price **7/6**

No. F. 4841. Preserve or Honey Jar. Crystal Glass. Silver-plated on nickel silver mount and spoon, **6/3**

No. F. 4810.

Honey or Jam Jar

Crystal Glass. (Assorted Shapes). Electro-plated on nickel silver cover and spoon. Price **2/3**

No. F. 2909.

Honey or Jam Jar.

Crystal Glass. Electro-plated on nickel silver cover and spoon. Price **1/9½**

No. F. 1683.

Double Shell Jelly Frame and Spoons.

Fitted with two glass linings. Silver-plated on nickel silver stand and spoons.

Price **13/9**

No. F. 13422. Handsome Stourbridge Glass **Preserve Dish.** Silver-plated on nickel silver frame & spoon, **9/9**

No. F. 2421.

Double Preserve Dish.

Rich decorated china. Silver-plated on Nickel Silver Frame.

Price **13/9**

SPECIAL NOTICE. TABLE DELICACIES BY POST.

Special Line.

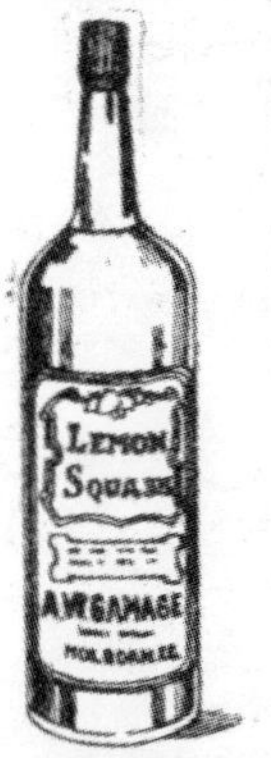

Lemon Squash

PREPARED FROM THE FRESH FRUIT.

Rept. Quart Bottles.

Per Bott. **6½d.**

Per Doz. **6/3**

Lime Juice Cordial,

PREPARED FROM THE FRESH FRUIT.

Same size as above.

Per Bott. **6½d.** Per Doz. **6/3**

UNRIVALLED AS A COOLING SUMMER BEVERAGE.

FOR the convenience of our many Customers we have opened a special Department for the sale of High-class Table Delicacies. Exceptional care has been taken in the choice of the various goods offered, and A. W. GAMAGE, LTD., can thoroughly recommend each article listed. Prices will be found to compare favourably with other firms, and our Customers can always depend upon new goods and prompt service and they can rely upon the highest grade of quality, purity and freshness. Our aim is to offer our Customers the pick of the World's Markets at the lowest possible prices.

Official Notice to our Mail Order Customers.

We suggest that, to save postage, these goods should be included when sending orders for other departments. They can of course be sent separately if desired, in which case postage is extra except Goods to the value of 10/- and upwards which are sent free by Parcel Post to any address in the United Kingdom, and to the value of £2 and over to any Goods Station in England and Wales, Scotland, Ireland, or the Channel Islands.

Free Delivery within our Wide Motor Delivery Area.

Goods not Listed.

We are always prepared to procure specially any Goods not in stock at lowest market prices.

We want you to make use of us, send us a trial order by Post or 'Phone (Holborn No. 2700, 12 lines). We feel confident of repeats.

Special and Seasonable.

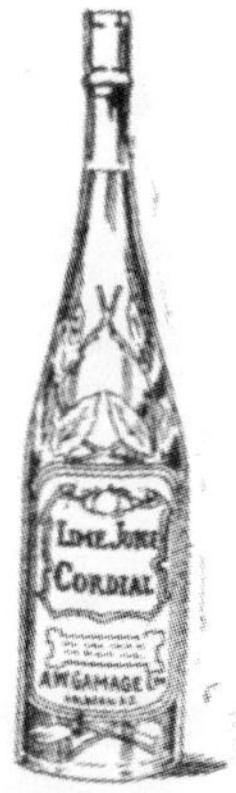

Lime Juice Cordial

Tall Spiral Bottles.

Floral Design.

Extra Strength.

PREPARED FROM THE FRESH FRUIT.

Usual Price 1/2

Per Bott. **10½d.**

Per Doz. **10/3**

Lemon Squash (CLOUDY).

Tall Spiral Bottle, as above.

Usual Price, 1/2

Per Bott. **10½d.** Per Doz. **10/3**

Makes a Delicious & Healthful Summer Beverage mixed with either plain or Aerated Waters.

We shall in future **issue a SPECIAL GROCERY LIST at intervals which will be sent to any address Post Free.**

Take advantage of our Free Motor Delivery Service. Drivers will take your order.

THE LATEST HIGH CLASS PRODUCT

In conjunction with Thermos or Spirit Stove.

Invaluable for Tourists, Travellers, Picnics, etc.

A. W. Gamage Ltd. can thoroughly recommend it for simplicity and delicious flavour. CAFE LIQUEUR.

Cafe Liqueur is ABOLUTELY PURE Coffee.

CAFE LIQUEUR IS PUREST COFFEE.	1/3 PER BOTTLE. Each bottle will make Half-a-gall of best After Dinner Coffee.	CAFE LIQUEUR IS ALL COFFEE.

"Café Liqueur" is a pure rich Coffee with an irresistibly delicate flavour made in liquid form for the sake of convenience.

"Café Liqueur" MUST NOT be confounded with the mixtures of coffee, chicory and sugar now sold.

"Café Liqueur" lastes even better than Coffee just made in a Cafetiere. THERE IS NOTHING LIKE IT.

NO CHICORY. NO SPIRIT. NO SUGAR.

It is the ONLY prepared Coffee retaining the TRUE FLAVOUR.

Buy a bottle of "Café Liqueur," then by carrying out the simple instructions any maid can make Coffee and Milk (Café au Lait) or Black Coffee (Café Noir) to perfection in two minutes. **CAFE LIQUEUR.**

SUGARS. In Cardboard Cartons.

Each package a cardboard carton packed at Refiner's thus saving dust and any impurities from contamination.

	Package Carton	Per lb.	Per doz.		Package Carton	Per lb.	Per doz.
LOAF, Sparkling	2lb.	2¾d.	5/3	GRANULATED	2lb.	2¼d.	4 3
,, ,, ...	1lb.	2¾d.	2 7½	,,	1lb.	2¼d.	2 2
,, Afternoon Tea Cubes	2lb.	2¾d.	5/3	CASTER ..	2lb.	2¼d.	4/7
,, ,, ,,	1lb.	2¾d.	2/7½	,, ..	1lb.	2¼d.	2 4

ICING SUGAR—Best English White, per lb. **6**d.

Good German White, per lb. **4**d. Best Pink, per lb. **6d.**

PURE CANE RAW—Golden Demerara, per lb. **2¼**d. Per doz. lbs. **2/2**

The A.W.G.

Pure Cocoa Essence.

Guaranteed free from all mixtures.

SURE TO PLEASE.

	Price
¼ lb. tins ..	**4½**d.
½ lb. ,, ..	**9**d.
1 lb. ,, ..	**1/6**

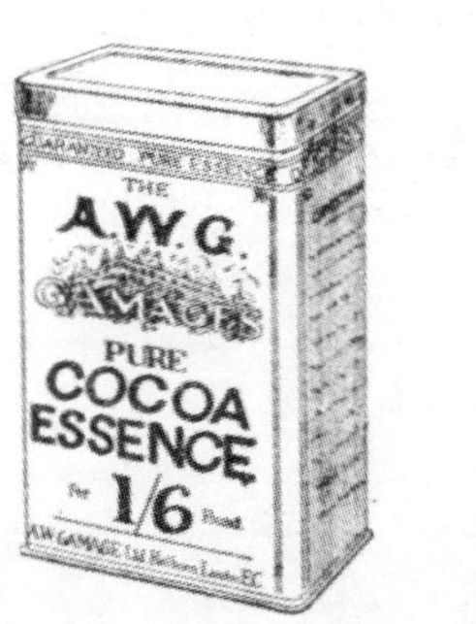

THE A.W.G. PURE COFFEE. Finest the World Produces.

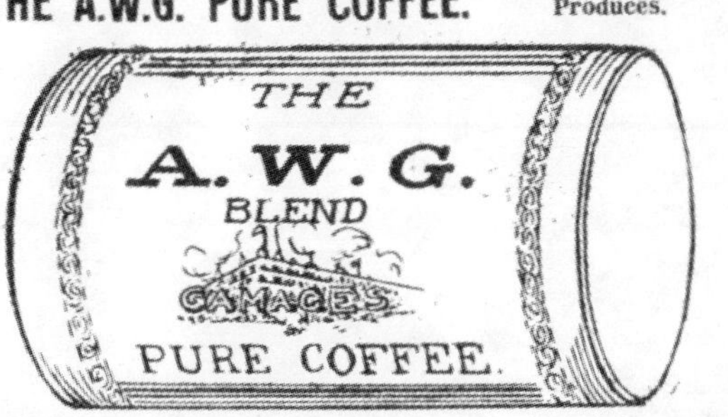

Specially recommended for Coffee Machines. It is composed of the finest growths and is perfectly Blended, which gives it its great strength and delicious flavour. Fine ground, **1/8** per lb. tin In Berry, same price, **10d.** per ½-lb. tin. THOROUGHLY RECOMMENDED.

The Famous Red White and Blue French Coffee

(COFFEE AND CHICORY MIXTURE).

This Coffee is ground immediately after roasting and forthwith secured together with the needful proportion of finest selected Bruges Chicory in perfectly closed tins which will for months preserve its aromatic piquant delicacy. 1 lb. tins, **1/5½** ½ lb. tins, **9**d.

TABLE DAINTIES. Suitable for Home Caravanning, Picnics, Camps, and for Abroad.

Noels' Potted Fish and Meats.

Specially recommended.

Oval Glass.  Small Flower Pot Glass. Miniature Glass.

		Each.	Doz.
Bloater	Strasbourg Meat		
Kippered Herring	Tongue	Small flower pot	5½d. 5/3
Lobster	Ham & Tongue	Specially Recommended.	
Salmon	Ham	Large flower pots 9½d.	9/3
Shrimp	Chicken & Ham	Oval glass .. 6d.	5/9
Salmon & Shrimp	Veal & Ham	Miniature glass 3¼d.	3/3
Crab	Chicken		
Sardine	Game		
Sardine & Anchovy	Grouse		
Smoked Cod's Roe	Goose		
Salmon & Anchovy	Wild Duck		
Beef ⎰Tongue	Pheasant		
Chicken, Ham &	Partridge		
Turkey and Tongue	Foie Gras		

Anchovy Paste.

Small tin ..	5½d.
Large ,, ..	10½d.
Small flower pot glass ..	6½d.
Large do. ..	11½d.

Galantines.

"Delicate and Appetising."
Chicken and Ham, Chicken and Tongue, Chicken, Ham, and Tongue Turkey and Tongue, Veal and Ham.

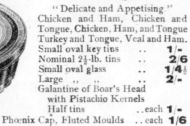

Small oval key tins ..	1/-
Nominal 2½-lb. tins ..	2/6
Small oval glass ..	1/4½
Large ,, ,, ..	2/-
Galantine of Boar's Head with Pistachio Kernels Half tins ..each	1/-
Phœnix Cap, Fluted Moulds ..each	1/6

Ox Tongues.

An ideal "piece-de-resistance" for Camp Storage.

Large size glass (one whole tongue)	5/11
,, ,, ,, (split)..	4/9
Medium size glass	3/9
Small ,, ,, ...	3/-
Calves' Tongues in glass	2/-
Lunch ,, ,, ...	1/9

Pates and Camp Pies.

Specially recommended for Camping-out Parties.

Chicken and Ham Pâté		
Chicken and Tongue Pâté	Small round Key Tins	6½d.
Chicken, Ham and Tongue Pâté	1-lb. oval Key Tins	1/3
Turkey and Tongue Pâté	Small round Glass	9½d.
Veal and Ham Pâté		

Camp Pies, Oval Tins 1-lb. Key opening	1/3
,, Small Tins, Key opening	1/-
,, ,, Oval Glasses	1/4
,, Large ,, ,, ...	2/-

Noels' Parmesan Cheese.

(Grated).

Large Bottles	1/5½
Medium Bottles	10½d.
Small Bottles	6½d.

Specially recommended for Country Use.

NOELS' & MOIRS' Fine quality Soups.

Real Turtle.

Pt. tins, **2/6**		Qt. tins, **4/6**
Pt. bot., **2/11**	½ pt. bot., **1/7**	

Ox Tail (thick or clear), Mock Turtle (thick or clear), Mulligatawny, Kidney, Chicken Broth, Hare, Tomato, Consomme.

Pt. tins, **10½d.**		Qt. tins, **1/8**
Pt. bot., **1/3½**	½ pt. bot., **9d.**	

Gravy. Julienne.

Pt. tins, **8½d.**		Qt. tins, **1/3**
Pt. bot., **1/-**	½ pt. bot., **8d.**	

Essence of Chicken.
½ pt. bot. **1/-**

GASTRONOMES SPECIALITIES.

Specially prepared for Hors d'Œuvre.

The goods listed are specially recommended, and are much sought after, being greatly used in High-class restaurants. We are enabled to offer them at prices much below the ordinary foreign produce shops.

Brand: MARTINACHE & CIE.

	Each
Filleted Smoked Herrings in oil. **9d.**	
Hors d'Œuvre Assortis ,, **11½d.**	
(specially recommended)	
Olives Farcies in oil .. **11½d.**	
Tunny Fish in oil, tomato. herbs or truffle **1/3**	

All the above are in round glasses, about 6 oz.

Anchovies, in Oil, small square bottles, **11½d.** each. Large, **1/8** each

Sardines des Aristocrates.

In oval glasses.

In Oil, Tomato or Herbs, large glasses	**1/5** each
Ditto, small glasses ..	**9½d.** ,,
In Truffle, Lemon or Curry, large glasses ..	**1/6** ,,
Ditto, small glasses ..	**10½d.** ,,

Cream Lucca Oil.

Guaranteed Pure Finest Tuscany.

¼ pt. bot., **5½d.**   ½-pt. bot., **9d.**   Pint bot., **1/4½**

Salad Cream (Parisian).

Large fancy bottles	**10½d.**
Small ,, ,, ...	**6½d.**

CHUTNEY.

A piquant appetiser for cold meats, sandwiches, etc.

	Pints.	½-pints. (Phœnix caps.)
Tirhoot, Col. Skinner's, ⎰ Cashmere, Major Gray's ⎰ ..	**9d.**	**6½d.**
Sweet Sliced Mango, ⎰ Bombay, Bengal ⎰ ..	**8d.**	**6d.**
Royal Naval Chutney		½d.

Goods to value of 10/- and over post paid.
Carriage paid in United Kingdom.

Wilts United Dairies Specialities.

Table Delicacies and Dainties. "Diploma Brand."
(In Hermetically Sealed Glass Moulds)

"Diploma" English Rolled Ox Tongues
Cooked and Glazed Ready for Table.

Medium size (1½ lb. nominal)	.. ..	**2/10**
Large size (2 lb. nominal)	.. ..	**3/11**
Extra large (2½ lb. nominal)	.. ..	**5/3**

"Diploma" English Sliced Ox Tongues

Small size (½ lb. nominal)	.. ..	**1/2**
Medium size (¾ lb. nominal)	.. ..	**1/3**
Large (1 lb. size)	.. ..	**1/10**

"Diploma" "Picnic" Tongues.

Medium (1 lb. size)	.. ..	**1/10**
Large (1¼ lb. size) "The Special"	..	**2/4**

"Diploma" Lunch Tongues.

Small size (½ lb. nominal)	.. ..	**1/2**
Medium size ¾ lb. nominal)	.. ..	**1/3**

"Diploma" Calves Tongues in Jelly.

1 lb. size	.. .. ..	**2/-**

"Diploma" Galantines.

Chicken and Ham, small size	..	**1/-**
Turkey and Tongue ,, ,,	..	**1/-**
Chicken and Ham, large size	..	**1/9**
Turkey and Tongue ,, ,,	..	**1/9**
Ham and Tongue ,, ,,	..	**1/9**

Diploma English Pressed Brisket of Beef
Ready for immediate use.

Medium size (1½ lb. nominal)	.. ..	**1/10**

"Diploma" Sardines.
In Hermetically Sealed Oval Glasses.

In oil, small	.. .. ..	**8½d.** each
,, large	.. .. ..	**1/3½** ,,
With Tomato, small	.. ..	**8½d.** ,,
,, large	.. ..	**1/3½** ,,
Truffle and Chili, large size	..	**1/8** ,,
With Lemon	.. .. ..	**1/8** ,,

"Diploma" Lobster in Jelly.
In Hermetically Sealed Glasses .. Price **1/9** each.

"Diploma" Soft Herring Roes.
In Hermetically Sealed Oval Glasses and Tins.

Small size. Oval Glasses	.. ..	**6½d.**
Large ,, ,,	.. ..	**1/-**
Medium size. In Oval Tins..	..	**6½d.**
Large ,, ,,	.. ..	**8½d.**

"Diploma" Potted Fish and Meat Pastes.
Packed in very attractive Vase-shaped Glasses, Hermetically sealed. Extra large size.

The Trade Mark "Diploma" carries with it a guarantee that these dainties are FREE FROM ALL COLOURING MATTER OR PRESERVATIVES, are of the FINEST QUALITY, being manufactured from the very BEST INGREDIENTS. There are none quite like them in flavour, as under our special process of preserving we have succeeded in retaining all the original flavour. **27 Varieties:—**

Salmon and Shrimp	Potted Beef	"Diploma" Relish
Salmon and Anchovy	Potted Ham	Turkey and Tongue
Crab and Lobster	Bloater Paste	Strasbourg
Devilled Cod's Roe	Lobster ,,	Ham and Beef
Shrimp Paste	Kipper ,,	Wild Duck
Salmon ,,	Sardine ,,	Ham and Tongue
Chicken and Ham	Anchovy ,,	Pheasant
Chicken, Ham and Tongue	Crab ,,	Partridge
Ox Tongue	Turkey and Ham	Grouse

We claim that our package is the best value of its kind before the public. Price .. **6**d. each. **5/9** .. dozen.

Midget Size.
Customers will note that this package is hermetically sealed under the Phœnix Patent, the same as larger package. This patent allows the jars to be filled to their utmost capacity, hence our package contains a much larger quantity of paste than similar shaped glasses sealed by the antomatic process, which requires a large air space between contents and cap to ensure a vacuum. **The best value of any 3½d. package.**

Salmon and Shrimp	Sardine	Bloater
Salmon and Anchovy	Devilled Cod's Roe	Lobster
Chicken and Ham	Ham and Tongue	Shrimp

"Diploma" Potted Meat and Fish.

We guarantee the paste to be our finest quality, and equal in every way to that packed in our larger sizes.
12 Varieties. Price **3½**d. each. **3/3** dozen.

	Anchovy	Kindly note to specify
	Turkey and Tongue	"Midget" when ordering
	Wild Duck	to avoid confusion.

Maconochie's Potted Meats and Fish Pastes, 3½d. & 6d., all fancy glass vases. Several new Pastes now ready.

"Diploma" Peeled Shrimps.
Very choice. In glasses.

Specially Recommended for Sauces.

Small	.. ..	**7**d. each
Medium	..	**11½**d. ,,
Large	..	**1/2½** ,,

"Diploma" Prawns in Aspic Jelly.
In Hermetically Sealed Round Glasses.

No. 1 size	.. .. ..	**8½**d. each
,, 2 ,,	.. .. ..	**1/3½** ,,

"Diploma" Herrings in Tomato Sauce.
Oblong Tins, extra large size, **6½**d. each.

Condensed Milk.

"Diploma" Full Cream.

1 lb. Tins	..	**6**d. each
½ lb. ,,	..	**3**d. ,,

Our Condensed Milk is PERFECT in quality—nothing but finest sugar and freshest milk are used in its manufacture.

"Diploma" is packed in patent lever-top enamelled tins—an IDEAL and very attractive package.

PAN YAN PICKLE

is composed of Fresh Fruits, Rare Spices and Choice Vegetables, and it is the most splendid Tonic and Digestive ever produced.

It gives Tone and Distinction to every dish. It makes the daintiest Sandwiches, and with Bread and Cheese, it is a delicious and easily digested supper.

SOLD IN TWO SIZES—

6½d. and 10½d.

☞ At GAMAGES ☜

PAN YAN PICKLE, 6½d. & 10½d.

MACONOCHIE'S LATEST SPECIALITY
IN FISH PASTE—

Lobster & Tomato.   Salmon & Shrimp.
Sardine & Lobster.   Sardine & Tomato.
And all other well known kinds.
Large Fancy Glass Vases, 6d.   Small, 3¼d.

Herbs (Dried).

FINEST PREPARED.

In Nickel Screw-Cap Bottles.
Screw-Cap Bottles very convenient for use.

Per Bott.	Per Doz.
5½d.	5/3

Assortment :—

Mint, Sage, Mixed Herbs, Parsley,   Thyme.

First & Best
GORDON & DILWORTHS
TOMATO CATSUP.
MADE FROM WHOLE FRESH FRUIT.

Gordon & Dilworth's
SPECIALITIES.

Tomato Catsup.

4-oz. Bottle	3d.	12-oz. Bottle	8½d.
8-oz. Bottle	5½d.	16-oz. Bottle	10½d.

Tomato Chutney.

8-oz. Bottle	8½d.	12-oz. Bottle	1/-

Tomato Soup.

No. 1. Tin .. 6½d.   About 1¼ pts. .. 10½d.   About 1 quart .. 1/4

Mushroom Catsup.

8-oz. Bottle	5½d.	16-oz. Bottle	10½d.

GORDON & DILWORTH'S MUSHROOM CATSUP
"Homestead" Brand
ABSOLUTELY PURE GUARANTEED
DELICIOUS WITH SOUPS GRAVIES MEATS CHOPS STEAKS ETC.

Gordon & Dilworth's Sweet Pickled or Spiced Fruits

Prepared with cane sugar, flavoured with finest Spices and Vinegar. Delicious with Poultry and Game. In 1½-pint Bottles.

Peaches, Pears, Pineapple, Greengages, Melons, Damsons and Red Cherries.

3/6 1½-pint bot.   Figs 4/9 1½-pint bot.   Cranberries 3/6 & 4/6 bot.

GORDON & DILWORTH'S
Tomato Soup
MADE ONLY FROM WHOLE FRESH TOMATOES & PRIME OX BEEF

GORDON & DILWORTH'S TART FRUITS

In Vacuum Bottles (abt. 24 oz.). Unsweetened.

Gooseberry ..	6½d.	Blackberry ..	8½d.
Red Plum ..	7½d.	Red Currant ..	11½d.
Golden Plum	7½d.	Raspberry and	
Victoria Plum	8½d.	Currant ..	11½d.

GORDON & DILWORTH'S
Special Quality Jams.

Prepared from rich ripe Fruits and maple Sugar.
NO PRESERVATIVES. IN GLASS JARS.

Apricot ..	1/-	Pineapple ..	1/-
Cranberry ..	1/-	Quince ..	1/-
Peach ..	1/-		

GORDON & DILWORTH'S
Tomato Chutney
Delicious and Appetising

Stewed Tomatoes,

A smooth pulp from which the skin and the seeds have been removed. Qrt. tins. Price 9½d.

CHINA & GLASS DEPT.

Tea, Breakfast and Dinner Services.

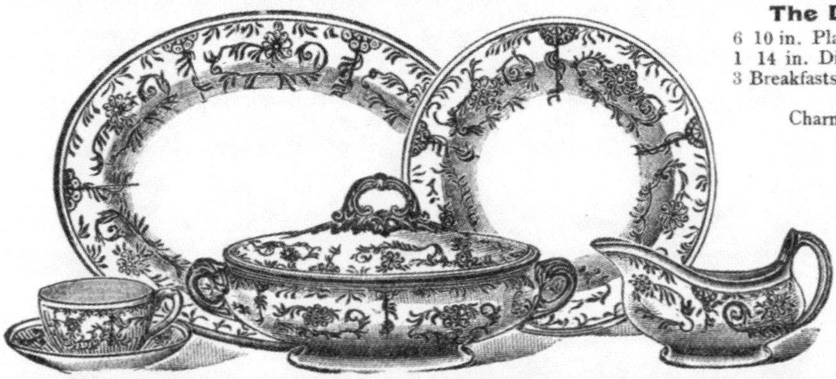

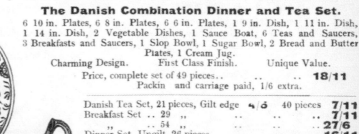

The Danish Combination Dinner and Tea Set.

6 10 in. Plates, 6 8 in. Plates, 6 6 in. Plates, 1 9 in. Dish, 1 11 in. Dish, 1 14 in. Dish, 2 Vegetable Dishes, 1 Sauce Boat, 6 Teas and Saucers, 3 Breakfasts and Saucers, 1 Slop Bowl, 1 Sugar Bowl, 2 Bread and Butter Plates, 1 Cream Jug.

Charming Design. First Class Finish. Unique Value.

Price, complete set of 49 pieces.. .. .. **18/11**

Packin and carriage paid, 1/6 extra.

Danish Tea Set, 21 pieces, Gilt edge **4/6** 40 pieces	**7/11**
Breakfast Set .. 29 ,,	**7/11**
,, .. 54 ,,	**27/6**
Dinner Set, Ungilt, 26 pieces	**16/11**
,, .. 70 ,,	**39/6**
Jugs, Ungilt, set of 3	**1/11**
Cheese Stands	**2/11**
Tea Set, 21 pieces	**3/11**

Packing and Carriage 1/- to 1/6 extra.

Ye Olde Delph Combined Dinner, Tea and Breakfast Set. In Dutch Blue Colouring

Comprising—
6 Meat plates. 6 Pudding plates.
6 Cheese ,, 3 Dishes.
2 Cover dishes. 1 Sauce Boat.
6 Teas and Saucers.
3 Breakfast and Saucers.
2 Bread and Butter Plates.
1 Slop Basin. 1 Cream Jug.
1 Sugar Bowl.

21/- for 49 pieces.
Packing and carriage **1/6** extra.

21 piece 'Ye Old Delph' Tea Set, **4/9**
Packing and carriage paid, **1/3** extra.

54 pieces Delph Dinner Set, **24/9**

70 pieces diitto, **38/6**

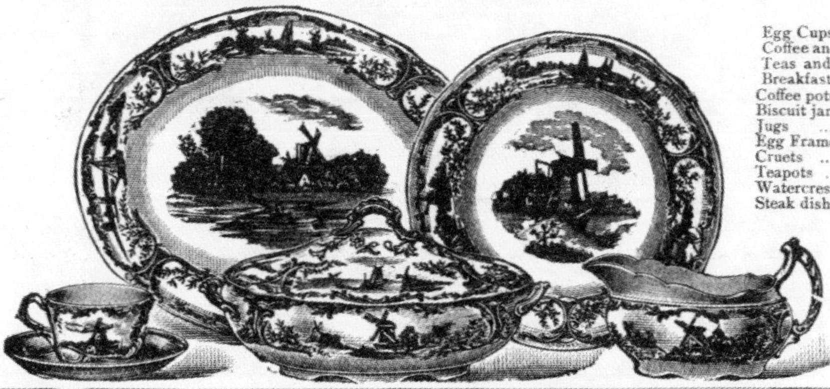

	Each.		Each.
Egg Cups ...	**2**d.	Cream Jugs ...	**5½**d.
Coffee and saucers	**2½**d.	Slop basin ...	**5**d.
Teas and ,,	**4½**d.	Bread & butter plates	**4½**d
Breakfast and ,,	**4½**d.	Sardine dishes ...	**2/3**

Coffee pots, patent strainers ... **2/9** **2/6** **2/3** each
Biscuit jars, with brass handle ... **2/6** each.
Jugs ... ... Set of 3, **1/7½** Set of 5, **2/9**
Egg Frames ... ... 6 cups, **2/9** 4 cups, **1/11**
Cruets ... ... **2/3** each.
Teapots .. ... **1/6½** **1/7½** **1/9½** **1/11½** ,,
Watercress stands ... **1/11½** ,,
Steak dishes, covered... **2/6** and **2/9** ,,
Butter dishes ... ... **1/3** ,,
Honey pots ... ... **1/8** ,,
Teapot stands ... ... **7½**d. ,,
Covered muffin dishes **1/10½** ,,
Triple trays ... ... **2/9** ,,
Cheese dishes ... ... **2/6** ,,
Salad Bowls ... ... **2/6** ,,
Hot water jugs. **1/6** **1/9** **2/-**
If with patent mounts. **4/6**

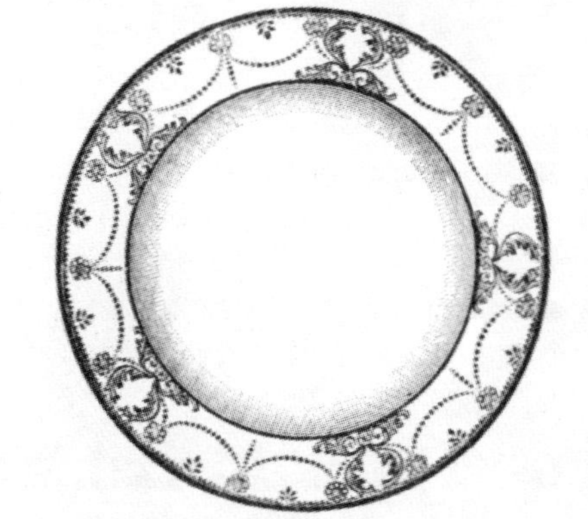

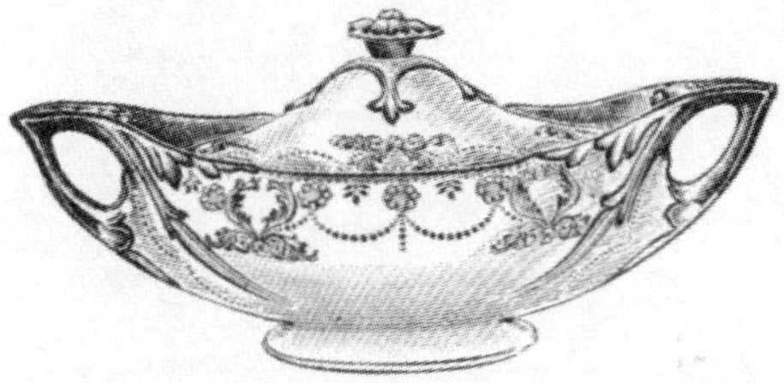

Venus Dinner Service.

54 pieces	**32/11**
70 ,, ...	**52/11**

Printed on fine English Earthenware Body and China Glaze.

Every Piece Gilt.

Packing 1/- and 1/6 extra on Dinner Sets.

Empress Shape Fluted White Earthenware.

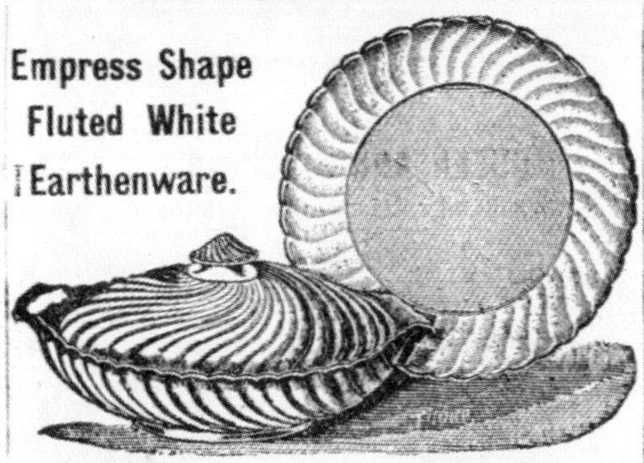

26 piece Dinner Set .. .. **9/11** complete
54 ,, ,, ,, ...**18/11** ,,
70 ,, ,, ,, ...**29/11** ,,
Meat plates .. 10 in... .. **3/6** per dozen.
Pie ,, .. 8 ,,.. .. **2/9** ,,
Cheese ,, .. 6 ,,.. .. **1/9½** ,,
Soup ,, .. 10 ,,.. .. **3/6** ,,
Vegetable dish, 1/9½ Sauce boats, **6½**d. each.
Sauce tureens, complete .. .. **1/9½** ,,
Dishes 9 in. 10 in. 12 in. 14 in. 16 in.
4½d. **6½**d. **9½**d. **1/3** **1/9** each.
Tea cups and saucers .. .. **2/6** per doz.
Breakfast do. .. .. **3/6** ,,
Teapots: Small **1/2**, medium **1/4½**, large **1/6½**

Divided Cover Dishes.

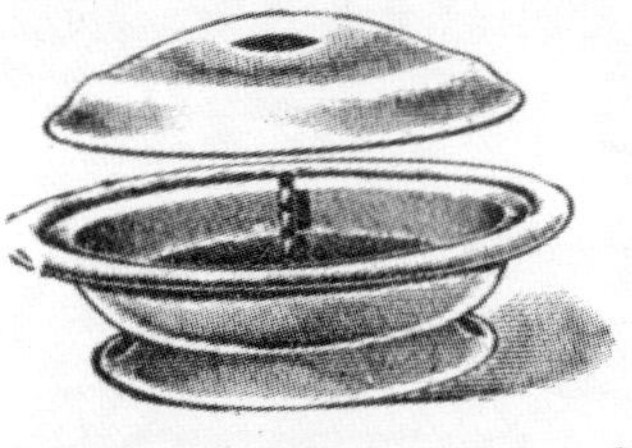

White .. .. **1/9** and **2/6**

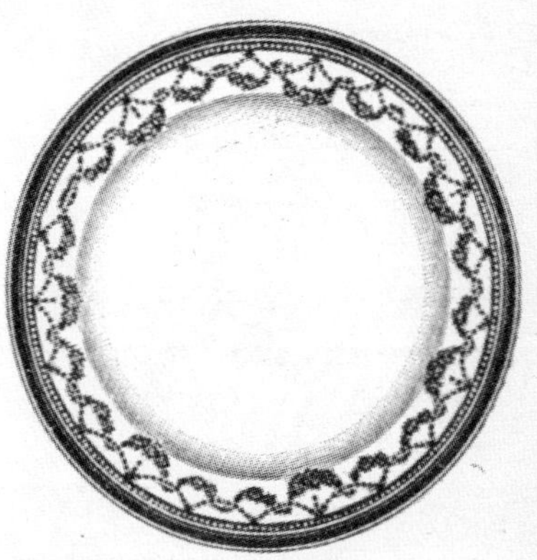

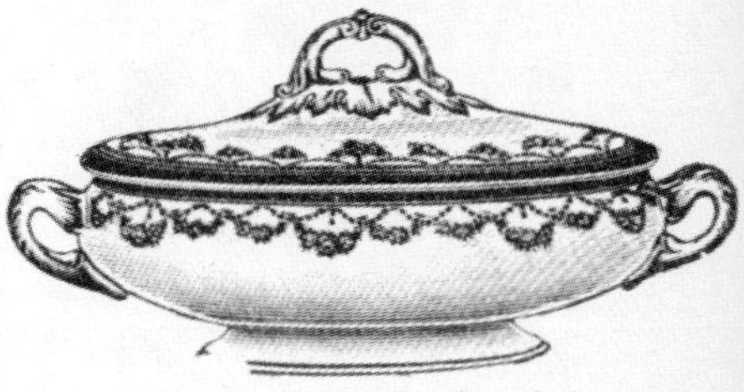

Louie Dinner Service.

54 pieces	**45/6**
70 ,, ...	**67/6**

As above, but without Mazarine Band.

54 pieces	**34/11**
70 ,, ...	**67/6**

Printed on best Eathenware Body and China Glaze.

Every Piece Gilt

Packing 1/- and 1/6 extra on Dinner Sets

Write for Full Departmental List sent post free anywhere.

SPECIAL OFFER.

The "Diana" (Wedgwood)

Finely printed in Peacock Blue or Canton.

Consisting of 54 pieces.

Special price **21/-** complete.

70 pieces, **32/9** complete.

Wedgwood & Co.'s Semi-porcelain (No. F. 8313).

Dinner Ware.

Perfect Body. With Green festoon and Purple ribbon and jewel.

Price, 54 pieces, **37/6**   70 pieces, **55/6**

Wedgwood & Co.'s Finest Semi-Porcelain.

Dessert Service.

18 pieces, price .. **21/-**

Choicely decorated in colours.

EXCEPTIONAL VALUE.

Ely Dinner Service.

26 pieces, price **9/11**   50 pieces, no gold, **18/11**

50 pieces, richly gilt, **28/6**

In Japan Blue and Bronze Green.

No. X. 20. Minton shape. Royal Mazarine Blue Band and Gold Line.

26-piece Dinner Set, **19/11** 54, **39/6** 70, **56/11**

The most popular set on the market.

The darker colour band showing up the gold lines. Very effective.

Special cheap line, 54 pieces, price **28/9**

X. 21.

First quality. Minton shape Royal Mazarine blue band and border.

26-piece Dinner Set .. **25/11**

54-piece   ,, .. **47/6**

70-piece   ,, .. **67/6**

40 Piece Tea Set, 10/9

QUEEN ANNE CHINA,

DELICATE FLUTED DESIGN.

40 Piece Tea Set, 10/9

Honey Jar and Stand, **1/4½**

Tea Cups and Saucers, **4/9** doz.

Tea and Breakfast Cups. Low or Tall Shape.

Breakfast Cups & Saucers, **7/3** doz.

Teapot, **1/11   2/4½   2/11**

Cream Jugs ... **7½d.**

Milk Jugs ... **1/-**

Hot Water Jugs **2/11   3/6   4/3**

Coffee Cups, doz. **4/9**

Low and Tall Shape.

Teapot Stands ... **7½d.**

Egg Cups, each ... **2½d.**

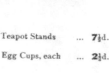

Sugar and Cream, **1/3** pair.

Covered Muffin, 8 in., **2/6**

Broth Bowls, **1/6½** and **2/3**

The Queen Anne China,

all white, and delicately fluted; is a very popular service and one we strongly recommend.

Jugs. **1/3   1/6   1/9**

Plates.

5 in.   6 in.   7 in.

3/-   **4/-**   **5/-** doz.

Bread and Butter Plates, **8½d.**

29-piece Breakfast Set,

Price .. **10/9**

Cocoa Jugs. **1/11½   2/3   2/9**

Tea Sets.

X. 1685. Low Doris Shape.
Decorated with wreaths of hand-painted roses and foilage. Best English China.

40-piece Tea Service .. **32/6**

29-piece Breakfast Service.. **32/6**

Packing 1/- Carriage paid.

The "Pansy."

X. 3297. "Pansy" English China Tea Service. 40 pieces. Beautifully hand-painted pansies and gold decoration. Price .. **21/-**
Packed in hamper and sent Carriage, paid, 1/- extra.

The "Rose."

X. 3607. "The Rose" English China Tea Service. 40 pieces. Beautifully decorated with Rose clusters, with gilt edges, **17/11**
Packed & carriage paid 1/3 extra.

X. 21. Mazarine Blue and All-colour Borders.

21-piece Tea Set **7/6**

40-piece **14/9**

29-piece Breakfast Set .. **14/9**

X. 1308. Bute Shape.
With sprays of blue and yellow flowers.

40-piece Tea Service .. **23/6**

29-piece Breakfast Service **23/6**

Packing 1/- Carriage paid.

X. 1133. Tall Doris Shape.
Decorated with ovals of green jewel work and pink roses, finished in burnished gold. Fine English china.

40-piece Tea Service .. **29 6**

29-piece Breakfast Service **29/6**

X. 6876. English china, green and gold line. Tea Cups & Saucers **4/6** doz.
Breakfast Cups and Saucers **7 3** ,,
Muffins, 5in. **3/3** 6in. **4/6** 7in. **5/6**
Bread and Butter Plates, Slop Bowls, Sugar Bowls & Cream Jugs, **7½d.** ea.
Milk Jugs, **1/3** each. Egg Cups, doz.
21-piece Tea Set, ... **6/6**
29-piece Breakfast Set **12/-**

No. X. 20.
Mazarine Blue band with gold line
21-piece Tea Set **6/9**
40-piece Tea Set **12 6**
29-piece Breakfast Set .. **12 6**

The "Ena" Globe.

No. X. 26. Mazarine Blue Band, in Green, Brown and Blue.

Tea Set, 21 pieces .. **6/11**

,, 40 ,, .. **13/6**

Breakfast Set, 29 pieces.. **13/6**

X. 1699. Windsor Shape.
In hair-brown pattern, and pink and yellow flowers.

40-piece Tea Service .. **23/6**

29-piece Breakfast Service **23/6**

Packing 1/- Carriage paid.

X. 1059. Windsor Shape.
Decorated with mauve bell flowers and green leafa e, gilt edge. Staffordshire China.

40-piece Tea Service .. **19/11**

29-piece Breakfast Service **19/11**

Mazarine Blue Band.

Same as No. X. 20, only in fine quality china.

Tea Cups and Saucers ..	**6/6** doz.
Breakfast Cups & Saucers	**11/9** ,,
6-in. Plates, Tea size ..	**6 3** ,,
7-in. Plates, Breakfast size	**7/11** ,,
Bread and Butter Plates..	**1/-** each
Slop Bowls & Sugar Bowls	**1/-** ,,
Cream Jugs	**1/-** ,,
Egg Cups..	**3/3** doz.
Milk Jugs..	**1/6** each

X. 1613. Low Doris Shape.
A real production of Old Chantilly Ware. In colourings—purple, green and pink.

40-piece Tea Service **25/9**

29-piece Breakfast Service.. **25/9**

Packing 1/- Carriage paid.

The "Poppy."

X 3614. The "Poppy" English China Tea Service. 40 pieces. Decorated with red poppies & gold, **13/9**
Packing 1/3. Carriage paid.

X. 3122. Tea Set. Decoration—Red, blue and richly gilded. Albert Shape, **18/11**

The "Danish." Special line.

Dark Blue with Gold edge. 21-piece Earthenware Tea Set, consisting of 6 Cups and Saucers 6 Plates, 1 Cream, 1 Slop Basin, and 1 Bread and Butter Plate. Marvellous value. Strong and Serviceable. **4/6** Packing and Carriage 1/-
40-piece Set, **7/11** 29-piece Breakfast, **7/11**
Packed and Carriage paid 1/3 extra.

Afternoon Tea Set on Wicker Tray.

Fine English China. Enamelled and printed colours.

Price, complete with Tray .. .. **6/11** Packing 6d.

The "Athena" Tea Set.

CHARMING DESIGN.

Printed in blue and green colours.

22 pieces .. **5/6**

Packing 6d.

Teapot to match .. **1/11**

Tray not included.

Write for Full Departmental List sent post free anywhere.

Selection of Toilet Sets.

Great variety of patterns in stock. New designs constantly arriving. We invite you to inspect our showrooms.

The "Sefton" Toilet Ware.
New lustre colours in Art Green, Red Blue and Heliotrope.
5 pieces, **11/9** 6 pieces, **14/6** 8 pieces, **21/9**
Slop Pail, to match .. **8/11**

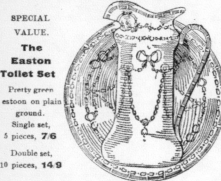

SPECIAL VALUE.

The Easton Toilet Set

Pretty green estoon on plain ground.
Single set, 5 pieces, **7/6**

Double set, 10 pieces, **14/9**

The Dane Toilet Set.

Art colours, Dark Green, Light Green, Crushed Strawberry,

5 pieces.	6 pieces.	8 pieces.	10 pieces.
11/6	**13/9**	**21/-**	**23/6**

Slop pail to match .. **9/6**
Packing 1/- and 1/6 ex. Carriage paid, over 20/-

Servants' Toilet Sets
At Remarkably Low Prices. If possible, intending customers should visit our showrooms, the charming designs and low prices will be a revelation to them.

Special Value.

New Shape.

Artistically Shaded in Green, Blue or Red.

5 Pieces.

Price .. **5/6**

The Holborn Toilet Set.

Gilt edges, coloured festoons and flowers.
Single set, 5 pieces, **8/11** Double set 10 pieces, **17/9** Slop Pail, **5/11** Sponge Bowl, **2/6**
Packing 1/- and 1/6

Shell Shape.

	5 pieces.	6 pieces.	8 pieces.
White	8/6	9/11	14/11
White and Gold	11/6	13/11	21/-
Flowers and Gold	15/11	18/11	29/6
Mother of Pearl & Gold		21/-	33/6

The "Iris" Toilet Ware.

Art colours, Green with Yellow Flowers.

Art colours, Pink with Yellow Flowers.

	Blue		Pink	
5 pieces.	6 pieces.	8 pieces.	10 pieces.	Slop pail.
13/9	**16/6**	**24/9**	**21/6**	**11/6**

The Rosary Toilet Set.
Beautifully Coloured Roses. 5 pieces, **13/11** set. 6 pieces, **16/11** Packing 1/-

No. X. 3813 Bromley Hand-painted
Toilet Sets. Beautiful designs. Staffordshire make.
5 pieces, **18/6** 6 pieces, **21/-** 8 pieces, **35/6**
Packing 1/- extra.

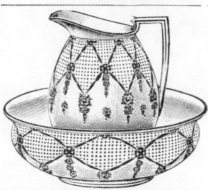

No. X. Bromley Hand-painted Ware.
Very choice, beautiful decoration, **18/6** set, 5 pieces, 6 pieces ... ... **21/-** Packing 1s.

Gem Shape.

	5 pieces	6 pieces	8 pieces	10 pieces
White and Gold	8/9	10/6	15/9	17/6
Flower and Gold	9/6	11/6	16/6	18/6

Gilt Bordered on Ivory Ground.

5 Pieces.

Price **5/11**

For further Selection see Furnishing List, post free anywhere

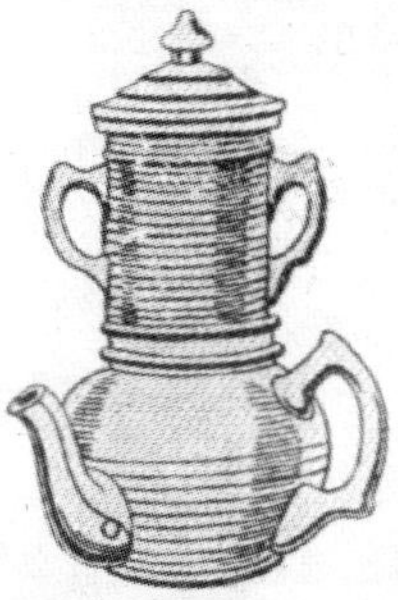

Coffee Pots and Filters

Brown or Green. Best Fireproof China.

Cups.	Each.	Cups.	Each.
1	1/6½	5	3/6
2	2/-	6	4/6
3	2/6	8	5/6
4	2/11	12	6/9

Covered Vegetable Entree or Breakfast Dish.

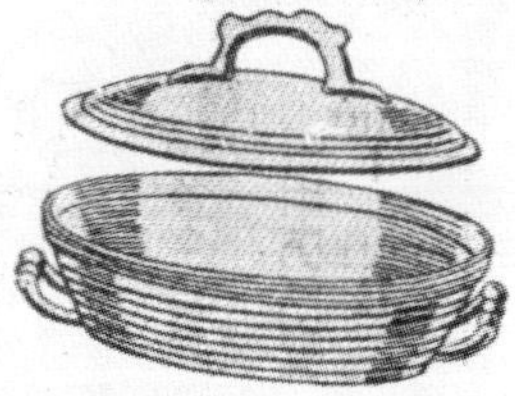

No. X. 103. Round.

6	7	8½	9	10 in. diam.
1/11	2/9	4/6	5/3	6/9 each.

No. X. 104. Oval.

8in.	9in.	10in.	11in.	Length.
2/4½	3/6	4/11	6/-	Each.

Fireproof Cooking Ware.

TERRE DE CHAMPAGNE.

Yellow Glazed inside and outside, superior finish and decorated Jaspé. This clay found in the department de la Champagne, is undoubtedly the finest clay in existence, and submits under enormous furnace heat (1,600-1,800 degrees Reamur) to a perfect glaze. Its composition is entirely free of any injurious substance, and has been passed by the French Government, by whom it has been analysed. Its fire resisting capacity is astounding and **if heated gradually at first and placed dry on the fire**, accidents are impossible.

The perfect glaze permits the cleaning to be done as easily as washing plates, and in the case of burnt crust, scrub with pumice stone, fine sand or a knife, which will at once remove all stains without injuring the glaze.

No. X. 66

Champagne Clay Casserole.

Flat English shape. Tubular handle. All Glazed inside and outside.

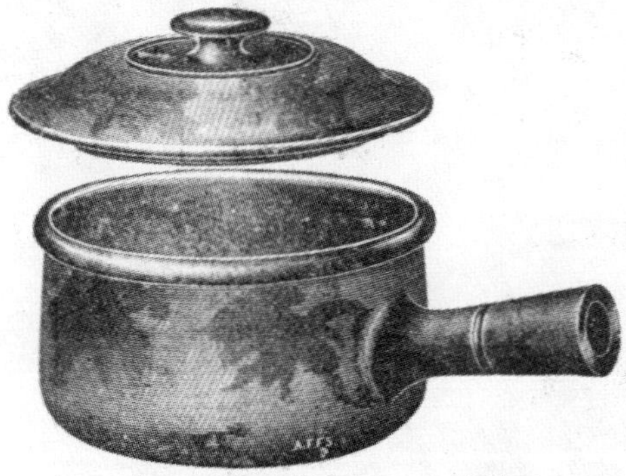

8	7	6	5	4	3	2	1	0	00 size.
4	4¾	5¼	6	6¾	7¼	8	9	10	11 in. in diam.
6½d.	7½d.	10½d.	1/2	1/6½	2/1½	2/9	3/6	4/6	4/11 each.

On account of its perfect glaze this article can be cleaned very easily.

No. X. 2 Casseorle (with lid).

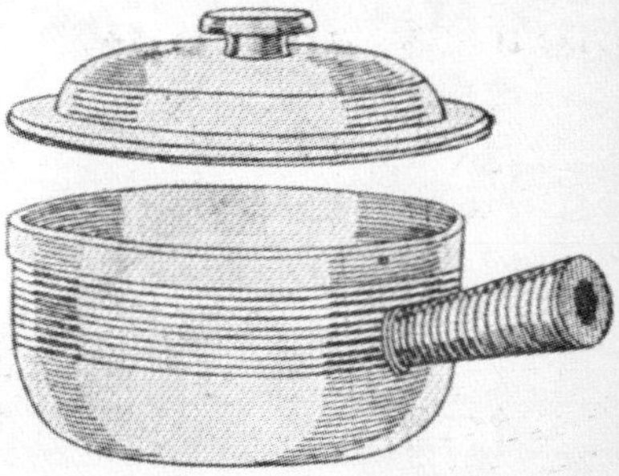

5in. diam.	6½d.	6½ in. diam.	10½d.	9½ in. diam.	1/6½
5½ ,, ,,	7½d.	7½ ,, ,,	1/-	10½ ,, ,,	1/11
6 ,, ,,	9½d.	8½ ,, ,,	1/3½	11½ ,, ,,	2/6½

Brown inside.

Lip Saucepan (without lid.)

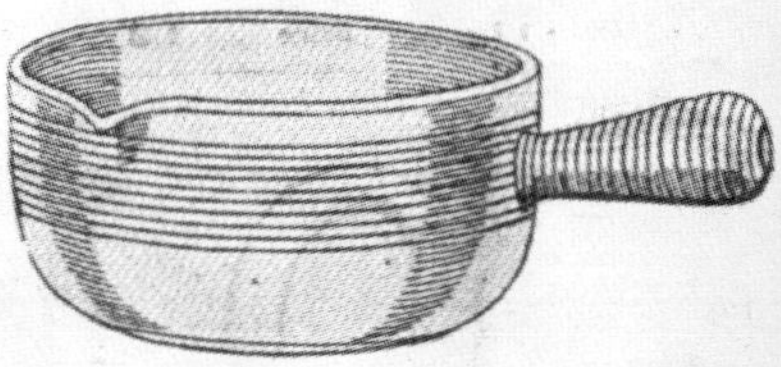

Diam.	Price.	Diam.	Price.
5½ in.	5½d.	8 in.	11d.
6 ,,	7½d.	8½ ,,	1/1
7 ,,	9½d.	9 ,,	1/4½

Casseroles No. X. 2 and Marmites No. X. 3.

For all kinds of Stews etc., where a slow and regular heat is required, and which is essential to retain the flavour and avoid burning.

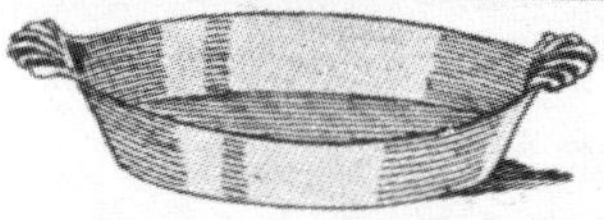

Fireproof China Oval Eared Dish.

No. X. 201. Length including ears.

6	7	8	9½	11	11½	12½	13¾	14½
5½d.	6½d.	8½d.	10½d.	1/-	1/3	1/11	2/6	2/11

No. X. 200. Round Eared Dishes.

5	5½	7	8	9 in. diameter without ears.
6½d.	7½d.	9½d.	11½d.	1/3 each.

Best quality White Fireproof China.

Ramikin, Fluted.

Inches diam.	cm. diam.	Crust Each.	White, best China, Each.
1¾	4	5d.	2d.
2	5	5½d.	2½d.
2¼	6	7d.	3d.
2¾	7	8d.	3½d.
3	8	9d.	4½d.

These are incomparable for the Frying of Eggs, Bacon, Tomatoes, Omelettes, Scrambled Eggs, Kidneys, etc. If these comestibles are fried in a little butter and served direct to table the difference in flavour is really wonderful.

China Egg Poacher.

No. X. 203.

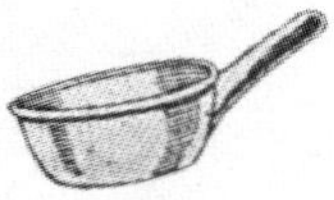

3	3¼	3¾	4½ diameter.
5d.	7½d.	8d.	9½d. each.

Special Instructions for use.

(1) It is most important to see that the utensil is perfectly dry outside before being exposed to the fire or stove. At first a SLOW HEAT should be applied, and at no time should the flame be allowed to extend beyond the bottom area. **Do not place an empty utensil on the stove or fire.**

(1) **On no account remove the utensil from the stove to a damp sink**, but place on a dry table. Allow same to cool before cleansing. Thoroughly clean both inside and outside of the utensil after use. If ordinary care is used, Fireproof Utensils will last twice as long as Enamel Ware, and no expense is incurred through cracking and breakages.

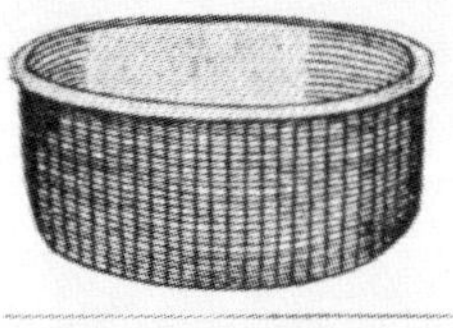

Round Souffle Fluted.

No. X. 202. In best White H.P. China.

4½	5½	6	6¾	7½	8 in. diam.
9d.	1/1	1/4	1/6	1/9	2/3 each.

No. X. 58.

Oval Roasting Dish.

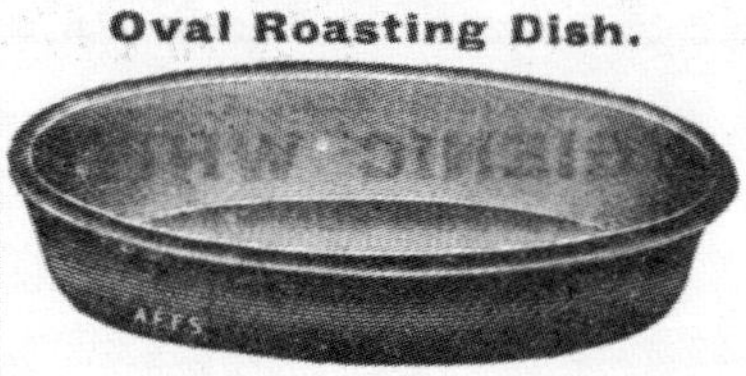

7	6	5	4 size.
11	12½	13½	15 in. in length.
11½d.	1/1½	1/11	2/4½ each.

No. X. 59.

Oblong Roasting Dish.

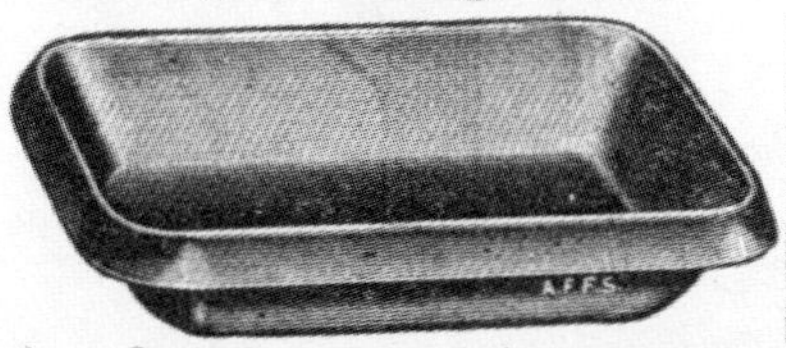

4	3	2	1	0 size.
8½	9½	10½	11½	13 in. in length.
11½d.	1/1½	1/6½	1/11	2/3 each.

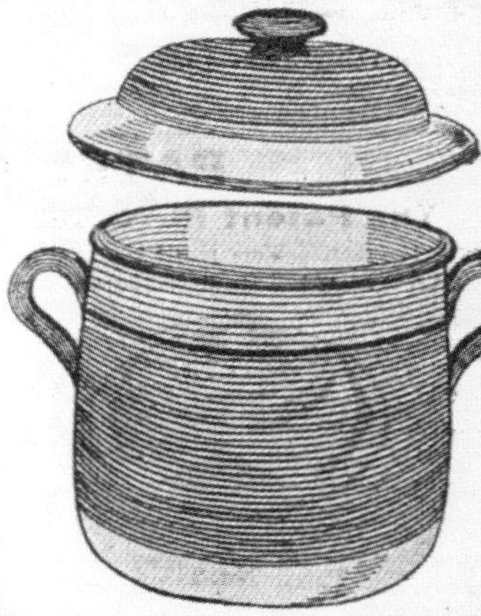

Marmite, High Shape (Fireproof, with Cover)

3½ in. diam.	7½d.	8 in. diam.	2/3
4½ ,, ,,	8½d.	9 ,, ,,	2/9
5 ,, ,,	10½d.	10 ,, ,,	3/6
5½ ,, ,,	11½d.	11 ,, ,,	4/11
6½ ,, ,,	1/3½	12 ,, ,,	6/6
7 ,, ,,	1/5½		

Milk Boiler. No. X. 5813 ... 15/- each
2 pint. 11½ in. high.

Oval Hot-water Bacon Dish.

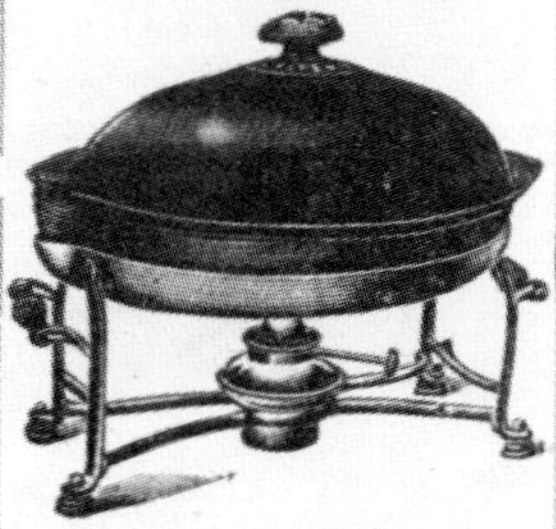

X. 5833. 26/6 each.
12½ in. long. 8½ in. high.

Entree Dish, Round or Oval. No. X. 5842.

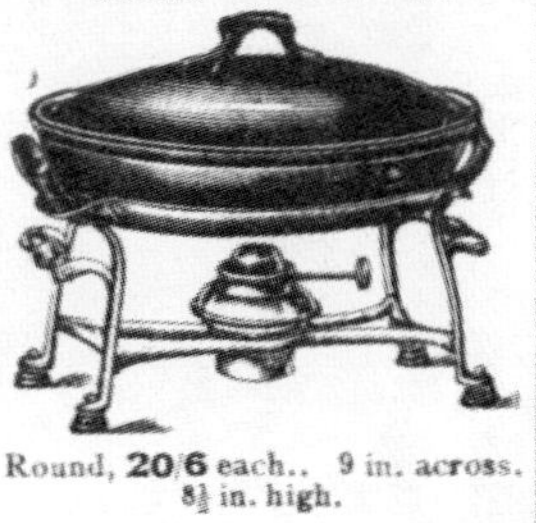

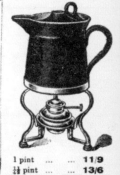

Round, 20/6 each.. 9 in. across. 8½ in. high.

No. X. 5828. Oval, 22/6
9 in. long. 8½ in. high.

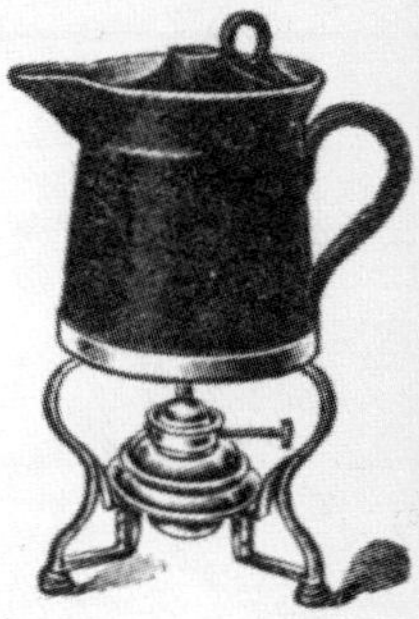

1 pint 11/9
1½ pint 13/6

Fireproof China, mounted on Alumininium Stands with Spirit Lamps underneath, is a delightful method of keeping food hot on the table, the lightness of the metal adding little to the weight of the china. The Stands are highly polished, having a beautiful appearance, resembling Silver-plate. They do not tarnish, and are kept in brilliant condition by simply rubbing with soft dry wash leather. Soda must not be used in cleaning.

Every type of French Fireproof Ware kept in stock, hundreds of different articles too numerous to list, all at competitive prices. A small amount is charged for packing on all the above. Goods to the value of 20/- and over Carriage Paid.

X. 365. Cut Glass Bottle. Price **1/6½**

X. 2600. Carafe & Up. Price ... **1/3**

THE CECIL Glass Carafe and Up. Price **5½d.** complete.

X. 211. Cut Glass Carafe and Up. Price ... **2/9**

X. 785. Cut Glass Carafe and Up. Price ... **2/9**

No. X. 36. Bohemian Crystal Cut Celery Glass. Price **2/3½** Posting and Packing, 6d.

X. 879. Bohemian Crystal Cut Celery Glass, **2/9** each.

Plain Crystal Glass Tankard Jug. 2-pt. ... **6½d.** each.

No. X. 29. Cut Glass. 1½-pt. **2/6** 2-pt. **2/11½d.**

X. 9070. Bohemian Crystal Cut Glass. 1-pt., **2/9** 1½-pt., **2/11½** 2-pt., **3/9½**

Goods to value of 10/- and over sent Carriage paid in England & Wales.

No. X. 879. Bohemian Crystal Cut Glass Jug. ½-pt. **1/6** 1-pt. **1/11** 1½-pt. **2/3** 2-pt. **2/11** 3-pt. **3/6**

THE TELL-TALE JUG. **10½d.** each. This Jug saves pounds in a very little time.

PATENT HYGIENIC WHITE WARE AND POTS.

The Patent Pie Dish.

Easy to clean. Very Hard and Durable. Oval Shape. Rounded Interior.

Grooved at bottom with four vents for air passage to prevent splitting or burning.

Just the thing every cook and house-keeper wants.

Paten. No. 23516. Registered Shape 531631.

Wide rim to form a good support for pastry.

All Sizes, 3 to 12 in. Shallow for fruit, or deep for meat.

SHALLOW, measuring edge to edge.

5½ in., **2½d.** 6½ in., **3d.** 7½ in., **3½d.**
8 in., **4d.** 9 in., **4½d.** 10 in., **5½d.**
10½ in., **6½d.** 11½ in., **7½d.** 12 in. **10½d.**
13 in., **1/2** each.

DEEP, measuring edge to edge.

6½ in., **3d.** 7½ in., **4d.** 8 in., **5d.**
9 in., **6d.** 10 in., **7d.** 10½ in., **8d.**
11½ in., **9d.** 12 in., **1/-** 13 in. **1/3** ea.

Brown Rock.
3½d. 4½d.
5½d. 6½d.
7½d.
Samian, same as above, with Salmon band.
5½d. 6½d.
8½d. 9½d.
10½d. each.

Cresswell Mottled, same shape as above.
7½d. 8½d. 10½d. each. Carriage forward.

Here is an article which will be a constant source of satisfaction to the user.

Made in Pearly White English Ware, Highly Glazed.

The Hygienic Jug.

Note its merits—

1. Non-Slpash Top.
2. Unchippable Edge.
3. Rounded Interior (easy to clean).
4. Perfect Pourer.

Provisional Patent 12834/09. Registered No. 533435.

10 Sizes. No sharp angles inside to hold dirt.

½ pt.	1 pt.	1½ pt.	pt.	2½ pt.
4½d.	**5½d.**	**7½d.**	**9d.**	**10½d.**

3 pt.	4 pt.	5 pt.	7 pt.	9 pt.
1/-	**1/3**	**1/6**	**1/10½**	**2/6**

Each Jug has the approximate measure stamped on the bottom.

Specially suitable for Hotels and Restaurants.

These Jugs fitted with the Patent Interchangeable "Flip-Flap" mount, make excellent Hot Water Jugs.

	½ pt.	1 pt.	1½ pt.	2 pt.
Prices of Mounts only	**6½d.**	**9d.**	**10½d.**	**1/-**

Other sizes proportionate.

Divided Vegetable Dish.

(Sunk Handle),

A very useful article for the mid-day meal. Actual Measure.

7	8	9 in.
10½d.	**1/-**	**1/3**

10	11 in.
1/6	**1/9**

Without division. 7 8 9 10 11 in.
7½d. 8½d. 11½d. 1/2 1/6

No untrimmed or sharp corners in which microbe or dirt can hide.

The Patent Safety Milk Bowl.

Incurved Top to prevent spilling. Very strong and Pearly White.

IMPORTANT.—When not in use this Bowl can be hung on a hook flat to the wall, and kept thereby free from dust.

Provisional Patent No. 5381/09.
Registered Shape No. 537320.

This invention quite supersedes the ordinary Milk Bowl, and is not so expensive.

7, **10½d.** 8, **1/2** 9, **1/-** 10, **1/4** 11 in, **1/6**
12, **1/9** 13, **2/-** 14, **2/9** 15 in. **3/9**

SPOUT COVERS to keep out flies. Recommended by doctors for preventing contamination.

7, **4½d.** 8, **5d.** 9, **5½d.** 10, **6½d.** 11 in., **7½d.**
12, **8½d.** 13, **9½d.** 14, **10½d.** 15 in., **1/-** ea.

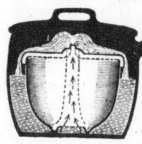

The Patent "Quick-Cooker" Pudding Bowl.

Scientific, Simple, Hygienic, Economical.

A central funnel through which boiling water rushes on thermosyphonic principle, cooking the pudding thoroughly in every part in half the usual time.

NO PUDDING CLOTH REQUIRED! Saves 25 per cent. of the gas bill when Cooking is done by Gas.

Prices.—

1 pint .. **1/-** 1½ pints .. **1/3** 2½ pint .. **1/9**
3½ pint .. **2/3** 4 pint .. **3/-**

Postage and packing 4d. to 9d. extra.

BOHEMIAN CRYSTAL GLASS. Etched & Cut.

Pall Mall Suite of Etched and Cut on Crystal Glass. The most handsome decorative and pleasing edition to the home yet introduced.

WELL WORTHY OF YOUR INSPECTION.

Ports .. per doz. **6/11**	Clarets .. per doz. **9/6**	½-pint Tumblers, per doz. **6/-**	Pint Decanters, each **5/6**
Sherries .. „ **6 11**	Champagnes.. „ **13/9**	Custards .. „ **12/-**	Claret „ „ **7/6**
Liqueurs .. „ **6/9**	½-pint Tumblers „ **6/9**	Quart Decanters, each **6/6**	

The Fish Suite of English Crystal Engraved Glass.

Very fine quality. Beautifully Engraved.

Claret Jug	.. each	**10/9**
2 pint Decanter	.. „	**7/9**
1 „ „	.. „	**6 3**
½ „ Tumbler	per doz.	**10/9**
8 to qt. „	„	**10/6**
Custard and Jelly	„	**13/-**

Champagnes, per doz...	**13/6**
Clarets	„ ..	**10/9**
Sherries	„ ..	**8/3**
Ports	„ ..	**8/3**
Liqueurs	„ ..	**7/11**
Finger Bowl	„ ..	**23/6**
Ice Plates	„ ..	**23/6**
Jugs, 1 pt. **2/3** 1½ pt.	**2/9**
do. 2 pint	..	**3/3**

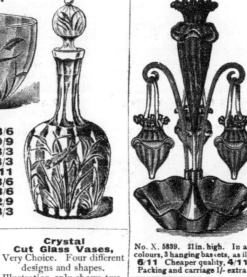

No. X. 5839. 21in. high. In all colours, 3 hanging baskets, as ill. **6/11** Cheaper quality, **4/11** Packing and carriage 1/- extra.

No. X. 4461. In all colours 21 n. high, 3 branches & 3 hanging baskets **9/11** Cheaper Type **7/11** Packing & Carriage 1/- extra.

Bohemian Crystal Cut-glass Spirit Bottle. Full-cut Hobnail **5/9** Half-cut Hobnail **4/9** Postage and packing 6d. xtra.

No. X. 6789. Rustic Flower Stand.

1 tube in clear or green glass, silver-plated and enamelled. 8½ in. high. **1/6½** Post 4d. No. X. 6786. Similar style, but longer, made up of 5 tubes, 17 in. long by 11½ in. high ... **10/6** Packing and carriage 9d. extra.

No. X 5821. 19in. high. In all colours, 2-branch ... **2/11½** 3-branch **3/11**

Dark green Epergne, similar to above, but perfectly plain, very rich ... **4/11** Packing and carriage 9d. extra.

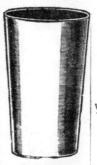

Cecil Plain. ½-pint Tumblers. **1/7½** doz. Postage & packing 6d. extra.

No. X. 340. Bohemian Crystal Cut Oval Dish.

6	7	8	9	10	11 in.
2/9	**3/4**	**4/3**	**4/11**	**5/6**	**6/9**

Very fine quality. Packing and carriage 3d. to 6d. extra.

No. X. 300. Bohemian Crystal Cut Glass Oval Dish. Cut edge, star bottom.

	6 in.	7 in.	8 in.	9 in.	10 in.	11 in.
Price ...	**1/6½**	**1/11½**	**2/4½**	**2/11**	**3 6**	**3/9**

Packing and carriage 4d. to 9d extra, according to size.

Crystal Cut Glass Vases,

Very Choice. Four different designs and shapes. Illustration only shows two. Crystal Cut Glass.

4½	6	8	10 in.
9d.	**1/-**	**1/3**	**1/9**

Postage and packing extra.

Postage and packing 9d.

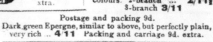

No. X. 885. Cut Handled Bohemian Glass Sweet Dish. Price .. **1/11** Post & packing, 6d.

No. X. 2. Pressed Salad Bowl, 9 in. **1/9** Post & Packing 6d. We have in stock a large variety of cheap English Pressed Glass Dishes. Cake Stands, **11½d.**

Oval or round, 6½ **4½**d., 7½ **5½**d., 8½ **6½**d., 9½ in. **7½**d. Cheap Salad Bowls, 7½d. 9½d. 11½d.

   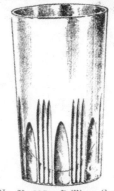

X. 400. Cut Hollow Polished bottom, Hand-made Tumbler ½-pt. **3/3** ½-pt. **3/11** ½-pt. **5/6**

Heavy bottom, plain. ½-pt. **1/11**   ½-pt. **2/6½** ¾ pt. **3/3.**

C. Circles. ½-pt. **2/6** ½-pt. **2/11** ¾-pt. **3/11**

No. X. 007. Brilliant Cut. Star Bottom. **6/11** doz. ½-pts. only.

ENAMEL WARE. Superior Quality and Finish.

The articles in this List are manufactured from best steel plates. The enamel is the best procurable, being perfectly coated and free from deleterious ingredients. In most cases it is entirely white with the blue rim, and presents the appearance of pure china. It is extensively used by large establishments, hospitals, and other places for its utility and reliability. Approximate dimensions and capacities stated.

Bread Bin.

No. Y. 703. Light Blue or Plain White outside, White inside. Capacity the same as Flour Bins. Lettered Bread.

Diam.	10	11	12	12½ in.
	4/9	**5/3**	**6/8**	**7/9**
Post	7d.	8d.	9d.	9d.
Diam.	13½	14	15	16 in
	8/3	**9/6**	**11/3**	**13/6**
Post	9d.	10d.	1/-	1/3

Wash-ups or Oval Baths.

No. Y. 510.

	13¾	15¾	17¾	19¾	21½	23½ in.
	3/-	**3/4**	**3/10**	**4/8**	**5/11**	**6/11**
Post	6d.	6d.	8d.	8d.	9d.	11d.

Child's Bath. Oval, Seamless

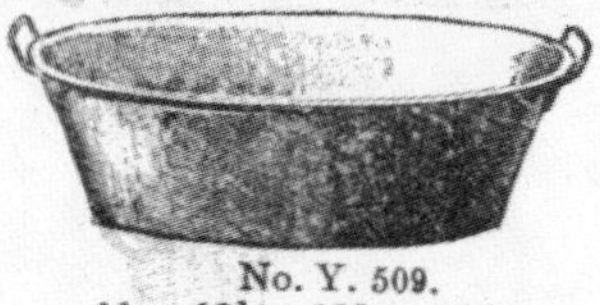

No. Y. 509.

	11	12½	13¾	15 in.
	1/7½	**1/8½**	**1/11½**	**2/2½**
Post	4d.	4d.	5d.	6d.
	16½	18	19¾	21½ in.
	2/6½	**2/9½**	**3/-**	**3/9**
Post	7d.	8d.	9d.	9d.

Stew or Stock Pot.

No. Y. 615.

Very suitable for Camp purposes. With Tin Covers.

Capacity about

Pints	4	6	9	12
	1/0½	**1/3½**	**1/9½**	**2/3½**
Post	3d.	4d.	5d.	6d.
Pints	16	20	25	27
	2/6½	**3/0½**	**3/6½**	**4/6**
Post	7d.	8d.	9d.	10d.

Flour Bin.

No. Y. 704. Light Blue or White outside, White inside.

Lettered Flour.

Best quality and finish.

Diam.	8	8¾	9½	10 in.
Capacity	7	9	12	bs
	2/9½	**3/3½**	**3/11½**	**4/6**
Post	5d.	6d.	6d.	7d.
Diam.	11	12	13½	15 in.
Capacity	18	21	30	42lbs
	5/3	**6/8**	**8/3**	**11/3**
Post	8d.	9d.	9d.	1/-

Toilet Pail.

No. Y 0594. With improved Drop-in Sanitary Cover, Detachable Cane Handle. White inside and out.

Diam.	..	10½	11 in.
Capacity about		2	2½ gals.
		4/3½	**4/9½**
Post	..	8d.	9d.

Toilet or Hot Water Cans.

No. Y. 652. Light Blue outside, White inside.

Pints	3	4	6	8
	2/11½	**3/9½**	**4/6**	**5/6**
Post	4d.	5d.	5d.	6d.
Pints	12	16	20	
	6/9	**7/11**	**9/9**	
Post	8d.	9d.	10d.	

Toilet Ewers.

No. Y. 542. White inside and out.

Pints	4	6	10
	1/8½	**2/2**	**3/3**
Post	4d.	5d.	6d.

Wash-Hand Basins.

No. Y. 505.

	11¾	12¼	13¼ in.
	8½d.	**9½d.**	**10½d.**
Post	3d.	3d.	4d.
	14½	15	15¾ in.
	11½d.	**1/0½**	**1/3**
Post	4d.	4d.	4d.

Extra Deep Basins.

No. Y. 507.

	10½	11	11¾	12½ in.
	9½d.	**11½d.**	**1/0½**	**1/2½**
Post	2d.		3d.	
	13½	14½	15	15¾ in.
	1/4½	**1/6½**	**1/8½**	**1/10½**
Post	4d.		5d.	

Pails or Buckets

No. Y. 590.

	10½	11	11¾ in.
	2	2½	3 gals.
	1/11½	**2/3½**	**2/6½**
Post	4d.	5d.	6d.

Y. 592. Toilet Pails

With Sanitary Drop-in Cover.

Cover.	2	2½	3 gals
	3/0½	**3/3½**	**3/9½**
Post	6d.	7d.	8d.

Toilet Jugs.

No. Y. 543. White inside and out.

Pints	2	4	5½	7
	1/3½	**1/6½**	**1/11½**	**2/3½**
Post	4d.	4d.	4d.	5d.
Pints	10	13	16	20
	2/9½	**3/3**	**4/3**	**5/3**
Post	6d.	7d.	8d.	10d.

Hand Bowls.

No. Y. 561. Or Dippers.

	8	8¾	9½	10½	11 in.
	9½d.	**11½d.**	**1/1½d.**	**1/3**	**1/6**
Post	3d.	3d.	4d.	4d.	4d.

Soap Dish

No. Y. 623A. Oblong to hang. 4¾ by 3½ in. **5½d.** 7½ by 4¾in. **6½d.** Post 2d. & 3d.

Commode or Chair Pans

No. Y. 524.

Top outside dimens.

	5½	7½	8¾ in
	6½d.	**9½d.**	**1/6½**
Post	3d.	3d.	4d.

10in. **1/9½** 11in. **2/3½**
Post 4d. 5d.

Frying or Omelette Pans.

Light Blue Outside, White Inside.

No. Y. 552

Deep ...	5½	7½	8¾	10½	11 in
	5d.	**7½d.**	**9½d.**	**11½d.**	**1/3½**
Post ...	2d.	3d.	3d.	4d.	5d. extra.

Saucepans.

No. Y. 614.

With Tinned Rim Cover.

Light Blue Outside, White Inside.

1	1½	2	3½	5	6½	9 pts
6½d.	**7½d.**	**8½d.**	**9½d.**	**11½d.**	**1/3½**	**–1/9½**
Post 2d.	2d.	3d.	3d.	4d.	5d.	5d.

Porridge Pot or Milk Sterilizer

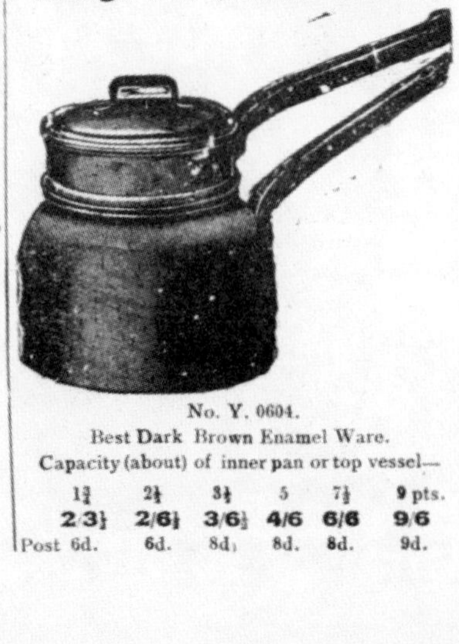

No. Y. 0604.

Best Dark Brown Enamel Ware.

Capacity (about) of inner pan or top vessel—

	1¾	2½	3½	5	7½	9 pts.
	2/3½	**2/6½**	**3/6½**	**4/6**	**6/6**	**9/6**
Post	6d.	6d.	8d.	8d.	8d.	9d.

Saucepans

Lipped.

No. Y. 610.

Capacity about

	¾	1	1½ pts.
	4½d.	**5½d.**	**6½d.**
Post	2d.	2d.	2d.
	2¼	2¾	4½ pts.
	7½d.	**9½d.**	**1/0½**
Post	3d.	3d.	4d.

ENAMEL WARE—*continued.*

No. Y. 705.
Household Canisters.

Plain or Lettered. 5⅛ by 6 in.
Plain .. **1/3½** Lettered .. **1/4½**
LETTERING: Tea, Sugar, Coffee, Sago, Tapioca, Raisins, Oatmeal, Currants, Biscuits. Post 3d.

No. Y. 518/29. **Candlesticks.**

White Ground, with Gold Band and Gold Edges.

5½ in.	..	6⅞ in.
6½d.	..	**7½**d.

Postage 3d.

No. Y. 518/14. **Candlesticks.**

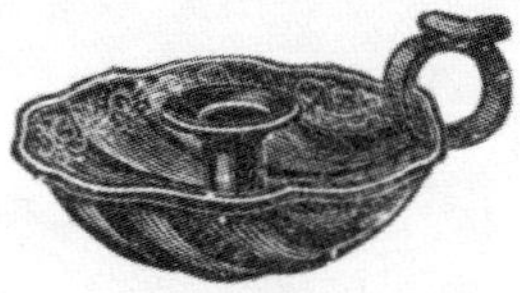

Shell Pattern.
Assorted Shaded Blue, Green, and Coral, with gold edges.
Price .. **6½**d. Post 3d.

No. Y. 522. **Chambers.**

Superior Quality.

	7½ in.	8 in.	8¾ in.	9½ in.
Price	**8½**d.	**9½**d.	**1/0½**	**1/1½**
Post	3d.	3d.	4d.	4d.

No. Y. 609.
Pudding or Navy Bowls.
Capacity about—

3/8	¼	½	¾	1	1¾ pt.
2½d.	**3**d.	**3¾**d.	**4**d.	**4½**d	**5½**d.
Post 1d.	1d.	1d.	1d.	1½d.	1½d.
2½	3½	4¾	6	7 pt.	
7½d.	**8½**d.	**10½**	**1/3½**	**17½**	
Post 2d.	2d.	2d.	2½d.	3d.	

No. Y. 743.
Pudding Basins.
China Pattern, Curled Edge.

Capacity about—

⅜	1¼	1⅝	2¼	3¼	4⅜ pt.
4½d.	**5½**d.	**7½**d.	**8½**d.	**10½**d	**1/0½**
Post 1d.	1½d.	1½d.	2d.	2d.	2d.

No. Y. 804. **Mugs.**

1 Pint. Government Stamped.
Price .. **8½**d. Post 2d.

No. Y. 713A. **Imperial Measures or Tankards.**
White with Blue Bands. Government Stamped. Taper or straight shape.

¼	½	1	2 pints.
11½d.	**1/3½**	**1/7½**	**2/0½**
Post 3d.	3d.	4d.	4d.

No. Y. 716. White Enamel **Egg Beater**, with improved Perforated Double Plunger, will beat from one to five eggs in one operation. Price ... **1/8½**
Postage 3d.

No. Y. 525/1.
Children's Tea Sets.

Cup,	Saucer,	Plate,
2¾ in.	4¾ in.	6¼ in.

Shaded, with Gold Rims and Gold Lines.
Price .. **11½**d. Post 3d.

Hot Water Jugs.
With Hinged Cover.

No. Y. 568. This Jug having a wide mouth can be thoroughly cleansed inside
Capacity about—

½	1	1½	2 pints
10½d.	**1/0½**	**1/3½**	**1/6½**
Post 2d	3d.	4d.	5d.

No. Y. 796. **Graduated Jugs.**

Seamless.

½ pts. graduated in ozs.	**6½**d.	Post 3d.
1 ,, ,, ,,	**9½**d.	,, 3d.
2 ,, ,, ¼ pts.	**1/0½**	,, 4d.

Y. 565. **Household Milk Jugs**

½	1	2	3 pts
8½d.	**1/1½**	**1/6½**	**1/10½**
Post 2d.	2d.	3d.	3d.
4	5	6	8 pts.
2/1	**2/7½**	**2/11½**	**3/6½**
Post 3d.	4d.	4d.	5d.

Graduated Jugs. Graduated Inside.
No. Y. 795. Best Enamel Ware. Exceedingly useful, Checking and for all Cooking purposes.

1 pint graduated in ¼ pints. ... **10½**d.
2 pints ditto in ½ pts. **1/1½**
3 pints ditto in ½ pts. **1/3½**

Postage 3d., 4d. and 5d.

Mugs.

No. Y. 587.
Seamless, best quality. Regulation Pattern.

½ pint ... **4½**d.
1 ,, ... **5½**d.
1¼ ,, ... **6½**d.
1½ ,, ... **7½**d.

In quantities not less than 1 dozen.
4/- **4/6** **5/-** **6/-** doz.

Cups and Saucers.

No. Y. 535.
Size of Cups 2¾ in. diameter.
,, Saucer 4 in. diam.
5½d. set.
Cup 3½ in. Saucer 4¾ in., diam., **7½**d. set.
Cup 4 in. Saucer 5½ in. diam. ... **8½** set.
Postage 2d. and 3d.

No. Y. 599.
Oblong Pie Dishes.

Size 5½ in., **4**d. 6½ in., **4½**d. 7½ in., **5**d. in., **6**d.
8¾ in., **6½** 9½ in., **7½**d. Postage 1d. and 2d.
Size 10½ in., **8½**d. 11 in., **9½**d. 11¾ in., **10½**d.
12½ in., **11½**d. 14½ in., **1/1½** Postage 2d. and 3d.

Y. 650. **Seamless Tumblers.**

½ pint **4**d. ¾ ptint **5**d.
1 pint **6**d.
Postage 2d

Enamel Ware Meat Dish

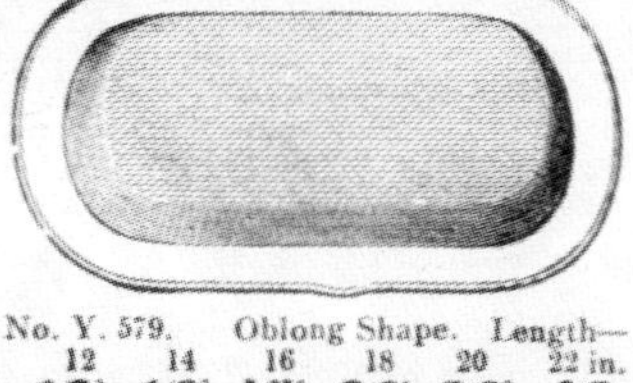

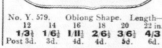

No. Y. 579. Oblong Shape. Length—

12	14	16	18	20	22 in.
1/3½	**1/6½**	**1/11½**	**2/6½**	**3/6½**	**4/3**
Post 3d.	3d.	4d.	4d.	5d.	6d.

Flat Meat Trays or Waiters

No. Y. 589. Enamel Ware. Length—

10½	12½	14½	16½	18½	20½ in.
1/0½	**1/3½**	**1/9½**	**2/3**	**2/11½**	**3/9½**
Post 3d	3d.	3d.	4d.	4d.	5d.

Enamel Ware Plates.

No. Y. 603. All White with Blue edge. Best quality. When ordering state whether Soup or Dinner Plates are required. Size 7 in., dia. **3d**
8 in., **3½**d. 9½ in., **4½**d. 10½ in., **5**d. Post 1½d. & 2d.

Special Prices for Mugs and Plates in quantities of not less than 1 doz. and upwards for the Army, Territorials, Schools, Brigades, Boy Scouts, &c.

Write for Full Deartmental List sent post free anywhere.

Enamel Ware Superior Quality and Finish.

No. Y.526. Cafetiere,
Or Coffee Filtering Machines.

Best Enamel Ware. Size about—

1	2	2½	3½ pint.
3	4	6	8 cups.
2/11½	**3/3½**	**3/6½**	**3/11½**
Post 4d.	4d.	5d.	6d. extra.

Collanders.

No. Y. 529. With foot, best extra extra deep.

8	8½	9½	10½ in.
11½d.	**1/3½**	**1/6½**	**1,8½**
Post 3d.	3d.	4d.	4½d.

No. Y. 689. Coffee Pots
with Percolators.

Best Enamel Ware, suitable for Boarding House.
Size about—

1¾	2½	3½	3¾	4½ pints.
4	6	8	10	12 cups.
2/3½	**2/6½**	**2/9½**	**3/0½**	**3/3½**
Post 4d.	4d.	5d.	6d.	6d. extra.

Stove Kettles Seamless.

No. Y. 753. Light blue outside and white inside. Superior quality, with fixed Handles.

2	3	4	5	6½	9 pts.
1/6½	**1/11½**	**2/3½**	**2/6½**	**3/3**	**4/3**
Post 3d.	4d.	5d.	5d.	6d.	7d.

The "Gamage" Tea Pot.

No. Y. 694. Best Green or Light Blue Enamel Ware, Seamless.

1½	2	3	4 pints.
1/4½	**1/6½**	**1/9½**	**1/11**
3d.	3d.	4d.	5d.

No. Y. 642. The "Canteen" Teapot.

Seamless, Assorted Colours.

Capacity about —

1¾	2	3	4	6	7	11 pints
1/2½	**1/4½**	**1/6½**	**1/9½**	**2/4½**	**3/6½**	**4/3½**
Post 3d.	3d.	3d.	4d.	4d.	5d.	6d

The "Cecil" Teapot.

No. Y. 680.

Seamless. White and Assorted Colours.

About	¾	1½	2	3	4 pints.
	1/1½	**1/3½**	**1/6½**	**1/7½**	**1/11½**
Post	3d.	3d.	4d.	4d.	4d.

Sink Baskets.

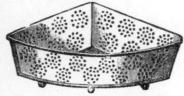

No. Y. 640. Sanitary, Triangular.
Perforated Bottom and Sides.

7½	8½	9	10 in.
11½d.	**1/2½**	**1/5½**	**1/10½**
Postage 3d·	3d.	3d.	4d.

Enamel Egg Poacher.

With Tin Fittings for four eggs.

Price .. **1/4½** Post 3d.

Fish Trowels.

No. Y 547A. .. **6½d.**

Fish Slices.

No. Y. 547.
Medium **6½d.**
Large **7½d.**

No. Y. 546. Oval Fish Kettles.

With Enamelled Cover and Drainer.

12	13	14¼	15¾	17¾	19¾ ins.
4/3	**4/11½**	**6/1½**	**7/3½**	**8/6½**	**9/11½**

Table Spoons.

No. Y. 618.
Medium **1/0½** doz. Large **3/-** doz.

Tea Spoons.

No. Y. 618A. **1/0½d.** doz.

The Servant.

All White.

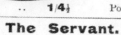

	Ewer	Basin	Chamber	Soap Dish	Tooth Brush Tray with Cover
	17	34	20	12	20 cm.
No. Y. 655.	6½	13½	8	4¾	8 in.

The Set complete .. .. **5/9** each.

Write for Full Departmental List sent post free anywhere.

QUALITY THE HIGHEST. PR'CES THE LOWEST.

THE CLARIDGE WARE.

Olive Green Outside **Pure White Inside.**

Is Fireproof Enamelled Ware, will stand any heat and will not crack. Highest possible grade. Articles illustrated are very reliable and the rich Olive Green Enamel is most serviceable and of pleasing appearance.

Saucepan with Enamel Cover.

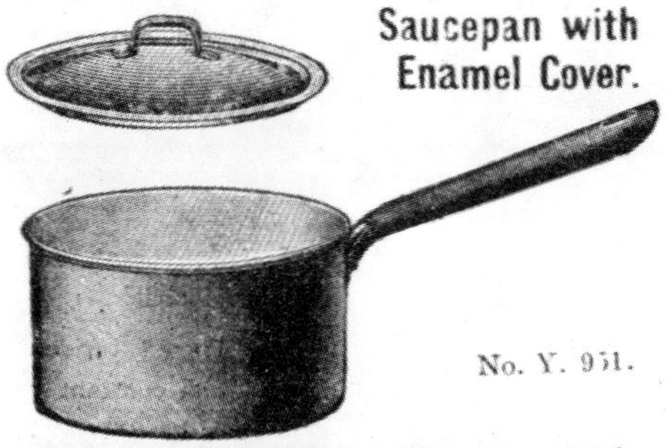

No. Y. 951.

Size	4¾	5½	6¼	7⅛	8	8¾	9¼ ins.
About	1½	2¼	3½	5	6½	9	12 pts.
Price	**10½d.**	**11½d.**	**1/3½**	**1/6½**	**1/9½**	**2/[illegible]½**	**2/6½**
Post	3d.	3d.	4d.	5d.	5d.	6d.	7d.

Kettle with Non-burn Handle.

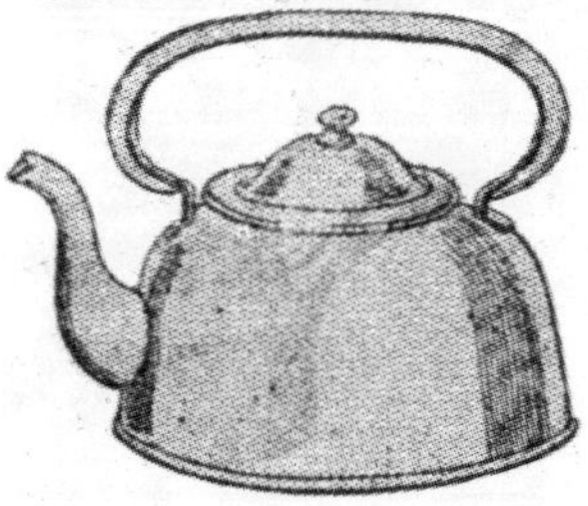

No. Y. 953.

Size about ..	2	3¼	4¾	6¼ pints.
Price ..	**1/9½**	**2/0½**	**2/3½**	**2/8½**
Postage ..	4d.	4d.	5d.	6d.

Toilet Jugs.

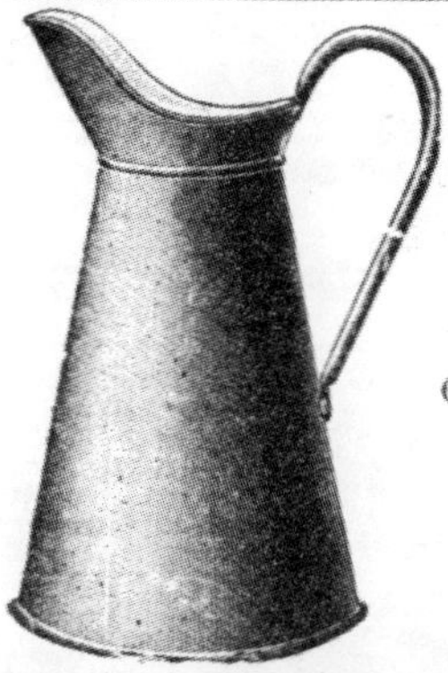

PARISIAN SHAPE.

With good pouring lip.

N. Y. 957.

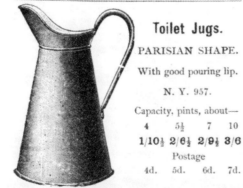

Capacity, pints, about—

4	5½	7	10
1/10½	**2/6½**	**2/9½**	**3/6**
Postage			
4d.	5d.	6d.	7d.

Porridge Saucepan or Milk Boilers.

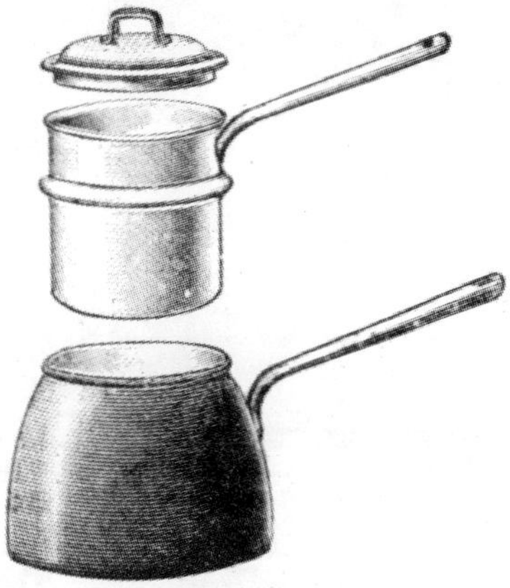

No. Y. 954.

Superior quality, with tubular handles.
Capacity of top vessel, about—

	2¼	3½	4½ pints.
	2/9½	**3/3½**	**3/11½**
Postage	7d.	7d.	8d.

Household Jugs.

SEAMLESS.

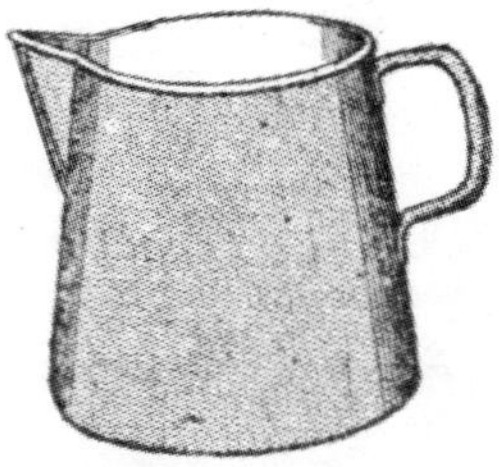

No. Y. 966.

Size, about—

	1	2	3	4 pints.
	1/0½	**1/3½**	**1/6½**	**2/2½**
Post	3d.	3d.	4d.	4d.

Deep Fry Pan.

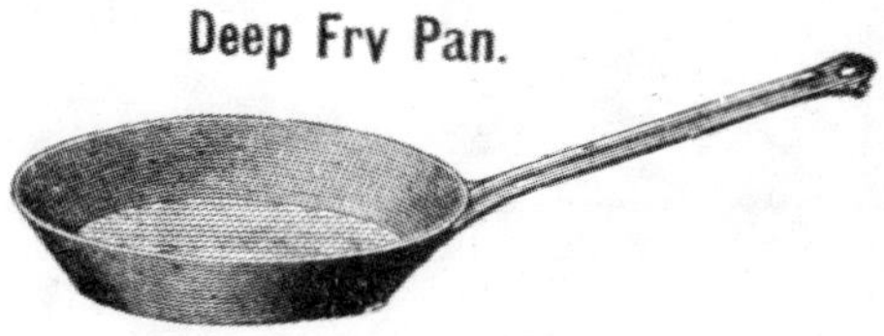

No. Y. 956.

	8	8¾	9½	10¼ in. top
	9½d.	**11½d.**	**1/1½**	**1/3½**
Postage	3d.	4d.	4d.	5d.

Lipped Milk Saucepan.

WITHOUT COVER.

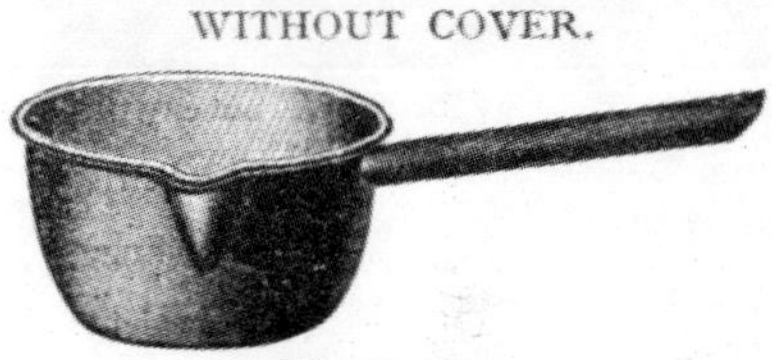

No. Y. 952.

Size, about ..	1½	2½	3½	4 pints
	6½d.	**8½d.**	**10½d.**	**1/0½**
Postage ..	2d.	3d.	3d.	4d.

Toilet Pails.

With

ENAMEL COVER

No. Y. 963.

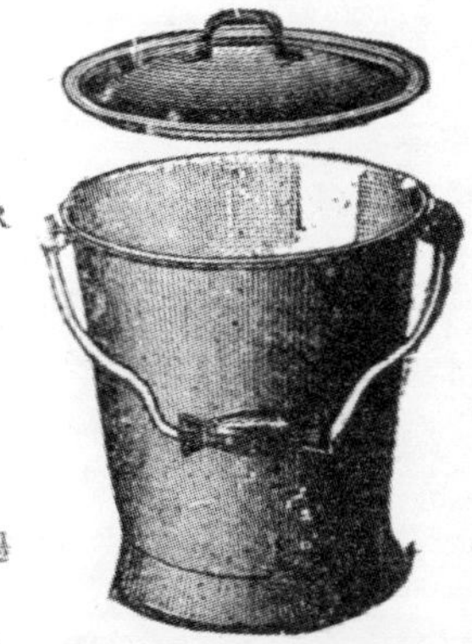

Size, about—

In gallons,

2	2½	3
2/11½	**3/6½**	**3/11½**
Carriage		
6d.	7d.	8d.

Extra Hard Quality. Warranted Fireproof.

Fire-proof Enamelled Hollow Ware.

Imitation Earthenware outside (Shaded)

Highly Finished. Enamelled Pale Grey Inside.

Saucepans with Enamel Covers.

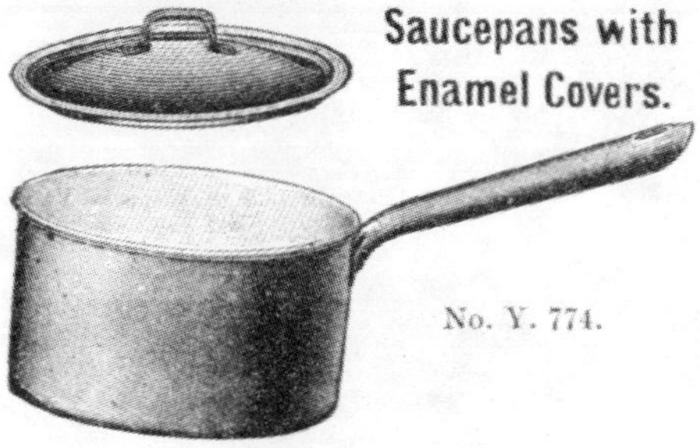

No. Y. 774.

Sizes, in pints, about—

	1½	2¼	3½	5	6½	9	12
	11½d.	**1/3½**	**1/6½**	**1/9½**	**2/0½**	**2/9½**	**3/3½**
Post	3d.	4d.	5d.	5d.	6d.	7d.	10d.

Porridge Saucepan.

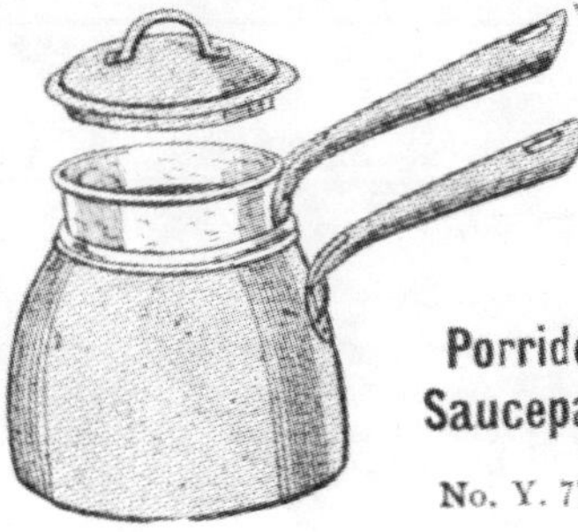

No. Y. 776.

Capacity of top vessel, about—

	1¾	2½	3½	5	7½ pints.
	2/6½	**3/3½**	**3/11½**	**4/11½**	**6/11**
Post	6d.	7d.	7d.	8d.	10d.

Lipped Saucepan.

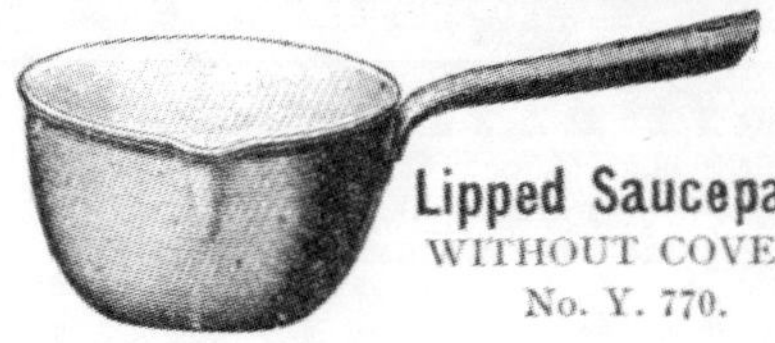

WITHOUT COVER.

No. Y. 770.

Capacity about	1	1½	2½	3½	4½ pts.
	6½d.	**9½d.**	**10½d.**	**1/2½**	**1/4½**
Postage ..	2d.	3d.	3d.	3d.	4d.

Deep Fry Pan.

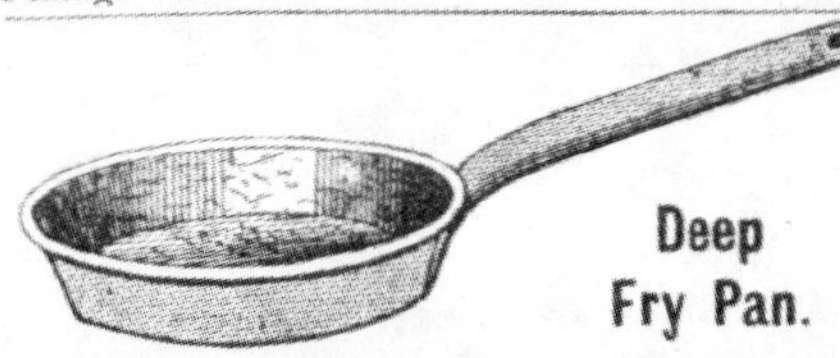

Y. 771. ..	7¼	8¾	10¼	11 in. top
	10½d.	**1/0½**	**1/4½**	**1/8½**
Price ..	3d.	3d.	4d.	5d.

Enamelled Ware, Utensils, etc. Orders to the value of 20/- and upwards sent carriage paid to nearest station England or Wales

Cooking Utensils. Guaranteed of the finest quality. London Manufacture and Improved Shapes and Superior Finish. Tinned with Pure Tin and Wrought Steel Hollow Ware.

Kettles and Pans.

Oval Iron Kettle.

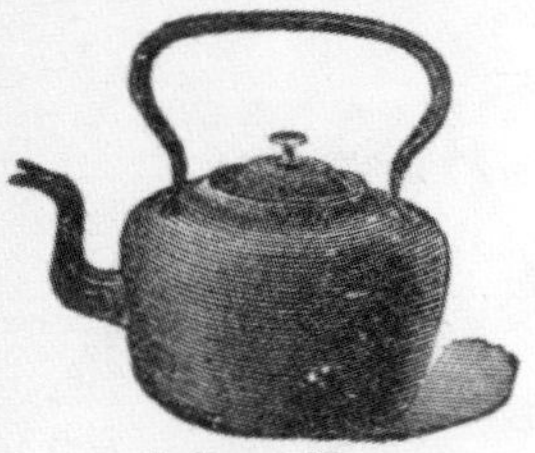

Ordinary Shape.
Strong and Useful.

4	6	8	10 pints.
2/6½	**2/11½**	**3/6½**	**4/3½**
4d.	5d.	6d.	7d. Post.

Range Kettle.

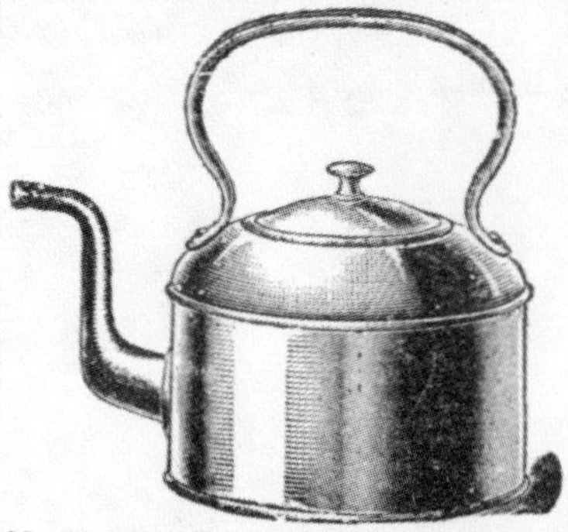

No. Y. 1113. Best quality block tin, copper bottom with iron handle and spout
4 pints **2/9½** 6 pints **3/3½** 8 pints **3/9½**
Post 5d. 6d. 7d.

Gas Stove Kettle

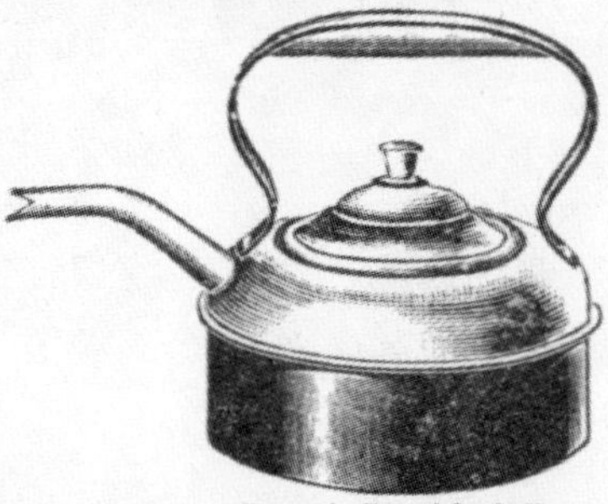

No. Y. 1339 – Round Burnished Top, Seamless Bottom.
3 pints, **6½**d. 4, **8½**d. 6, **10½**d.
No. Y. 5—Ditto, Copper Sides & Bottom.
2 pts., **1/9½** 4, **2/6½** 6, **3/6½** 8, **3/11½**
Postage 4d. 5d. 6d. 6d.

Wrought Iron Kettle.

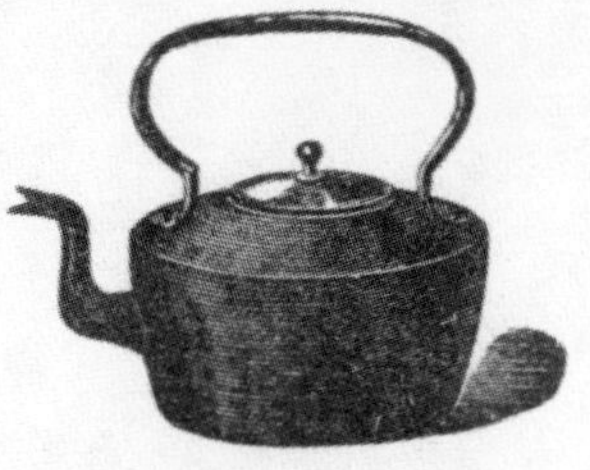

London Shape.
Pure Tinned Inside.
For hard and constant use.

6	8	10	12	14	16 pts.
4/9	**5/6**	**6/3**	**7/3**	**7/11**	**8/6**
5d.	6d.	7d.	7d.	8d.	9d.

The Whistling Kettle.

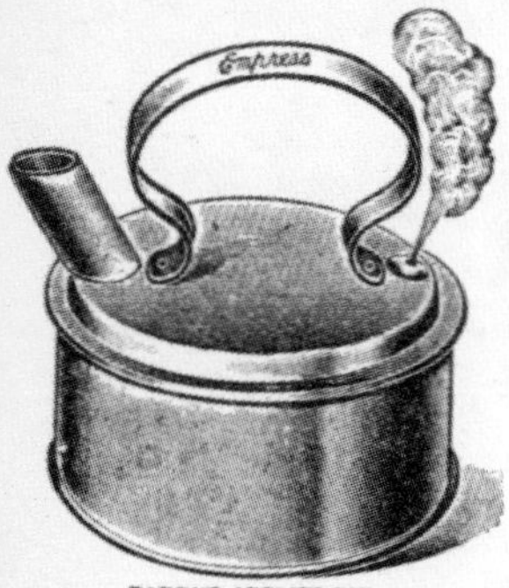

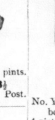

PATENT APPLIED FOR

A novelty in a quick-boiling kettle, whistles when boiling. Prevents many accidents and waste of gas.

3	5	7 pts.
1/3	**1/6½**	**1/9½**
3d.	3d.	4d. 5d. Post.

Gas Stove Kettle.

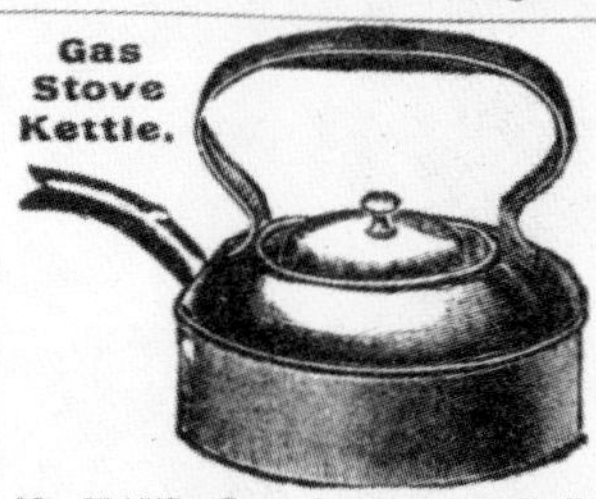

No. Y.1557. Straight Sided Gas Stove Kettle. Best London made, block tin with iron handle. Thoroughly recommended for hard wear.
2 pts. **1/7½** 4, **2/-** 6, **2/11½** 8, **3/6**
Post 3d. 4d. 5d. 6d.

Best Steel Tea Pots

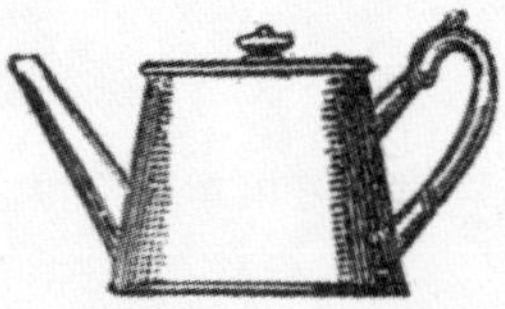

1½ pts., **1/3½** 2, **1/6½** 3, **1/9½**
4 ,, **2/6** 6, **3/3** 8, **3/11**
Postage 3d. 4d. 5d. 6d.

Copper Kettle.

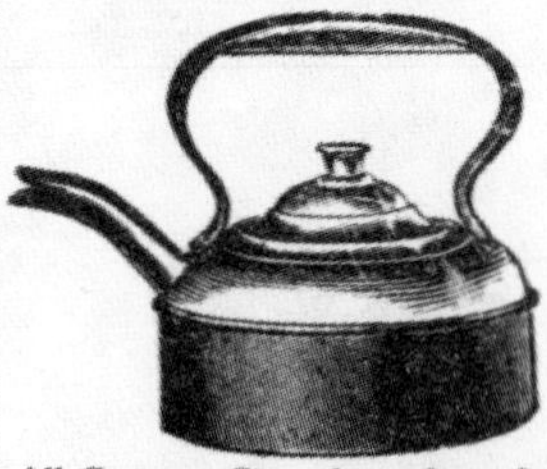

All Copper. Strongly made, with Brass Handle. Best Finish.

2	4	6	8 pints
3/6	**4/3**	**5/6**	**6/6**
3d.	4d.	5d.	6d.

Copper Kettles.

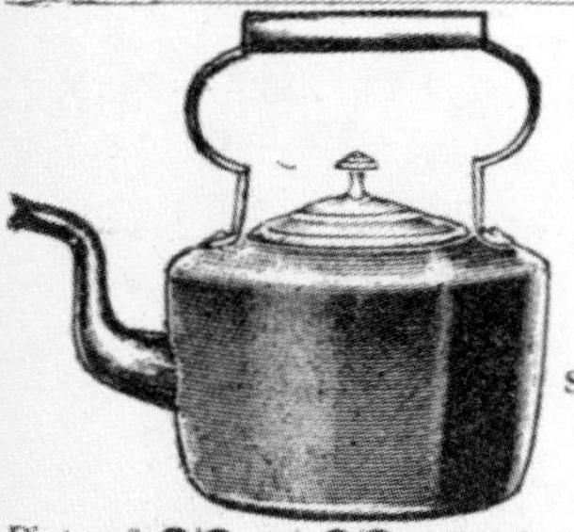

Best Seamless.
With barrel handle.
Superior quality
Oval Shape.

Pints. 3 **8/6** 4 **9/9** 6 **10/9** **13/6**
Postage 4d. 6d 6d. 6d.

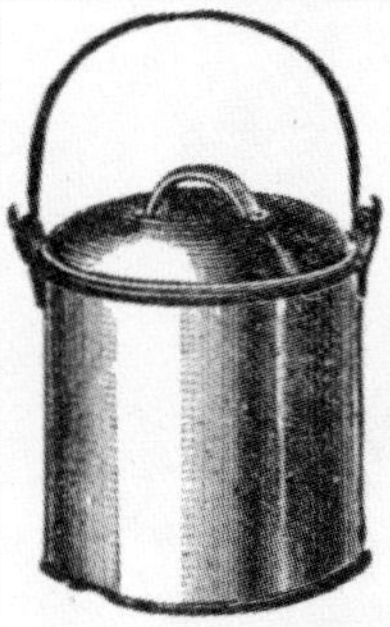

Camp Kettle.
Strong Tin.

2 quart, **9½**d. Postage 4d.
4 ,, **1/3½** Postage 5d.
6 ,, **2/3** Postage 6d
8 ,, **2/11** Postage 7d.
10 ,, **3/9** Postage 8d.
12 ,, **4/3** Postage 9d.

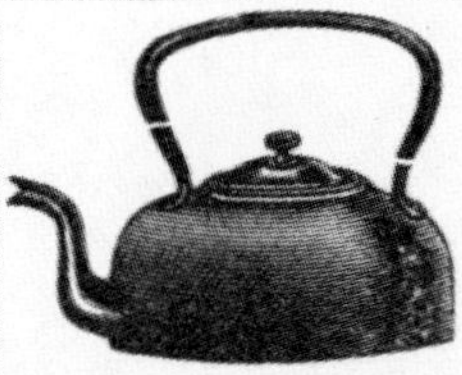

Useful Gas Stove Kettle.
Much superior and more durable than an ordinary tin kettle.

3	4	5	6	8 pts.
1/11	**2/3**	**2/6**	**2/6**	**2/9½**
4d.	4d.	5d.	5d.	6d.

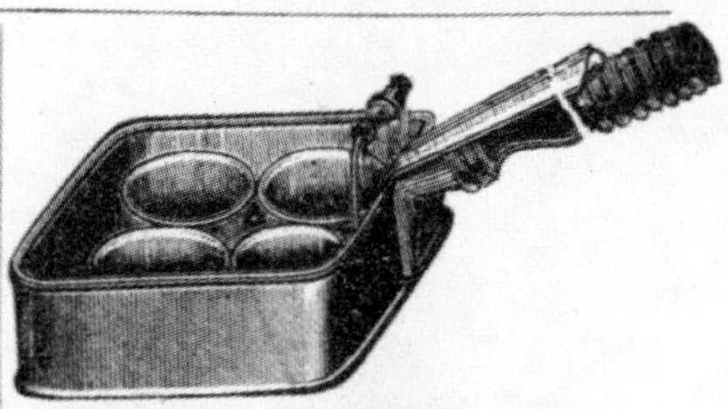

No. Y. 1254. Wood handle, best quality.
For 2 eggs, **1/0½** For 3 eggs, **1/3½** Post 3d.
,, 4 eggs, **1/6½** ,, 6 eggs, **2/3½**
Post 4d. Post 5d.
Cheaper quality, for 3 eggs, **9½**d. 4 eggs, **11½**d.
Post 3d. Post 4d

Baking Plates.

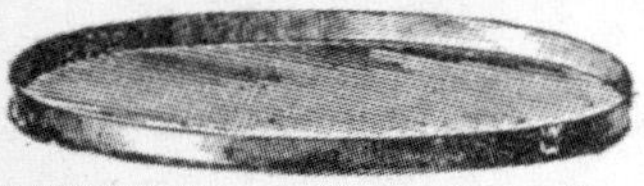

ROUND Copper Pattern, turned up all round.

9	10	11	12	13	14 in.
1/6	**1/9**	**1/11**	**2/3**	**2/11**	**3/3**
3d.	3d.	4d.	4d.	4d.	5d.

No. Y. 195. Oblong shape.

10	11	12	13	14	15
1/6	**1/8**	**1/9**	**1/11**	**2/3**	**2/11**
3d.	4d.	4d.	4d.	5d.	5d. Postage

No. Y. 197. **Baking Plates**

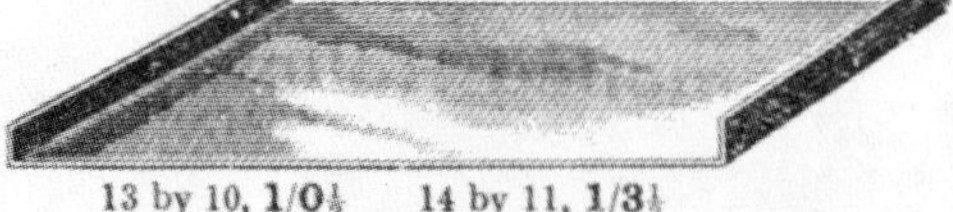

13 by 10, **1/0½** 14 by 11, **1/3½**
16 by 12, **1/7** 19 by 14, **2/0½** Post 4d. 5d. 6d

Fish Kettle.

Best London Make,

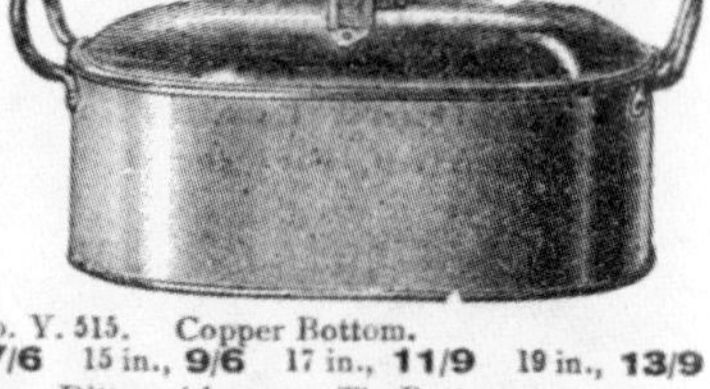

No. Y. 515. Copper Bottom.
12 in., **6/3** 13 in., **7/6** 15 in., **9/6** 17 in., **11/9** 19 in., **13/9**
No. Y. 503. Ditto, with strong Tin Bottoms.
12 in., **3/9** 13 in., **4/2** 15 in., **6/3** 17 in., **7/6** 19 in., **9/9**
No. Y. 1303. Ditto, lighter quality, but very Special Value.
12 in., **2/3** 13 in., **3/3** 15 in., **3/11** 17 in., **5/9**
Carriage 7d. 8d. 9d. 10d. 11d.

Yorkshire Pudding or Baking Pan.

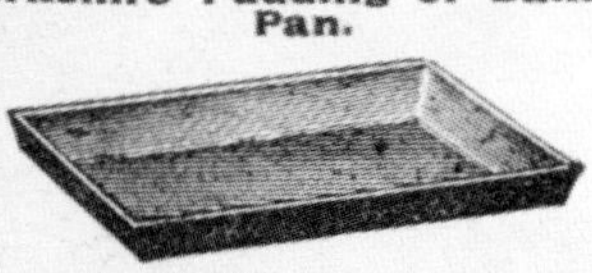

No. Y. 3335. Extra strong.

8½ in.	10½ in.	12½ in.	14½ in.	17 in.	18 in.
5½d.	**7½**d.	**1/0½**	**1/3½**	**1/6½**	**1/11½**

Postage 3d., 4d. and 6d.

No. Y. 936. Square Pattern.
8 in. **11½**d. 10 in., **1/3½** 12 in. **1/6½**

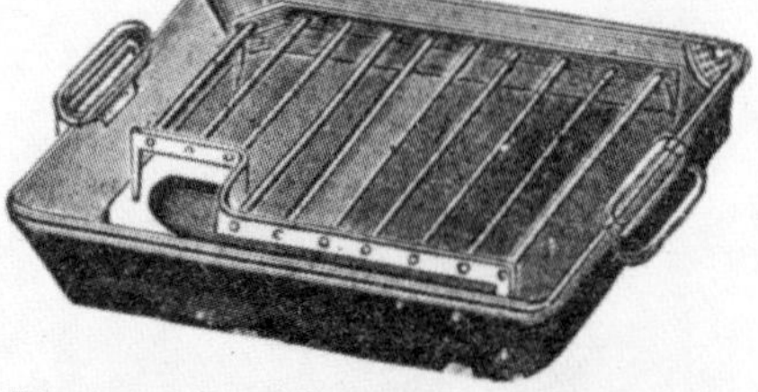

Stamped Double Range Pans with **Grid**

No. Y. 889. Stamped Oblong Baking Pan.
12 by 9 **3/11½** 13 by 10 **4/3½** 14 by 11 in. **4/8½**
15 by 12 **5/3** 16 by 12½ **5/6**
Carriage 6d. 6d. 7d. 7d. 8d.
No. Y. 888. Do. Square shape.
12 in. **4/9** 14 in. **5/6** 16 in. **6/11** 18 in. **8/3**
Carriage 6d. 7d. 7d. 8d.

Baking Pans.

Stamped
Extra
Strong.

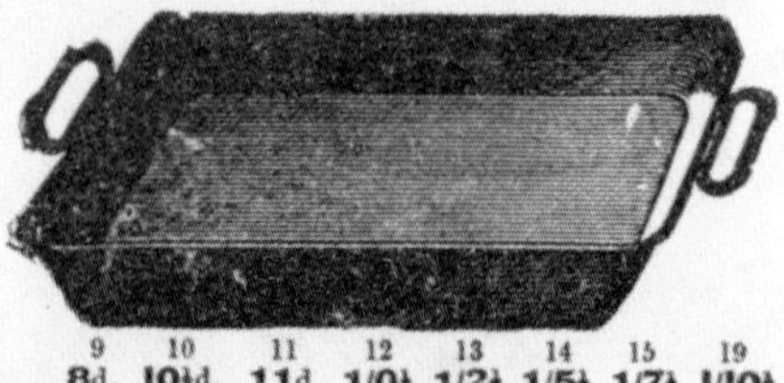

	9	10	11	12	13	14	15	19
No. Y. 942. Oblong Shape.	**8**d.	**10½**d.	**11**d.	**1/0½**	**1/2½**	**1/5½**	**1/7½**	**1/10½**
Post	3d.	3d.	3d.	4d.	4d.	4d.	5d.	5d.

	9	10	11	12	13	14	15
No. Y. 941. Square Shape.	**8½**d.	**11½**d.	**1/2**	**1/4**	**1/5**	**1/8**	**1/10**
Post	3d.	3d.	4d.	4d.	4d.	4d.	5d.

Write for full Departmental List sent post free anywhere.

Copper Cooking Utensils.

Y. 502. Copper Stewpans.

4½	5	5½ in.
8	8 9	9/9

6	6½	7	7½	8	8½	9	10 in.
11/-	13/-	14/6	16/-	19/-	21/-	24/6	29/3

Y. 504.

Copper vegetable Stewpans.

6 in.	...	...	21/6	9 in.	...	38/-
7 in.	...	...	27/-	10 in.	...	46/
8 in.	...	...	32/6	11 in.	...	50/-

Y. 556. **Copper Sugar Boiler.**

4	5	6	7	7½ in.
9/6	11/6	14/6	19/6	21/6

Y. 528. **Copper Saucepans**

2	4	6	8	10	12	14 pts.
11/3	13/6	15/9	19/-	23/3	26/3	30/6

Y. 516. Copper Stock Pots.
With Tap.

9	10	11	12	13	14	15 in.
57/9	72/6	81/-	93/9	105/-	134/-	156/-

Without Taps

| 32/9 | 55/- | 65/6 | 74/- | 86/- | 109/- | 129/- |

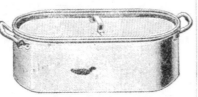

Y. 515. Copper Fish Kettles.

14	16	18	20	22	24 in.
51/-	60/-	73/-	90/-	109/-	122/6

Y. 516. **Fish Fryers.**

Y. 521. Bain Marie Pans.

6	7	9 vessels.
79/-	92/6	117/6

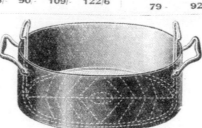

Y. 552A. **Copper Preserving Pans.**

11 in.	...	19/-
12 in.	...	21/-
13 in.	...	24/6
14 in.	...	25/-
15 in.	...	30/-
16 in.	...	36/6
17 in.	...	42/-
18 in.	...	46/6

Y. 613. **Copper Kettles.**

2	3	4	5	6 pts.
6/-	6/3	6/9	7/-	7/6

Y. 536. Copper Omelet Pans.

7	8	9	10	11	12	13 in.
5/6	6/6	8/6	10/6	11/9	12/9	14/-

14	15	16	18 in.
46/-	50/-	58/-	68/8

Fish Fryer.

Wrought Steel, tinned with purest silver. Tinning and fitted with strong wire suspending drainer.

14 in.	...	11/6
16 ,,	...	14/-
18 ,,	...	18/3
20 ,,	...	22/6

Carriage 10d. 1/- 1/3 1/5

Preserving Pan.

Cast Iron Enamelled.
Best quality ... Size 12 14 16 18 in.
Approximate capacity 13 18 25 36 pt
5/9 6/9 7/11 10/3
Carriage Forward.

The "Gamage" Roaster.

For Roasting Beef, Mutton, Pork, Rabbits Fowls, Fish, &c.

Ham and Tongue cooked in Roaster is most delicious. Will make the toughest meat tender, or an old fowl like chicken. Apple dumplings, &c., steamed in the Roaster retains all the natural flavour, none of which is evaporated in the Roaster.

12½ in. by 8½ in.	...	2/9½
12 in. by 11 in.	...	3/3½
14 in. by 12 in.	...	4/6½

Carriage 6d., 7d., 8d.

No. Y. 1521. Japanned Red. Size—

To hold 4 saucepans .. Price **5/6**

To hold 8 do., .. ,, **6/6**

Carriage 10d. and 1/- extra.

Saucepan Stand

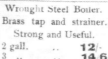

Wrought Steel Boiler.
Brass tap and strainer.
Strong and Useful.

2 gall.	...	12/-
3 ,,	...	14/6
4 ,,	...	17/3
5 ,,	...	19/11
6 ,,	...	22/6

5 & 6 Galls. to Order only.

Wrought Steel Stock Pot.
With Best Brass Tap and Stamped Steel Cover and Strainer.

2 gal.	...	12/6
3 gal.	...	17/6
4 gal.	...	22/6
5 gal.	...	27/-
6½ gal.	...	30/-
8 gal.	...	36/-

4 gal. upwards to order.
Carriage paid.

No. Y. 34.

No. Y. 73. **A. w. G. Self-Basting Roaster or Cooker.** No Attention Required. Stout Tin Roaster, with iron straps round bottom. The top is fitted with a tin Dish with perforated bottom to hold the spare fat from the joint cut into pieces, which bastes the meat whilst cooking. Note our cut prices. When ordering send measurements of your oven. 12 by 9, **2/11½** 13 by 10, **3/9** 14 by 11 in., **4/3½** Carriage 6d. 7d. 8d.

RELIABLE HABERDASHERY AT VERY LOW PRICES.

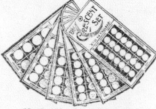

No. S. 151. Box of Linen Buttons, containing 12 doz. assorted sizes. 10½d.

No. S. 152. The Secure Box of Best Brass Pins containing ½-lb. full weight, mixed or short whites 4½d. per box.

No. S 153. 'Gamage' Value Packet of 100 Best Sewing Needles, assorted ... 3d.

No. S 154. Linen Buttons. Plain or with Two-Holes. 8½ doz. assorted sizes ... 4½d.

No. S. 155. The Protector Garment Shield. The Latest Shape. Sizes 3, 4 or 5 11½d.

No. S. 156. Best 3-ply Mending Wool Black, White and Colours ... 6 Cards 4½d.

No. S. 157. Bracelet of Safety Pins, containing 100 assorted sizes 2½d.

No. S. 158. Lace and Ribbon Threader, for running ribbons through Insertions without crease 3½d.

S. 159. The 'Gem' Box of Best Linen Buttons, containing 12 doz. assd. sizes 11½d.

S. 160. Berry Toilet Pin Basket, contains 60 pins, black and assorted colours 3d.

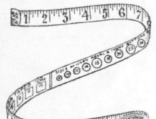

No. S. 161. "Quiver" Needlefulls, Patent Mendings. No more tangled skeins. No more waste. Each need'eful ready cut. Packet contains 100 needlefuls and Darning Needle. Black and Colours... 2d.

No. S. 162. Workbasket Companion Tape Measure, showing sizes of Buttons, Tapes, Pins, etc. 5½d.

S 168. Pearl Buttons Card of 6 doz. assorted sizes, 1/3½

No. S. 163. Toilet Pin Cube, Black or Assorted Colours. 4½d.

No. S. 164. Best Quality Linen Buttons. Any size, Plain or 2-hole. 2d. per card.

No. S. 165. The Concise Roll of Best White Tape contains 12 pieces. 4½d.

No. S. 166. The 'Simplex' Darner, fitted with neat nickel-plated Bands to hold the darn in position ... 3½d.f

68 S. 177. Hose Suspender with rubber buttons. 6½d.

S. 167. Hose Suspender, Double Ends, Rubber Buttons, 10½d.

No. S. 171. The 'Silkwave' Collar Support, all sizes. Packet of 12 4½d.

No. S. 170. Shield Safety Pins, containing 50 assorted sizes, including Gilt Lace Pins. 5½d. box.

No. S. 269. Diamond Box of Linen Buttons. Plain or 2-Hole, assorted sizes. 5½d.

No. S. 172. Best Mending Wool, Black only. 1 oz. Ball. 3½d.

No. S 173. The 'Aluminium Red Box of Good White Tape, contains 12 pieces of various widths ... 6½d.

No. S175. The 'Verineat Blouse Holder, an elastic band with rubber grips that holds the blouse down securely. Black or white. 6½d.

No. S. 174. Double Covered Nainsook Dress Shields. Size 1 2 3 4 4½d. 5½d. 6½d. 7½d.

No. S. 176. The Cameo Box of 12 rolls of Best White Tape ... 10½d.

No. S. 175. Fashionable Wide Shoe Laces, mercerised ... 3½d. pair.

No S. 179. Corset Shields, Size 1. For Corsets up to 24 in. Size 2. " " over " 5½d.

No.178. Box of 1 doz. Superior Ladies' Black Boot Laces 4½d.

HOLBORN GRAMOPHONES (1914 Models).

The Holborn Model IV.

Cabinet.—15 by 13 by 7 in., highly polished Oak with hinged door admitting to the wooden sound chamber. Turntable - 10 inch nickel-plated. Tone Arm.—Tapered inverted nickel-plated. Motor—Reliable playing 1 12-inch Record. Sound Box—Tresor.　Price .. **25/-**

The Holborn Model II.

Cabinet—Dark Oak, ornamental base, size 12½ by 12½ by 6 in. Turntable—10 in. covered green baize. Tone Arm—Tapered, highly nickel-plated. Motor—Superior, playing one 12 in. record. Sound Box—"Alexophone," fine tone. Horn—18 by 18 in., seamless.　Price .. **25 6**

The Holborn Model VI.

Cabinet—Handsome polished Oak, 16 by 16 by 12 in., with hinged doors to sound chamber. Large size lid as illustration. Can be closed down while playing, with lock and key, and handle at side for carrying. Motor—Strong latest type spring motor playing 2 10-inch Records. Tone Arm—Inverted, nickel-plated. Sound Box—Model B, latest pattern, improved model with a human tone .. **55/-**

The Holborn Model III.

FINEST VALUE ON THE MARKET

Cabinet—English Solid Oak, 13 by 13 by 7 in. with hinged lid to Motor. Turntable—10 in. covered green baize, nickel-plated. Tone Arm - Tapered, nickel-plated, highly polished. Motor—Extra strong worm gear, silent running and perfectly reliable. Speed Indicator. Sound Box—Gamage Famous Model B. Horn, size 19 by 19in. seamless .. **32 6**

The Holborn Model VIII.

MOST PERFECT OBTAINABLE.

Cabinet—Best English manufactured Oak, finely polished, hinged top to Motor. Motor—New Patent worm gear, silent running, extra strong double spring, accurate speed indicator. 12 in. Turntable. Tone Arm—Finely adjusted with patent swivel, extra heavy and well tapered. Sound Box—The Famous "Crescendo." Horn—Dark Oak polished, new design, Bell 22 in., length 26 in.

Price **£3 15 0**

The Holborn Model V.

Cabinet—English Oak Case, 15 by 15 by 7 in., fitted with wooden grill and hinged doors to sound chamber. Turntable—10-inch covered Green Baize. Tone Arm—Patent extension, tapered, giving a rich tone. Motor—Powerful worm gear, thoroughly reliable and silent running. Sound Box—Gamage special rubber insulated, fitted with speed indicator.

Price .. **33/-**

The Holborn Model I.

Cabinet 12 by 12 by 5½in. Oak polished. Turntable, 10 in. green felt. Tone Arm, tapered and nickelled. Motor plays one 10 in. record. Sound Box — "Expression." Horn — Size 17 by 17 in., seamless pattern. As illustration **18/6**

The Holborn Model IX.

Cabinet—14½ by 14½ by 9½ in., solid Dark Oak, English manufacture. Folding doors. Concealed wood Horn, giving a fine reproduction. Very powerful double spring Motor, playing three 10 in. records. Speed indicator. Strong nickel plated tone arm with extension. Model C Sound Box, giving a clear mellow tone.

Price **47/6**

H 1..

'His Master's Voice' GRAMOPHONES

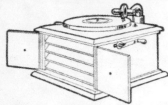

Hornless—Model No. 1.
Price £4.
Specification

CABINET.—Fumed Plain Oak, nickel-plated fittings; internal horn with wooden grille. Size 6¾ in. high 14½ in. wide.
MECHANISM.—Single-spring spiral-drive motor; 10 in. turntable, playing 10 in. and 12 in. records; speed indicator; "His Master's Voice" tapering tone-arm with patent "Gooseneck"; Exhibition sound-box.
Nett weight, 16¾ lbs. Gross weight, when packed, 34 lbs.

Cabinet Grand—Model No. 10. £20.
Specification

CABINET.—Highly Polished Mahogany, brass gilt fittings; internal horn of special metal which enhances the tone; wooden grille and needle bowl. Under the horn is a chamber for storing 72 records in albums. Size—height 42½ in., width 16 in., depth 20 in.
MECHANISM—Double-spring spiral drive motor; 12 in. turntable; new automatic brake and speed indicator; "His Master's Voice" tapering tonearm with patent "Gooseneck"; Exhibition sound box.
Nett weight, 77 lbs. Gross weight when packed, 225 lbs.

Also Manufactured in Oak at same price.

Hornless—Model No. 3.
Price £6.
Specification

CABINET.—Polished Quartered Oak with solid moulded doors; nickel-plated cabinet fittings; full size internal horn with wooden grille. Size—base 17 in., height 9 in., depth 17 in.
MECHANISM.—Small double spring spiral-drive motor; 12 in. turntable; speed indicator; "His Master's Voice" tapering tonearm with patent 'Gooseneck'; Exhibition sound-box.
Nett weight 52½ lbs. Gross weight when packed, 48 lbs.

Table Grand—Model No. 6. £8 8s.
Specification

CABINET.—Dull Polished Quartered Oak; nickel-plated fittings; internal horn with wooden grille; wooden needle bowl. Size—base 15¼ in.; height 12¾ in.; depth 19 in.
MECHANISM.—Small double-spring spiral-drive motor; 10 in. turntable; speed indicator; "His Master's Voice" tapering tonearm with patent "Gooseneck"; Exhibition sound-box.
Nett weight, 31 lbs. Gross weight when packed, 87 lbs.

Table Grand Model No. 8. £12 10s.
Specification

CABINET.—Dull Polished Quartered Oak, brass gilt cabinet fittings; internal horn with wooden grille; needle bowl. Size—base 18¼ in., height 14½ in., depth 22½ in.
MECHANISM.—Double-spring spiral-drive motor; 12 in. turntable; speed indicator; "His Master's Voice" tapering tonearm with patent "Gooseneck" Exhibition sound-box.
Nett weight 26 lbs. Gross weight when packed, 115 lbs.

Columbia Graphophones

No. 3. ("Junior Regal")

CABINET.—Mahogany or Oak throughout, piano finish, round corners, size 13½ by 13½ by 7
MOTOR.—Columbia, powerful double-spring to run about three 10 inch records, silent running.
TONE-ARM.— Columbia tapered arm, with sound-tight universal joint, detachable "Regal" sound box.
HORN.—Wood horn (oak) to match cabinet, bell 21 in., length 23½ in.

No. 3. Brass Horn .. **£5 10 0**
No. 4. Wood Horn .. **£7 10 0**

No. 18. ("Crescent" Hornless).

"The Open Tone that Surprises."
CABINET. Solid oak piano finish, round corners, hinged lid, size 16½ by 16½ by 8½
TONE CHAMBER.—Specially large interior amplifying chamber, fitted with new tone shutters, controlled by a button, for regulation of volume.
MOTOR—Genuine Columbia, powerful double-spring to run about three 10-inch records, silent running.
TONE ARM.—Columbia tapered arm, with sound-tight universal joint, nickelled horn-bracket and elbow, detachable "Regal" sound box.
No. 18 Oak, **£5 10 0** No. 19 Mahogany, **£6 6 0**

No. 17 ("Phœnix." Hornless).
Similar to above, but smaller cabinet and lighter finish. Powerful double spring motor to run two 12 in. records. "Regal" sound box. Price .. **£4 10 0**

No. 2. ("Regent")

CABINET.—Solid oak, highly polished, round corners, size 13½ by 13½ by 7
MOTOR.—Columbia, powerful double-spring to run about three 10 in. records, silent running.
TONE ARM.—Columbia tapered arm, with sound-tight universal joint, detachable "Regal" sound box.
HORN.—New style metal horn, enamelled oak finish to match cabinet, bell 20½ in., guaranteed not to rattle or spoil reproduction with vibratory noises.
Price .. **£4 4 0**

PIANOS AND PLAYER PIANOS.

COTTAGE PIANO.
15 guineas.

Ideal instruments for the Drawing Room. Made of selected well-seasoned material. These Pianos have an ideal touch and a brilliant tone, combined with durability.

Cottage Piano. Iron Frame, Full Trichord, 7 Octaves, Check Action, Moulded Door, Lined Panel with either Shell or Flower Centre, Gilt Sconces, Walnut Case. Height 3 ft. 10 in., width 4 ft. 6 in.

The Boudoir Model.—Iron Frame, Full Trichord, 7 Octaves, Check Action, Bushed Keys, Moulded Top Door and Lock Board, Square Columns Pearl and Marqueterie Panel, Brass Pedals, Gilt Sconces, Black or Walnut Case. Height 4 ft. 2 in , width 4 ft. 7 in. Price **17 guineas** (As illustration).

The ' ALL-BRITISH PLAYER " Piano.
38 guineas.
The Most Perfect and Up-to-date Player Piano.

Well made of best seasoned wood with fine finish. Has a singing tone and splendid touch. The Player answers readily to the levers, both the finest crescendo to dim, being easily obtained either in treble or bass. Only very light pedalling required. A child can play it. Best workmanship throughout.

Specialities.—Standard Compass, 65 Notes. Perfect Repetition. New Four-fold Motor. Noiseless Tracker. Divided Key-board. Accentuation Stops. Forte and Tempo Stops.

Height 4 ft. 2 in., width 4 ft 10½ in., depth 2 ft. 2 in.

New Improved Overstrung Piano.
20 guineas.

Iron Frame, Full Trichord, 7 Octaves, Overstrung, French Type Check Action, Bushed Keys, Moulded Top Door and Lock Board, Marqueterie Centre, Square Columns, Gilt Sconces, Brass Pedals, Walnut Case. Height 4 ft. 2 in., width 4 ft. 8 in., depth 2 ft.

Emil Dressler Overstrung. Model A.
28 guineas.

These Pianos being so well known need little comment They are of German production and by one of the best makers.

Height 4 ft. 2 in. Depth 2 ft. 2 in. Width 4 ft. 11 in.

Overstrung Full Iron Frame, Underdamper Action, Ivorine Keys, Walnut, Rosewood or Black Case.

ORGANS AND HARMONIUMS.

The "Baby" Portable Organ.
Best English Manufacture.

DESCRIPTION.

Style A.—Solid Oak Case, 1 row of 8 ft. Reeds, 4 Octaves C to C, Kneeswell. Weight about 42lbs. Closes up to form an oblong box 2ft. 5in. 12in. by 17in. **£4 15**

Style 1.—Ditto, Superior finish, lighter model weighing only 40lbs. (as illustration) .. **£5 0 0**

Style 2.—2 rows of Reeds, 4 Octaves, Compass C to C, Bass 2 Octaves, Treble 2 Octaves. 4 Stops, viz., Diapason 8 ft., Principal 4 ft., Melodia 8 ft., Flute 4 ft. With Kneeswell. Weight about 48 lbs. **£6 7 6**

These Organs are made with Full-size Keys. The Reeds are most carefully voiced, and possess powerful, strong, rich, sympathetic tones Strongly made for hard wear. Suitable for Parlour or Mission Hall.

The ANGELUS Organ.

Height 61 in. length 41 in., depth 18 in.
DESCRIPTION OF CASE. — Case in Walnut Veneer, highly polished; large Bellows; Removable Panel over pedals, giving access to Webbings; large bevelled Mirror; fitted with Actions 1, or 3.

With Action 1: One Row of 8-ft. Reeds; 61 Notes; No Stops; Forte Kneeswell.

£7 2 6

With Action 3 : One row of 8-ft. Reeds; 61 Notes; Five Stops; Diapason, Dulciana, Melodia, Echo, Vox Humana. Forte Kneeswell.

£7 17 6

Imperial Linenized Music Rolls.
For use with all makes of Piano Players.

From **9d.** each. Write for Catalogue of Titles.

These Rolls are Standard size, with 65 or 88 Notes, and will suit all Standard Piano Players.

Join our Lending Library for Music Rolls.

Terms of Library :—

24 Rolls per Month.		12 Rolls per Month.	
Period.	Subscription.	Period.	Subscription.
One Year ..	**63/-**	One Year ..	**42/-**
Six Months ..	**42/-**	Six Months ..	**25/-**
Three Months ..	**21/-**	Three Months..	**15/-**

Carriage free both ways on One Consignment each Month, within our Vans' district.

H 1

ACCORDIONS.

"Gamage" Accordions.

Black moulded case, single bellows, nickel key pallets, 1 set of reeds, 2 stops, 10 keys.
Price .. .. .. **3/-** Post 6d.

Same as above, but with double bellows.
Price .. .. .. **3/9** Post 6d.

Black moulded case, blue tops, open action, nickel keys, double bellows, 6 folds, 10 keys, 2 stops, 2 sets of reeds .. .. .. **4/6** Post 6d.

Black mouldings, nickel pallets, double bellows, nickel corners to folds, imitation crocodile skin covered bellows, 2 stops, 2 sets of reeds, 10 keys (as illustration) .. .. **5/6** Post 6d.

Black mouldings, nickel pallets, 8-fold treble bellows, with nickel corners to each fold, fancy sides, 2 wood stops, 2 sets of reeds, 10 bone keys .. .. .. **6/6** Post 6d.

The "Empress" Brand, 8-fold treble bellows, with nickel corners to each, fancy coloured cloth sides, open key action, moulded case, 3 stops, 3 sets of extra broad reeds, 10 keys.
Price .. .. .. **11/6** Post 6d.

The "Empress" Brand, new Improved Model, walnut finish, 11-fold bellows, with nickel corners to each, fancy coloured cloth sides, open key action, moulded case, 3 stops, 3 sets of extra broad reeds, 10 keys.
Price .. .. .. **12/9** Post 6d.

"Imperial" Accordions.

"The Prince of Wales," extra small size, 10 keys, 2 stops, 2 sets of extra broad reeds, polished case, light panels **8/6**

"Little Lord Fauntleroy," black polished mouldings, nickel border to panel, nickel pallets, new action keys, 2 sets of reeds, 2 stops (as illus.) .. **10/6**

Ten keys, black polished case, white moulding, patented simplex key action, fine nickel baguettes, double bellows, each fold entirely fitted with steel wire riveted nickel rims, 2 sets of reeds .. **11/-**

Ten keys, the smallest size with 3 sets of reeds, very loud music, by means of the stops the tones can be changed five times.. .. .. **14/-**

"Virtuose Grandini," stained rosewood tops, nickel edges, 10 keys, 3 stops and bass stop, 3 sets of steel reeds and 2 sets in bass, 20th Century patent key action **21/-**

Chromatic Accordion.

"Gamage" Chromatic, the "Empress" Brand, black moulded case, 11-fold treble bellows, with nickel corners to each, variegated coloured sides, 2 stops, 2 sets of reeds, 19 keys, 4 bass chords, **15/9**

Imperial Chromatic Accordions.

19 keys, 2 stops, the smallest Imperial with 2 rows of keys, with open key action, 2 sets of broad reeds, black polished case **21/-**

19 keys, 2 stops, ebonized moulding, open nickel valves, silver stamped bellow frame, 8-fold double bellows, leather straps, 2 sets of broad reeds **25/-**

19 keys, 2 stops, 4 bass chords, Vox humana, oak case, nickel pallets, double bellows, leather straps, broad reeds **31/6**

Italian Accordions.

No. W. 345. Size 10 by 5½ in. Imitation rosewood with nickel corners, 12-fold bellows with nickel corners to each fold, fretwork tops, 10 pearl keys, 4 pearl bass keys, cloth lined straps, 2 sets of reeds .. **9/9**

No. W. 346. 11 by 6 in. Imitation rosewood with nickel corners, 14-fold bellows with nickel corners to each fold, fretwork tops, 19 pearl keys, 8 pearl bass keys, cloth straps, 4 sets of reeds **16/9**

No. W. 347. 12 by 6 in. Imitation rosewood with nickel corners, 14-fold bellows with nickel corners to each fold, fretwork tops inlaid, 21 pearl keys, 8 pearl bass keys, cloth lined leather straps, 4 sets of reeds .. **22/6**

No. W. 289. Sovereign Professional. 11 by 6 in. Rosewood tops, ebonized frame with nickel corners, 14-fold bellows with nickel corners to each fold, fretwork tops, 21 pearl keys, 8 pearl bass keys, cloth-lined leather straps, 4 sets of steel bronzed reeds .. **27/9**

CONCERTINAS.

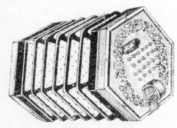

ENGLISH CONCERTINA.

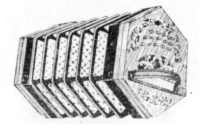

ANGLO-GERMAN CONCERTINA.

Lachenal's English Patent Concertinas.

Keys, Double Action, Screwed Notes, and Warranted. Compass, 3½ Octaves from G below to second C above stave.

MAHOGANY—In Deal, paper covered box	...	**35/9**
ROSEWOOD—Superior tone and finish, mahogany box	...	**44/9**
ROSEWOOD—Extra superior tone and finish, five-fold bellows, mahogany box	...	**53/6**
ROSEWOOD—Best finish five-fold morocco bellows, moulded edges, keyholes, bushed with cloth, to prevent rattling, rosewood box	...	**72/-**
ROSEWOOD—Extra best finish, five-fold morocco bellows, German Silver keys, rosewood box	...	**95/-**
ROSEWOOD—Newly improved, ornamented throughout, silver-tip keys, fine and pure tone, rosewood box	...	**99/-**
ROSEWOOD—Same finish as No. W 4, with tempered steel reeds, rosewood box	...	**112/-**

Lachenal's Anglo-German Concertinas.

All with separately fitted Screwed Notes.

MAHO-	20 keys.	26 keys.	28 keys.	30 keys.	MAHO-	20 keys.	26 keys.	28 keys.	30 keys.
GANY	**19/6**	**26/9**	**27/6**	**29/6**	GANY	**23/9**	**32/6**	**35/-**	**38/9**
	With Yellow Metal Reeds.					With Steel Reeds.			

Special Quotations given for any of Lachenal's Concertinas not Listed

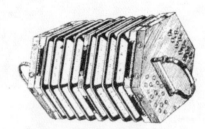

German Concertinas.

		Post
20 keys, imitation rosewood, hexagon ..	**2/9**	6d.
20 Ditto do. G.S. bound trumpet holes	**3/9**	6d.
20 keys, rosewood, hollowed, double G.S. bound trumpet holes	**5/9**	6d.
20 bone keys, rosewood, 6 folds, double bellows, bellows clasps, trumpet holes	**6/9**	7d.
20 bone keys, Anglo-German, rosewood ..	**8/6**	7d.
20 bone keys, Anglo-German, rosewood, steel reeds, 6 folds	**12/9**	7d.
20 keys, Anglo-German, rosewood, 8 folds, broad reeds, in wood case	**14/9**	7d.

MUSICAL BOXES.

Hand Organs.

In wooden case, 4 by 2 by 1¾ in.
To play one tune.   As illustration.
Price   ..   ..   **1/6**   Post 3d.
Do., 4 by 3¼ by 2¾ in.   To play two tunes.
Price   ..   ..   **2/6**   Post 3d.
Do., 4½ by 3½ by 3 in.   To play four tunes.
Price   ..   **3/6**   Postage 4d.
In Round Nickelled Cases.
To play 1 tune **1/2**
Do.   2 tunes **2/-**

Edelweiss Hand-Organ.

With Changeable Tunes.

Polished wood case, 6 by 4½ by 3 in. and
three interchangeable tunes   ..   **7/11**
Do., 8¼ by 6 by 5¼ in. with carrying sling and
three interchangeable tunes **10/6** Post 4d.
Extra tunes 4d. each.
Polished Walnut, 11 by 9¼ by 6½ in., with
six tunes.
Long tunes, superior music and motor..**22/6**
Extra tunes 8d. each.

Musical Piano.

Light oak.   To turn by hand.
Size of piano 9 by 4 by 9½ in.
Price including 6 metal tunes   ..   **12/6**
A very fine Present.

Polyphons.

These boxes are auto-
matic with the
exception of No. 28
and have a strong
well-made motor
and cabinet.
New Tunes always
to be obtained.
When ordering, men-
tion the diameter of
your tunes or send us
one as a sample.

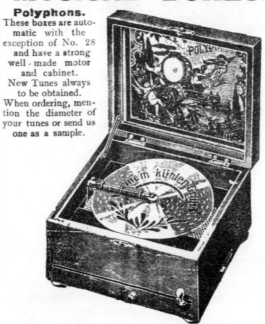

Polyphon No. 28.   To turn by hand, 30 notes, in Rose-
wood case, 7½ by 7¼ by 3½ in.
Price, including 3 tunes **14/6**
Diameter of tune 6½ in.   Price per dozen 4/-

Polyphon No. 28 S.   30 notes, rosewood case, 7⅝ by 7¼
by 4¾ in.   Price, including 6 tunes   ..   **25/6**
Diameter of tunes 6½ in., price per dozen ..   **4/-**

Polyphon No. 41.   41 notes, polished walnut case, size
10⅛ by 9¾ by 6⅜ in.
Price, including 6 tunes **38/6**
Diameter of tunes 8½ in., price per doz.   ..   **6/-**

Polyphon No. 46.   46 notes, highly polished walnut case,
size 12 in. by 10¾ by 7½ in.
Price, including 6 tunes **57/6**
Diameter of tunes 9⅝ in.
Price per dozen **11/-**

Automatic Musical Boxes.

In highly finished imitation rosewood cabinets.

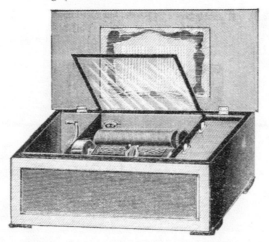

W. 1.   Has 3½ in. barrel, plays 8 tunes, 14 by 7½ by
5 in. **23/6**
W. 2.   Has 6 in. barrel, plays 10 tunes, stop, start,
change, repeat levers, 17½ by 8½ by 5½ in.   ..   **35/-**
W. 4.   Has 7 in. barrel, plays 12 tunes, 4 bells, stop,
start, change, repeat levers, 20 by 11 by 9..   ..   **45/-**
W. 5.   Has 7½ in. barrel, plays 20 tunes, start, change
and repeat lever, with optional mute, size 22 by
12 by 7½ in. **59/6**

Self-acting Musical Boxes.

Plays 2 tunes, in polished wood box,
4¾ by 3¼ by 2½ in.   ..   **3/9**   Post 3d.
With glass cover to works, winds at side.
Plays 8 tunes   ..   **4/9**   Post 3d.
Plays 4 tunes, in polished wood box, 4¾ by 3¼
by 2½ in., with glass cover to works, winds at
bottom   ..   **5/6**   Post 3d.
Highly polished Walnut 4¾ by 3½ in.
Extra long superior music.
Playing 2 tunes **6/6**
Do.   3 „ **8/-**
Do.   4 „ **9/6**

Edelweiss Automatic.

With Changeable Tunes.

Polished mahogany wood case, strong clock-
work motor.
Complete with 6 tunes, **12/6**   Post 6d. each.
Extra tunes, 4d. each.

Musical Tobacco Jar.

(Plays when lifted).   Height 7 in.
With 2 tunes.   As illustration.   Price **9/6**

Useful Household Requisites.

"Hygienic."
True Disinfectant.
GERMICIDE.
INSECTICIDE.
BACTERICIDE.

This invaluable preparation is compounded with the object of incorporating the most recent discoveries of Hygienic Research as revealed in relation to the science of bacteriology. See Reports from most eminent Analysts and Bacteriologists, which are irrefutable proof of the power and efficiency of **Hygienic** TRUE DISINFECTANT.

The quantity required for drains, &c. is 2 teaspoons to a pint of water.

	Price.	Carr. extra.
Size, 8 oz. bottle.	**9**d.	2d.
Per pint can	**1/1**	4d.
Per quart can	**1/9**	6d.
Half-gallon	**3/-**	8d.
Per gallon	**5/3**	10d.
Five gallons	**23/-**	Carr. paid.

Cask of 40 gallons, at **4/-** per gallon, sent carriage paid direct from works. ALL CANS FREE.

'Comet' Metal Polish.
LIQUID. NON-POISONOUS.

This unique preparation is based on an entirely new formula, being of a *Pleasant aromatic odour,* entirely free of paraffin, petrol or methylated spirits.

For Silver, Sheffield Plate, White Metal Articles, Brass, Copper, Steel, Tin, Zinc, Culinary Utensils, Cutlery, Cycles, Harness Fittings, Motor Cars, etc.

Perfectly harmless to the hands.

Four-ounce can ..	**3½**d.	Post 1d.
Half-pint can	**6**d.	1½d.
One-pint can	**1/-**	4d.
One-quart can.. ..	**1/9**	6d.
Half-gallon can ..	**3/-**	8d.
One-gallon can ..	**5/6**	10d.
Five-gallon can ..	**22/6**	Carr. paid.

ALL CANS FREE.

"Seal" Brand
Liquid Metal Polish.

FREE from GRIT, ACID or POISON.

Will move the most troublesome stain.

⅓-pint ..	**3½**d.	Post 1d.
½-pint ..	**5**d.	,, 1½d.
⅔-pint ..	**10**d.	,, 3d.
1¼-pint ..	**1/8**	,, 4d.
1 quart..	**2/6**	,, 6d.

Per gallon, **7/6**, carriage extra 10d.

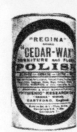

"Regina"
Brand
'Cedar Wax.'
Furniture and Floor Polish Antiseptic Aromatic.
Lasting and Pure.

The Ideal Polish for Linoleum, Parquet Floors, Furniture, Cabinets, Pianos, &c.

Used in large quantities by Hospitals and other large Public Institutions, Schools, Restaurants, Hotels in all parts of the country.

Size about—			
6-oz. Tin ..	**6**d.	Post	2d.
14-oz. ,, ..	**1/-**	,,	4d.
3-lb. Canisters	**3/6**	Carr.	6d.
7-lb. ..	**7/-**	,,	9d.

"Dusmo."

A Hygroscopic Sweeping Powder for preventing dust flying into the air. It cleans the carpet.

No Oil or Grease.

1¼ lbs.	**4½**d.
2 lbs. (decorated tin) ..	**9**d.
12 lbs.	**2/6**
35 lbs.	**8/6**
75 lbs.	**15**/-

Dusmo "B," for the plain floors of Hospitals, Schools, Churches, Ball-rooms, etc.,

18 lbs. ..	**2/6**	56 lbs. ..	**8**/-
112 lbs. ..	**14**/-		

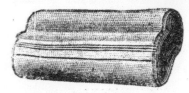

Household Flannel.

Best White	**7**d. per yard.
Per roll of about 45 yards ..	**25/6**
Strong Check	**5½**d. per yard.
Per roll of about 45 yards ..	**19/6**
Good Quality	**4½**d. per yard.
Per roll of about 45 yards ..	**16**/-

Windolene.

The most useful invention of modern times.

Cleans windows without water.

Made in 5 sizes.

0	1	2	3	4
4½d.	**6½**d.	**1/-**	**1/9**	**3/-**

The 'Instantaneous' Floor Polish
MAKES A PERFECT DANCING FLOOR BY MERELY SPRINKLING.
NO DUST!

By using this preparation, you may produce a well polished floor, ready for dancing, in a few minutes. Price, medium size tin, **1/-** Large size tin, **1/6**

Postage 3d.

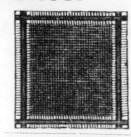

Sponge Cloths.

22 in. by 15 in.
1/0½ doz.

22 in. by 22 in.
1/6½ doz.

24 in. by 30 in.
2/- doz.

Postage 3d. doz.

Floor Cloths or Wearwell Scourers.
The "Whitecross" Floor Cloth.
As illustration.

		Each.	Doz.
Best on the market 22 by 22 in. ..		**3½**d.	**3/3**
Blue stripe Floor Cloth, 22 by 22 in.		**3**d.	**2/9**
Good quality ,,	22 by 22 in.	**2½**d.	**2/3**

Housemaids Gloves. CHAMOIS LEATHER

		Pair.	Doz. pair
Special ribbed backs ..		**1/1**	**12/6**
First quality Gloves ..		**11**d.	**10/6**
Second ,, ..		**8½**d.	**8/3**
Gauntlets ..		**1/-**	**11/6**
White Cotton, lined ..		**5½**d.	**5/-**

Chamois Leathers

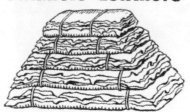

Best selected skins. Thoroughly recomended for hard wear. When ordering state whether for window or silver cleaning.

Sizes about 14 by 14in.	**8½**d.	16 by 16in.	**1/0½**
Postage	1¼d.		2d.
Sizes about 19 by 19in.	**1/8½**	22 by 22in	**2/3½**
Postage	3d.		3d.

Best quality Chamois Housemaid's Gloves, 1st quality **1/2½**, 2nd quality **9½**d. pair. Post 1½d.

Chamois Dusters

Each hemmed ready for use.
Best quality,

			Doz.		
24 by 22 in. ..	**4/11½**	26 by 24 in. ..	**5/11½**		
Each .. **5½**d..		..		..	**6½**d.

Check Dusters.

Superior quality.

	Doz.			Doz.
22 by 22 in. ..	**3/9½**	22 by 24 in. ..		**4/6½**
Each ..	**4½**	.. ..		**5**d.

The Polivit Cleaner.

Made in 3 sizes.

No.	1	2	3
	1/3	**2/6**	**4/6**

Post 1d. and 2d.

A New Method of cleaning Silver and Electroplate.

The old plan of cleaning Silver is superseded, no more pastes, powders, cloths, or brushes.

The Polivit—the new cleaner—does the work by itself. You simply place the Polivit in water with washing soda, and as if by magic the dirt flies from the silver to the Polivit, leaving the silver ware as clean and brilliantly polished as when new.

AWARDED GOLD MEDAL, LONDON, 1902

Patent Food Choppers.

Tinned or Enamelled.
Clean and Hygienic.
Easy to keep Clean.

Each Machine complete with Five Knives and Plates, all of case-hardened steel, reversible and self-sharpening.

Full Instructions and Cookery Recipe Book with each Machine Gratis.

No. Y. 1a.   Cuts 1½ lbs. per min.   **3/6½**
„ Y. 2a.   „   2½ lbs.   „   **3/11½**
Carriage extra, 6d. and 8d.

Note the oblique Clamp. Saves stooping down.

Dr. Klein's Meat Juice Extractor.

A Boon to Invalids and Convalescents.

Adopted by leading Hospitals all over Europe and recommended by medical authorities for **USE IN THE HOME** for preparing Beef Teas, etc.

Each Extractor holds 2½ lbs. of Meat.

SIMPLE, EFFECTIVE & HYGIENIC.
PRICE **18/9**

The "Gamage" Fruit Press.

Invaluable for making } **Wines, Syrups, Summer Drinks, etc.**

The Press separates the juice of the fruit from the pulp and throws them out at different ends.

No. Y. 376.   As illustrated **6/11**   Carriage 10d.

The "Gamage" Bread and Bacon Slicer.

Cuts Bread, Bacon, Meat, &c.,

EASILY AND QUICKLY.

Thickness can be adjusted to a nicety.

Knife of best cutting steel.

Frame tastefully japanned.

Base in one piece   ..   **11/6**

With Folding Base   ..   **14/6**

The "Gamage" Fruit and Lard Press.

No. Y. 165.   Enamelled white inside, with tinned lining.
Suitable for Pressing Apples for Cyder.

Capacity	½	1	2	3	5	10	20 qts.
Price	6/9	10/6	13/6	16/6	30/-	55/-	86/-
Weight	6½	10	20	30	54	88	166 lbs

Sizes 2 to 20 quarts, **TO ORDER.**

The "Gamage" Efficient Knife Cleaner.

Triumph of Simplicity and Utility.

Polishes Cutlery like Silver.

Visible Cleaning.

Household Size **10/6**

The "Gamage" Bean Cutter.

Fitted with three adjustable rotary knives of best cutting steel.

Quick and easy working guaranteed.

Price **3/6**

The "Gamage" Improved Bread Vegetable and Nut Grater.

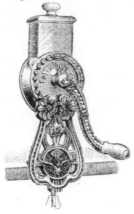

Both medium and fine cut may be obtained in the same machine by reversing the handle.

Price   ..   ..   **2/3**   Post 3d.

Smaller Size, for Nuts, Almonds, etc.   **1/3**
Post 3d.

The "Gamage" Meat Juice Extractor.

Unequalled for Making Beef Tea, etc.

Strongly made and well finished.

Tinned or enamelled.

Price **2/9**

The "Gamage" Lemon Squeezer.

Made of Cast Iron.

Well finished.

Can be had either tinned or enamelled.

Price **1/0½**

The "Gamage" Christmas Tree Holder.

Holds the tree firmly and securely.

Prevents accidents.

Tree cannot topple over.

Price **1/3½**

The "Gamage" Latest Pattern Coffee Mill.

Mounted on polished beech board for fixing to wall or dresser.

Complete with measuring glass, and regulator for grinding coarse or fine.

Price, to hold ½ lb. berries,
5/6

Price, to hold 1 lb. berries,
7/6

Write for full Departmental List sent post free anywhere.

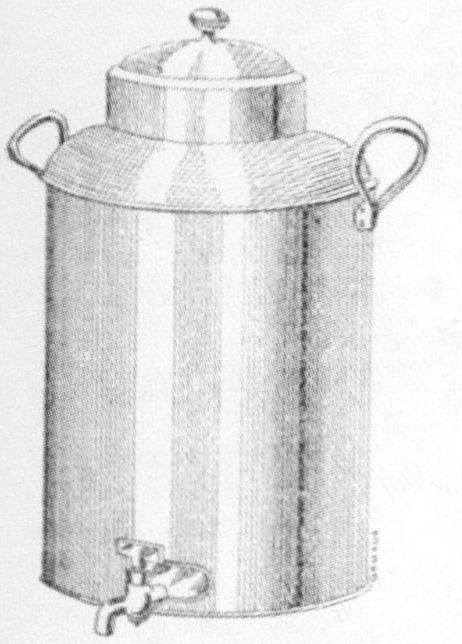

Tea Urns or Water Boilers.

With best brass taps. These Urns are very convenient where a considerable quantity of hot water is required. Can be used on a coal range or gas stove.

Invaluable for bathing purposes, etc.

Made extra strong and durable.

WITH TIN BOTTOM.

1	2	4	6	8	10	12 gall
5/3	**7/9**	**10/6**	**16/9**	**19/6**	**26/6**	**28/6**

DITTO, WITH COPPER BOTTOM.

9/3	**11/6**	**15/-**	**19/6**	**24/6**	**29/6**	**35/-**

Y. L364. Ditto, Best quality. COPPER BOTTOM.

9/9	**12/6**	**18/3**	**26/6**	**32/-**	**41/-**	**47/-**
Carriage extra.		Carriage free 20/- and over.				
7d.	8d.	1/-	1/3	1/6	1/6	1/9

Household Scale.

Complete with Weights. As illus. To weigh 14 lbs. by ¼ o

Price **11/9**

Ditto, Government Stamped, for trade purposes, **26/-**

The "Gamage" Scales and Weights.

Best London Manufacture. Not Stamped.

No kitchen should be without a set of reliable Scales. Most useful for fancy or French cooking, checking tradesmen. In purchasing a set of these Scales is money well spent. Highest possible value at the lowest possible price and which is unobtainable elsewhere.

Scales as illustration with 8 in. diam. solid Copper concave loose pan tinned and polished inside and Bright Copper outside, complete with set of Round Weights, weighing ¼ oz. to 7 lbs.

Our price **6/11**

Scales as illustration, but with 11½ in. oblong tin Scoop pan, complete with weights.

Gamage's price, **5/6** Carriage extra.

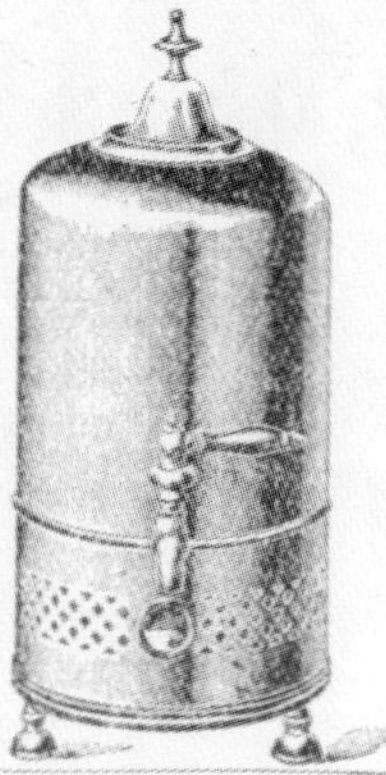

No. Y. 2.

Tea or Water Urns.

Suitable for Hotels, Restaurants, Tea Rooms, etc.

Capacity.	Brase or Copper.	Copper Nickel-plated.	Silverite.
1 gall., 1 tap	**22/6**	**36/-**	**45/-**
1½ „ 1 „	**28/6**	**41/-**	**52/6**
2 „ 1 „	**31/6**	**48/-**	**55/6**
2 „ 2 „	**48/-**	**58/6**	**71/6**
3 „ 1 „	**43/-**	**56/-**	**69/6**
3 „ 1 „	**59/6**	**76/-**	**85/-**

Carriage and Packing paid.

TO ORDER ONLY.

Cheap Provision Dealers' Scales.

Government Stamped

Fitted with Square China Plate, Iron Weight Pan and loose Lead Box.

Size of Plate,	7 by 8	8 by 9	9½ by 10	10 by 11 in.
To Weigh	4	7	10	20 lbs.
	14/6	**15/6**	**17/6**	**21/6**

Stamped Weight extra. Listed as below.

Provision Dealers' Scales.

BEST QUALITY.

No. Y. 315. Fitted with Iron Weight Pan and Best Glazed China Pan. Government Stamped. Ready for use.

To weigh 7 lbs.	**17/6**
14 lbs. ..	**23/-**
28 lbs. ..	**30/-**

Confectioners' and Greengrocers' Scale.

B Pattern Scale with iron stand, T iron beam steeled in all parts, fitted with brass pan and scoop. Stamped and adjusted ready for use.

NOTE—10 lb. to 20 lbs. Scale is for Greengrocers with large brass scoop.

To weigh	1 lb.	2 lbs.	4 lbs.	10 lbs.	20 lbs.
Price ..	**7/9**	**8/11**	**10/9**	**17/11**	**19/11**

Weights extra as below.

Carriage and packing extra—				
5d.	6d.	7d.	8d.	9d.

Polished Flat **Brass Weights**
Stamped ready for use.

½ lb. to ¼ oz.	**1/6½** set.
½ lb. to ¼ oz.	**2/9½** „
1 lb. to ¼ oz.	**4/3** „
2 lb. to ¼ oz.	**7/3** „
4 lb. to ¼ oz.	**13/-** „

Flat **Iron Weights,** stamped ready for use, with ½oz. to ¼ oz. in brass—1 lb. to ¼ oz. **2/3** 2 lb. to ¼ oz. **2/9** 4lb. to ¼ oz. **3/9** 7 lb. to ¼ oz. **5/9** per set.

Japanned and Gilt Iron Ring Weights.

ALL WEIGHTS are GOVERNMENT STAMPED.

56 lb. to ¼ lb.	**18/6** set	7 lb. to ¼ lb.	**5/9** set
28 lb. to ¼ lb.	**12/-** „	4 lb. to ¼ lb.	**3/9** „
14 lb. to ¼ lb.	**8/-** „	2 lb. to ¼ lb.	**2/6** „

Round Brass Weights, stamped, 2 oz. to ¼ oz., **1/6½**

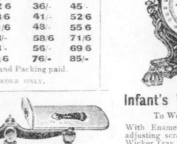

Infant's Weighing Scales.

To Weigh 25 lbs. by 2 oz.

With Enamelled Dial and fitted with adjusting screw. Price, complete with Wicker Tray, as illustration ... **6/6**

Carriage 9d. extra.

Do., best quality Hughes' pattern, **12/6**

Ditto Salters, as used by the Medical Profession, weighing up to 28 lbs. by 2 oz. **18/9** To order.

No. Y. S 48. **Hughes' Family Balance Scale,** with round pan, detachable. Enamelled dial.

To weigh.		Price.	Postage.
20 lbs. by 1 oz.	...	**5/9**	7d.
28 „ 2 „	...	**6/3**	7d.

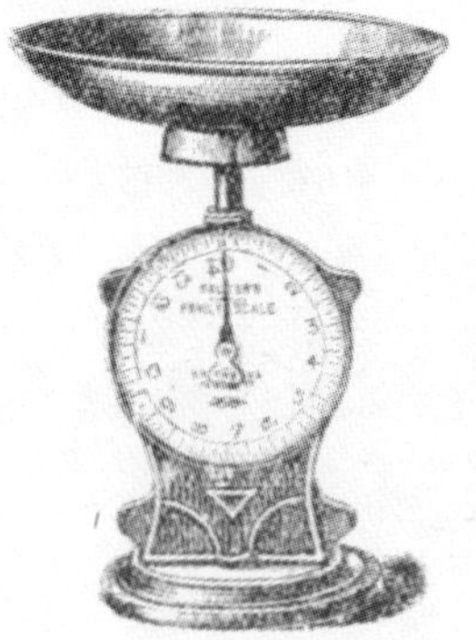

No. Y. S 50.

Household Balance Scale,

with round pan, detachable, and solid brass dial.

	lbs.	oz.	Price.	Post.
To weigh ...	7	by ¼	**8/3**	7d.
„	14	by 1	**8/9**	8d.
„	28	by 2	**10/3**	8d.
„	50	by 2	**17/6**	10d.

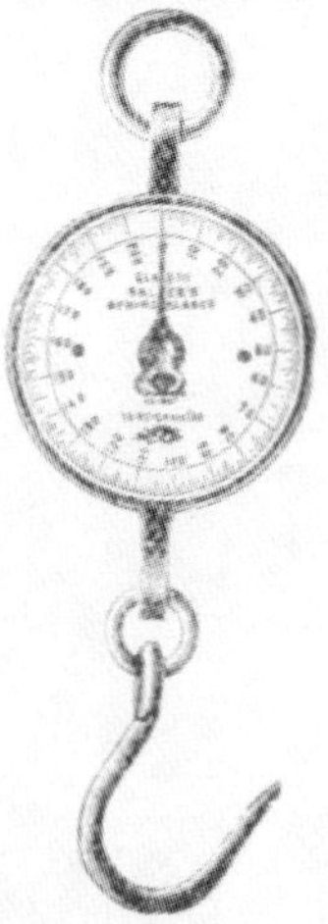

No. Y. S20.

Balance Scale,

with Circular Brass Dial and Hook.

To weigh

50 lbs. by ½ lb., 5 in. dial **13/9** Post 5d.

100 lbs. by 1 lb. 5 in. dial **12/-** Post 6d.

200 lbs. by 1 lb. **14/-** Post 6d.

300 lbs. by 1 lb. 8 in. **21/-** Post 8d.

Barford & Perkins' Water Ballast Rollers.

Universal" Water Ballast Garden Roller

"Universal" Water Ballast Tennis Ground Rollers.

For Pony or Manual Power.

With Rounded Edges.

A most useful combination Roller, adopted for Lawn Tennis Grounds, Gravel Walks, etc.

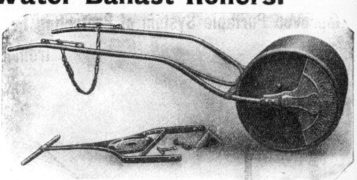

Width and Diameter.	Weight Empty. cwt. qrs.	Weight Full. cwt. qrs.	GAMAGE'S PRICES. With Shafts and Handle.	With Shafts only.	With Double Cylinders, extra
27 by 27 in. (for donkey or small pony)	7 2	10 3	£9 15 6	£8 10 0	£2 11 0
30 by 30 in. (for pony)	9 2	14 2	12 15 0	11 9 6	2 11 0

The light tubular iron Shafts can be removed in a few moments and the handle substituted.

The Double Cylinders increase the Weight.

Width and Diam. Inches.	Weight, Empty. Cwt. qrs. lbs.	Weight, Full. Cwt. qrs. lbs.	GAMAGE'S Price. £ s. d.
18 by 18	2 3 0	4 0 0	3 3 9
21 ,, 21	3 2 0	5 1 0	3 16 6
22½ ,, 22½	4 0 0	6 1 0	4 13 6
24 ,, 24	4 2 0	7 0 0	5 6 3
27 ,, 27	6 3 0	10 0 0	7 4 6
30 ,, 30	9 0 0	14 0 0	10 4 0

The larger sizes of these Rollers can be supplied with DOUBLE CYLINDERS at the following prices :

21 in. ..	£5 11 9	27 in. ..	£9 14 3
22½ in. ..	5 17 0	30 in. ..	12 17 3
24 in. ..	6 9 3		

There is a corresponding increase in the weight.

New Double Cylinder Cast-Iron Water-Ballast Rollers,

With Balanced Frame of Wrought-iron, Tubular-iron Shafts, and rounded outside edges, adapted for rolling Parks, Tennis and Cricket Grounds, etc. Shafts are fitted for carriage harness when desired.

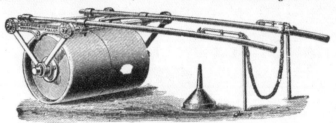

Diameter. Feet. Inches.	Width. Feet. Inches.		Weight Empty. cwts. qrs. lbs.	Weight Full. cwts. qrs. lbs.	Prices. £ s. d.
1 9	by 3 6	(for pony) ..	9 2 0	12 2 0	12 6 6
2 0	by 4 0	(for cob) ..	10 2 0	15 2 0	13 16 3
2 3	by 4 6	(for carriage horse)	15 2 0	22 0 0	20 3 9
2 6	by 5 0	(for cart horse) ..	19 0 0	28 0 0	24 17 3
3 0	by 6 0	(for two horses) ..	35 0 0	50 0 0	45 18 0

Seat for Driver 21/3 extra.

New Roller Cart.

FOR GOLF LINKS.

Diam.	Width.	App. Weight.	Price.
30 in.	36 in.	10 cwts. ..	£19 11 0
30 in.	48 in.	13 ,,	22 2 0

Edges of Cylinders rounded.

A most useful implement for Seaside or Inland Golf Courses.

"Universal" Water Ballast Cricket Ground Rollers.

WITH SHAFTS OR WITH MANUAL FRAMES.

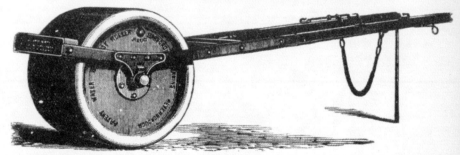

Diam. Inches.	Width. Inches.		Weight, Empty. Cwts. qrs. lbs.	Weight, Full. Cwts. qrs. lbs.	PRICES. £ s. d.
30	30	(for cob	10 2 0	15 2 0	£13 3 6
36	36	(for carriage horse)	16 2 0	25 0 0	20 16 6
36	42	double cylinder	21 0 0	30 0 0	27 8 3
42	42	double cylinder	28 0 0	41 0 0	36 11 0
*48	54	double cylinder, for cricket grounds	39 0 0	55 0 0	51 0 0

N.B.—The 30-in. an 36-in. sizes can be supplied with double cylinders. Price **38/3** and **80/9** extra respectively. *The double cylinders increase the weight* Shafts fitted for carriage harness when desired. Seat for Driver, **21/3** extra. Removable wooden crossbar for use when a horse is not available. Price 21 3. Cricket Ground Rollers with manual frames, same price as with shafts.

* This Roller is made with ordinary frame and shafts, as shown, or with tipping shafts to turn right over if ordered specially.

For Complete List of Garden Tools and Accessories, see Horticultural Catalogue. Post free.

GAMAGE'S IMPROVED CHAMPION No. 2 LAWN MOWER.

The very best low priced Lawn Mower on the Market.

Five Blades.

This Mower has screw adjustments throughout, and is very light working.

Five Blades.

Extra large Cylinders. Large strong Half-open Driving Wheels.

New Design.

Close Cutting.

Blades and Cutter Bar of high-grade Steel. Carefully tempered.

All parts are machined and fitted to insure accurate construction.

Reel Shaft made with adjustable brass bushings for taking up wear.

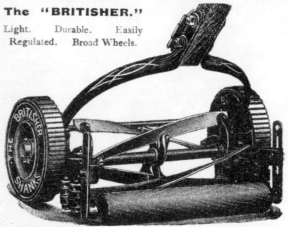

Sizes	8	10	12	14	16	18 in.	CARRIAGE
Prices	13/6	14/6	15/9	17/-	18/6	20/-	PAID.
Grass Boxes	3/-	3/3	3/6	3/9	4/-	4/6	

SHANKS' LAWN MOWERS.

The "BRITISHER."

Light. Durable. Easily Regulated. Broad Wheels.

Ideal Machine for Small Lawns.

Size.	Price.
10 in.	22/3
12 in.	23/9

Grass Boxes
3/9 4/9

Size.	Price.
14 in.	25/6
16 in.	27/3

Grass Boxes
5 - 6/-

STANDARD CHAIN or GEAR HAND LAWN MOWERS.

Size.	Price.		
10 in.	£3	10	0
12 in.	4	9	3
14 in.	5	8	3
16 in.	6	7	6
18 in.	7	4	6
19 in.	7	10	9
22 in.	8	5	9
24 in.	8	14	3

Prices include Grass Boxes. Steel Axle Springs. Easily Handled. Splendid work. A good machine for Bowling Greens and Cricket Grounds. It must be specially stated on order when a machine is required for Bowling Greens and Cricket Grounds.

Drawbow for Pony, 22 or 24 in. Machine, **3/6** extra.

Standard Gear Machines, specially constructed for Pony and Donkey draught, fitted with gear clutch, lifting out grass box and whipple tree—

20 in. **£11 1 0**   21 in. **£11 18 0**   24 in. **£12 5 0**

Shanks' Mowers carriage paid from factory.

Grass Boxes, when ordered separately are not sent carriage paid.

The **"Gamage" Mower** and **Implement Oil.** Non-freezable, specially prepared for mowers, garden rollers, wheelbarrows, etc. Postage extra.

The "Gamage" Garden Roller.

IMPROVED DESIGN.

ROUNDED EDGES OUTSIDE

TURNED EDGES INSIDE.

BALANCE HANDLES.

DOUBLE CYLINDERS WELL FITTED AND NEATLY PAINTED

SOLID ENDS SUPPLIED AT SAME PRICES.

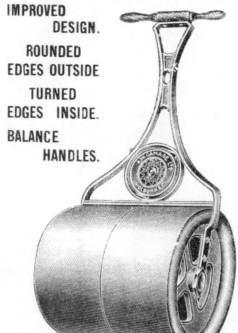

Carriage paid to any Railway Station in England, Scotland or Wales

		SIZE.		Weight about c. q. lb.			PRICE.
No. Z. 1	..	14 by 14 in.	..	1	2	0	.. 30/-
,, 2	..	16 ,, 16 ,,	..	1	3	14	.. 32/6
,, 3	..	18 ,, 18 ,,	..	2	2	0	.. 39/9
,, 4	..	20 ,, 20 ,,	..	3	0	14	.. 43/6
,, 5	..	22 ,, 22 ,,	..	3	2	14	.. 55/6
,, 6	..	24 ,, 24 ,,	..	4	0	14	.. 70/-
,, 7	..	26 ,, 26 ,,	..	5	2	0	.. 105/6
,, 8	..	28 ,, 28 ,,	..	7	0	0	.. 130/-

A. W. GAMAGE, Ltd., were awarded Two Gold Medals at the CHILDREN'S WELFARE EXHIBITION 1914, for the best Exhibit of TOYS AND INDOOR GAMES and the best General Exhibit appropriate to CHILDREN'S WELFARE.

LAWN MOWERS AND EDGE CUTTERS.

GREEN'S LAWN MOWERS.

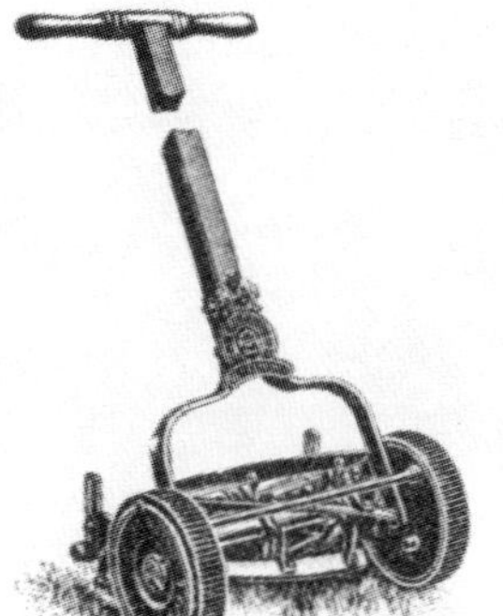

"New Century Light Side-Wheel Mower.

Well adapted for Mowing Lawns, Tennis Courts, Slopes and Banks.

5 Blades

9 in.	22/3	Grass Boxes ...	3/6
11 in.	23/9	,, ...	3/9
13 in.	25/6	,, ...	4/3
15 in.	27/3	,, ...	4/9
18 in.	29/9	,, ...	5/6

"Silens Messor," including Grass Boxes.

6 in.	36/-
in.	51/-
10 in.	70/-
12 in.	89/3
14 in.	108/3
16 in.	127/6
18 in.	144/6
20 in.	157/3
22 in.	165/9
24 in.	174/3

Rope and Handle, 1/6 extra.

RANSOMES' LAWN MOWERS,

"Lion" Lawn Mower.

Light in Weight. Easy to Work.

9 in.	11 in.	13 in.	15 in.
22/3	23/9	25/6	27/3

GRASS BOXES, extra—

3/6	3/9	4/3	4/9

Patent Edge Cutter.

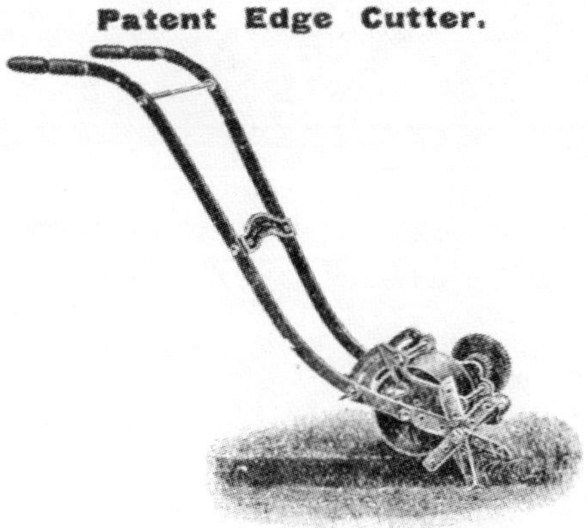

Can be Guided with the Greatest Ease.

Price 34/-

"Anglo-Paris" Mower.

Fitted with Patent Screw Adjustment.

Light and Easy

6	8	10	12	14	16	18	20 in.
25/6	29/9	34/-	40/3	46/9	55/3	63/9	72/3

Grass Boxes extra—

4/3	4/3	4/3	6/-	[illegible]	6/-	6/9	6/9

Patent Gear Automaton.

Prices of Gear and Chain Automaton.

Including Grass Boxes—

8 in.	£2 11 0		16 in.	£6 7 6
10 in.	3 10 0		18 in.	7 4 6
12 in.	4 9 3		20 in.	7 17 3
14 in.	5 8 3		22 in.	8 5 9

24 in. .. £8 14 3

Whippletree for Pony or Donkey .. 10/- extra.

Side Rollers for Cutting Long Grass 2/- to 4/6 extra

"Automaton Minor" Mower.

Special Light Machine. Runs easily.

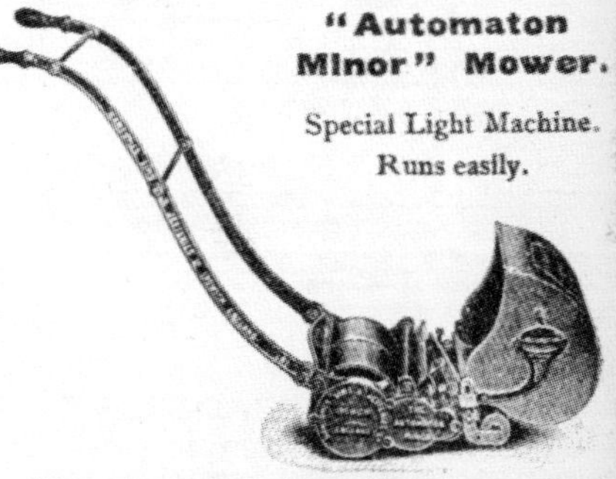

6 in., 34/- 8 in., 46 9 10 in., 61/9 12 in., 72/3 14 in., 85/- 16 in., +7/9

G & R.'s Mowers, Carriage Paid from Factory. Grass Boxes, when ordered separately are not sent carriage paid

Solid Lawn Mowing Horse Boots. (PATENT).

These Boots effect a saving of at least 50 per cent. They are Block Sole and Upper in one piece, fit better, are more compact, and much more durable than any others. They retain their shape, cannot cut up or mark the lawn having no sharp edges, and are superior in every way to the ordinary Boot. As illustrated. The vamp is secured with Patent Bifurcated Steel Rivets.

Size.	Inside Measurment.	
Donkey	4 by 3 in.	20/-
Pony	5 by 4½ in.	25/-
Cob	6 by 5¾ in.	30/-
Horse	7 by 6½ in.	33/-
Van	7¾ by 7 in.	40/-
Cart	8 by 7½ in.	47/6

Carriage paid.

When ordering these boots kindly give size or rough outline of animal's hoofs.

Old Style Lawn Boots, strong hand-sewn throughout.

Soles of prime solid Leather, well-dressed good hide uppers.

Pony or Donkey size	5 by 4 in.	15/6
Small Horse size..	6¼ by 5 in.	21/-
Van	7 by 6¼ in.	25/6
Cart	9 by 8 in.	30/-

FLOWER POTS.

No. of Pots to Cast.	Diam. Inside.	Price Per Cast.	No. of Pots to Cast.	Diam. Inside.	Price Per Cast.
72	2 in.	2/6	28	7 in.	5/-
*72	2½ in.	2/6	24	7½ in.	5/-
*Small 60	2¾ in.	2/6	16	8½ in.	5/-
Mid 60	3 in.	2/6	12	10 in.	6/-
*Large 60	3½ in.	2/6	8	11 in.	6/-
54	4½ in.	3/-	6	12½ in.	6/-
48	5 in.	3/-	4	14 in.	6/-
40	5½ in.	3/6	2	15½ in.	6/-
32	6¼ in.	3/6	1	18 in.	6/-

* LONG TOMS. WITHOUT RIMS.

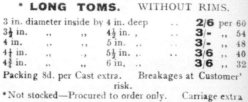

3 in. diameter inside by	4 in. deep	2/6	per 60
3½ in. ,, ,,	4½ in. ,,	3/-	,, 54
4 in. ,, ,,	5 in. ,,	3/-	,, 48
4¼ in. ,, ,,	5½ in. ,,	3/6	,, 40
4¾ in. ,, ,,	6 in. ,,	3/6	,, 32

Packing 8d. per Cast extra. Breakages at Customer' risk.

*Not stocked—Procured to order only. Carriage extra

Palm Leaf Portmanteau.

Y. 3. Best Quality.

Length	16	18	20	22	24 in.
Price	4/6	5/6	8/3	11/3	14/3
Postage	5d.	6d.	6d.	6d.	7d

Ladies' or Gent's Suit Cases.

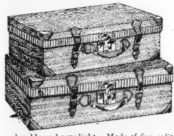

Strong, durable and very light. Made of fine split cane, has a patent spring lock, two leather straps and leather corners and handle.
Dimensions : Length. Width and Depth.
21 by 11½ by 6½ in.   23 by 13 by 7 in.
9/6 Postage 6d.   **11/6** Postage 6d.

Laundry or Travelling Hampers

Unlined. Best make. Trunk Lid. Cane Loops.

	22	24	26	28	30	32	34 ir.
White	8/9	10/3	11/6	12/9	14/3	16/-	17/9
Buff	10/6	11/6	12/9	13/9	15/6	17/3	19/3

Carriage extra.

Wicker Dog Kennel, white wicker, nicely made.
Suitable for pet dogs.   Length 14 in. .. **13/6**
Length 16 in. .. **16/9**   18 in. .. **19/6**
Cheaper make, buff wicker, with a brass wire door
to take off and on.   Size 14 in. .. **11/6**
Length 16 in , **13/6**   Carr. 6d.   18 in., **1**
21 in. .. **19/6**   Carriage 7d.
Estimates given for Larger Sizes.

Travelling Hampers.

(Carriage forward.)

These Hampers, being London Made, are exceedingly strong and durable, lined with the best Waterproof. They are an ideal travelling requisite for home or foreign use, and will stand a tremendous lot of rough usage.

Y. 1. With iron hoops and bar for padlock, as illustration, without rollers or runners.

	Inside Measurements.					Prices.
1.	Length 24 in.	Width 14 in.	Depth 14 in.		..	14/9
2.	,, 26 in.	,, 16 in.	,, 16 in.		..	17/3
3.	,, 28 in.	,, 18 in.	,, 18 in.		..	19/6
4.	,, 30 in.	,, 20 in.	,, 20 in.		..	23/6
5.	,, 33 in.	,, 21 in.	,, 21 in.		..	27/C
6.	,, 36 in.	,, 22 in.	,, 22 in.		..	32/-

No. 3.—All close best willows and hard cane; iron hinges, iron bands on lids, rope handles, spring lock, two best straps, lined waterproof cloth, two hardwood battens, and rollers; strongly recommended for hard wear.

	Inside Measurements.					Prices.
12.	Length 26 in.	Width 16 in.	Depth 16 in.		..	33/6
13.	,, 28 in.	,, 18 in.	,, 18 in.		..	36/-
14.	,, 30 in.	,, 20 in.	,, 20 in.		..	39/-
15.	,, 33 in.	,, 21 in.	,, 21 in.		..	46/9
16.	,, 36 in.	,, 22 in.	,, 22 in.		..	51/6

Trays, well made, can be fitted to the above Hampers at an extra charge.

Length of Hamper :

24	26	28	30	33	36 in.
3/9	4/6	5/9	6/6	7/6	8/6

Picnic Hampers.

Flat Lid.   Buff

Outside Dimensions.

Long.	Wide.	Deep.	Price.
10	7	6 in.	1/3½
12	8	7 ,,	1/9½
14	9	8 ,,	2/3½
16	10	9 ,,	2/9½
18	11	10 ,,	3/6½

Carriage extra :

4d.   5d.   5d.   6d.   6d.

Japanese Travelling Hampers.

Best quality Hampers extra wide, complete with a pair of Leather Straps.
22½ in., **2/9**   24 in., **4/9**   26 in., **5/9**   27 in., **6/9**   30 in., **8/9**   Carriage extra.

Dog Baskets.

Round.   Buff wicker.
Best quality.
Dimensions across top.

16	18	20	22	24 in.
2/9	3/-	3/6	4/6	5/6
Carr. 4d.	5d.	6d.	6d.	7d.

Larger Sizes Made to Order.

Buff Wicker Portmanteau.

Y. 2. Fixed Handles. Cane Fasteners.
Dimensions : Length and Width.

18 by 11½	21 by 13	24 by 14½	27 by 16½ in.
Price 8/6	11/9	15/9	19/6
Postage 5d.	6d.	7d.	8d.

Ladies' Travelling Cases.

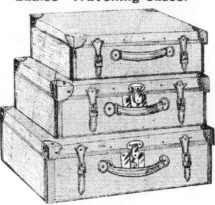

Y. 38/4.

Light and strong, with four leather cap corners, leather handle, two straps, lock and key.

Size—24 in. by 17 in. by 7 in.   **12/6**
22 ,, by 14½ ,, by 6 ,,   **10/6**
20 ,, by 12 ,, by 5 ,,   **8/6**
Carriage extra 7d., 8d., 9d.

Ladies' Dress Cases.

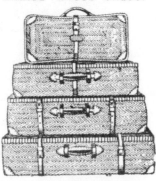

Y. 108.

Superior quality, 4 leather corners, complete with straps.

27 by 15½ by 8 in.	..	6/11
26 ,, 14 ,, 7½ ,,	..	5/11
25 ,, 12½ ,, 7 ,,	..	4/11
23 ,, 11 ,, 6½ ,,	..	3/11
21 ,, 9½ ,, 6 ,,	..	3/3½

Carriage 4d., 6d., 7d., 8d.

Wicker Dog Baskets & Kennels any desired shape can be made to order. Estimates free.

Bag, Trunk, Portmanteau and Travelling Equipage Department.

Every description of TRUNKS, BAGS, PORTMANTEAUS and CASES for Home and Foreign Travel.

SPECIAL REQUIREMENTS MADE TO ORDER WITH DESPATCH.

Lettering and Stamping on Bags and Trunks executed at a cost of 3d. per letter. Goods over 20/- value marked free up to four letters.
Name and Addresses, or Names of Regiment, 1/- per line.

BRIEF AND SQUARE BAGS.

No. K. 2. Full cut brown cowhide Brief Bag. Well lined, strong nickel handle plates, lock, and end clips. London made.
12 in., **4/11** 14 in., **5/11** 16 in. **6/11**

No. K. 3. Good quality brown Cowhide Brief Bag. Drill lined, strong gilt lock and handle plates, strong handle. London made.
12 in., **6/11** 14 in., **8/6** 16 in., **9/6**

No. K. 4. Better quality brown cowhide, strong covered steel frame, good nickel lock and handle plates, super drill lining.
12 in., **8/6** 14 in., **10/6** 16 in., **12/6**
No. K. 4a. Specification as No. K. 4, but roan leather lined.
12 in., **10/9** 14 in., **12/6** 16 in., **14/-**

No. K. 5. Superior quality cowhide Brief Bag. Good Brass lock and handle clips, lined best drill. London made, on a strong steel frame.
12 in., **11/6** 14 in., **15/9** 16 in., **18/-**
No. K. 5a. Specification as No. K. 5, but lined roan leather.
12 in., **16/6** 14 in., **19/6** 16 in., **21/9**

No. K. 6. Useful brown cowhide square Hand Bag. Nickel lock, clips, and handle plates, lined drill. London made on a steel frame.
12 in., **8/6** 14 in., **9/6** 16 in., **10/6**
18 in., **12/6**

No. K. 7. Better quality brown cowhide square Hand Bag. Stronger nickel clips, lock, and handle plates, drill lined, good handle. Extra full cut bag.
12 in., **11/6** 14 in., **13/6** 16 in., **15/-**
18 in., **17/6**

No. K. 8. Superior quality brown cowhide square Hand Bag. Gilt turn-over clips, lock, and hand plates, strong drill lining, good handle. London made.
12 in., **13/-** 14 in., **15/6** 16 in., **17/6**
18 in., **19/6**

No. K. 10. Best quality hide, superior finish, leather lined, good lock and fittings.
12 in., **22/6** 14 in. **26/6** 16 in., **30/-**
18 in., **33/6**
A smart, reliable bag.

Commercial Sample Bag.

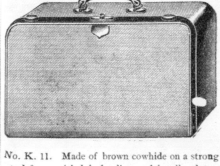

No. K. 11. Made of brown cowhide on a strong steel frame, nickel lock, clips and handle plates, drill lined. An ideal bag for commercial use.
14 in., **14/6** 16 in., **16/6** 18 in., **18/6**
20 in., **21/6**

Commercial or Dome Bag.

No. K. 12. Made of well selected brown cowhide, strong visible steel frame, good lock and clips, lined drill.
14 in., **25/-** 16 in., **29/6** 18 in., **32/6**

No. K. 12a. Specification as above, but leather lined.
14 in., **32/6** 16 in., **37/6** 18 in., **39/6**
Useful for Commercial or Week-end Bag.

Gamage's Bank Bag.

No. K. 13.
Made of extra stout brown cowhide, lined leather, strong steel frame, good brass lock.
12 in., **17/-** 14 in., **18/6** 16 in., **21/-**

Hand and Travelling Kit Bags.

No. K. 16.

Hand Kit Bags, Made of Brown Cowhide, brass clips, lock and handle plates, lined drill.

14 in.	..	**14/6**
16 in.	..	**16/6**
18 in.	..	**18/6**
20 in.	..	**21/6**

Leather-covered frame.

No. K. 21.

Made of brown Cowhide on a strong steel frame, lined drill, brass slide nozzle lock, brass fastening 2 strong handles. An Ideal Bag for Travelling.

20 in.	..	**29/6**
22 in.	..	**33/6**
24 in.	..	**36/6**
26 in.	..	**39/6**

No. K. 21½. Similar Bag to K. 21, but better hide and finish, good drill lining, slide nozzle, brass lock and brass fittings

20 in. .. **37/6**	22 in. .. **41/6**	24 in. .. **44/6**	26 in. .. **47/6**

No. K. 22. Superior quality Hand-sewn. Best selected Hide, good brass lever lock, end clips and end straps, drill lined.

20 in. .. **54/-**	22 in. .. **58/-**	24 in. .. **64/-**	26 in. .. **69/-**

No. K. 17.

Useful Hand Kit Bag, made of selected Brown Cowhide, good brass side lock, all brass fittings, lined good drill.

14 in. ..	**16/6**		18 in. ..	**21/6**
16 in. ..	**18/9**		20 in. ..	**23/6**

No. K. 18.

GAMAGE'S SPECIAL Kit Bag, Made of superior Brown Cowhide, good brass lock and fittings, best drill lining.

London Made.

16 in. ..	**28/6**	20 in. ..	**35/**
18 in. ..	**31/6**	22 in. ..	**39/6**

No. K. 23.

Kit Bag, superior quality Cowhide, nut colour, full cut, lined drill, made on a strong steel frame, brass lock and 2 keys, 4 large corners, drop handles, end straps and end clips.

20 in. .. **55/-**	22 in. .. **59/6**	24 in. .. **65/-**	26 in. .. **70/-**

No. K. 19.

GAMAGE'S "Hand Sewn" Kit Bags. Made of best quality Cowhide, super drill lining, all brass lever lock and fittings. Best London Finish.

16 in. ..	**37/6**	18 in. ..	**42/6**	20 in. ..	**45/-**

No. K. 19½. Same Bag, lined leather.

16 in. ..	**45/-**	18 in. ..	**50/-**	20 in. ..	**55/-**

No. K. 20. Super quality Brown Cowhide, best brass lever lock, and all brass fittings, lined best drill. London's Best Production.

16 in. ..	**40/-**	18 in. ..	**45/-**	20 in. ..	**50/-**

No. K. 20½. Same Bag, leather lined.

16 in. ..	**52/6**	18 in. ..	**57/6**	20 in. ..	**65/-**

GAMAGE'S "UNIVERSAL" Hand-made Kit Bag. The finest value procurable. Made of best selected Cowhide, good brass lever lock and fittings, drop end clips, 2 short straps and 2 drop handles, lined best quality drill.

20 in. .. **70/-**	22 in. .. **75/-**	24 in. .. **80/-**	26 in. .. **82/6**

Initials free.

Gladstone Bags, Portmanteaus, &c.

The Gamage G. 1 Gladstone.

Made of strong cowhide, on a good steel frame. 1 nickel lock 2 slides, 2 straps all round, lined drill. Useful Week-End Bag.

18 in.	.. ..	**15/6**
20 ,,	.. ..	**16/9**
22 ,,	.. ..	**18/6**
24 ,,	.. ..	**20/-**
26 ,,	.. ..	**22/6**

The Gamage G. 5 Gladstone.

Made of best selected cowhide good brass lever lock and fittings, 2 saddler made straps all round, lined good drill.

Hand Sewn Throughout.

20 in.	..	**49/6**
22 ,,	..	**52/6**
24 ,,	..	**57/6**
26 ,,	..	**62/6**

The Gamage G2. Gladstone.

Made from well selected hides, nickel lock and clips, lined drill straps inside, 2 good straps all round. London made.

18 in.	.. ..	**18/-**
20 ,,	.. ..	**20/-**
22 ,,	.. ..	**22/-**
24 ,,	.. ..	**24/-**
26 ,,	.. ..	**26/-**

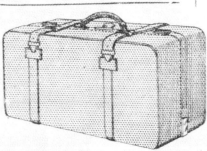

The Gamage G 6.
(2 locks.)
Gladstone.

Specification as above, but stouter hide on a better frame and fitted with 2 good brass locks.

Hand Sewn Throughout.

20 in.	..	**55/-**
22 ,,	..	**60/-**
24 ,,	..	**65/-**
26 ,,	..	**72/6**

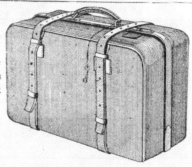

The Gamage G. 3 Gladstone

A most popular bag, being cut wide. Made of brown cowhide, brass lock and 2 clips, 2 good straps all round, brass clips and shoes.

20 in., **25/-**   22 in., **27/6**   24 in., **30/-**   26 in., **32/6**

The Gamage G. 4 Gladstone.

Good quality hide, 2 nickel locks and fitting, straps inside. A real smart bag at a popular price.

20 in.	..	**29/-**
22 ,,	..	**32/6**
24 ,,	..	**35/-**
26 ,,	..	**39/-**

The Gamage G. 7 Gladstone.

This bag represents the highest grade it is possible to put on the market. Best selected hides, high class locks, large pocket inside and finest possible finish throughout.

Two sizes only. — 24 in. .. **102/6**   26 in. .. **110/-**

Folding Portmanteaus.

Brown hide (as illustration), with 8 capped corners, straps all round, D.A. lock.

30 in.	..	**79/6**
33 in.	..	**87/6**
36 in.	..	**95/-**

Superior quality selected hide on "Flaxite," hand-sewn, 8 solid leather capped corners, etc.

30 in. **102/6**   33 in. **132/6**   36 in., **147/6**

Extra good quality Sole leather with cap corners, superior D.A. lock, and finish straps round, etc.

30 in. **140/-**   33 in. **150/-**   36 in. **160/-**

Expanding Top Coat Case.

Solid hide, lever lock, two keys, lined linen, division inside, first class finish throughout.

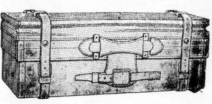

27 in.	30 in.	33 in.
72/6	**79/6**	**89/6**

Do., lined drill, with solid top, first class lock, and best London finish.

27 in. **98/6**   30 in. **115/-**   33 in. **130/-**

Most Convenient for Continental Use.

Compressed Cane and Fibre Suit Cases.

This Popular Compressed Fibre Extension Case

Has completely taken the place of the old-fashioned expanding Basket.

It is just as light, absolutely waterproof, and exceptionally Strong.

SIZES.

14 in. by 10 in. by 5 in.	..	**4/-**
16 in. ,, 11 in. ,, 5 in.	..	**4/9**
18 in. ,, 12 in. ,, 5 in.	..	**5/6**
20 in. ,, 13 in. ,, 5 in.	..	**6/-**
22 in. ,, 14 in. ,, 5 in.	..	**6/9**
24 in. ,, 15 in. ,, 5 in.	..	**7/6**
26 in. .. 16 in. ,, 5 in.	..	**8/6**

The "Edmund" Week-end Case.

Smart Week-end or Blouse Case, made on a 3-ply wood foundation, covered green canvas, 4 leather corners, 2 slide nozzle locks, lined green Moire twill. Light and exceptionally strong.

22 in. **24/-** 24 in. **27/-** 26 in. **30/-**

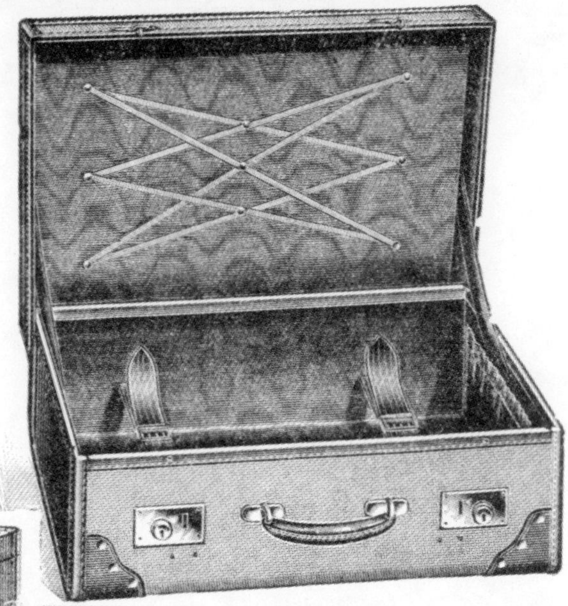

Genuine Fibre Suit Case.

No. K. 31½. Brown in colour. The lightest serviceable case ever produced. 2 good nickel locks, lined smart green drill, 8 fibre corners; absolutely waterproof

16 by 13 by 5	..	**9/6**	22 by 14½ by 6½	**13/6**
18 ,, 13½ ,, 5½	..	**10/9**	24 ,, 15 ,, 7	**14/6**
20 ,, 14 ,, 6	..	**12/-**	26 ,, 15¼ .. 8	**15/6**

No. K. 32. Brown Fibre Case, extra stout, 2 good brass locks, drill lined, 8 hide corners, cut extra deep.

20 by 14½ by 7½	**15/-**	24 by 15½ by 8½	**18/6**
22 by 15 by 8	**16/6**	26 by 16 by 9	**19/6**

No. K. 34. Flaxite Fibre Case, covered with Willesden Canvas, 2 good brass locks, drill lined, stout handle, 8 hide corners.

18 by 14 by 5½	**15/9**	24 by 15½ by 7	**21/-**
20 by 14½ by 6	**17/6**	26 by 16 by 7½	**22/6**
22 by 15 by 6½	**18/9**	28 by 16½ by 8	**25/-**

No. K. 36. Same case as No. K. 34, but cut deeper.

18 by 14 by 7 in.	**21/6**	24 by 15½ by 8½ in.	**29/6**
20 ,, 14½ ,, 7½ ,,	**23/6**	26 ,, 16 ,, 9 ,,	**31/6**
22 ,, 15 ,, 8 ..	**27/6**	28 ,, 16½ ,, 9½ ,,	**33/6**

Brown to order in three days.

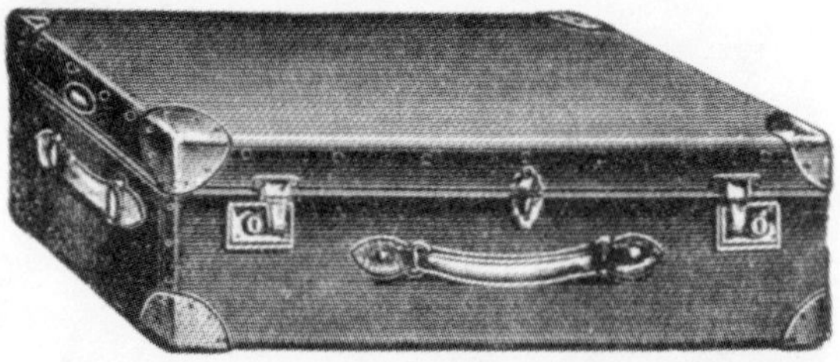

No. K. 42.

Fibre Suit Cases.

Best quality Willesden canvas, on stout Flaxite Fibre, 8 solid hide corners, 3 stout hide handles, visible steel frame, 2 good brass locks and centre clip.

24 by 15 by 8½ in.	..	..	**32/6**
27 by 16 by 9 in.	..	..	**36/-**
30 by 17 by 9½ in.	..	..	**39/6**

No. K. 43.

"Improved" Week-end Travelling Case.

Gamage's

CONTINENTAL TRAVELLING CASES.

Made on a strong 3-ply birch wood foundation, covered brown canvas, brass locks and clips, visible steel frames, lined drill.

LIGHT, STRONG, SMART.

20 by 14½ by 6 in.,	**20/-**	26 by 16½ by 8½ in.,	**26/-**
22 ,, 15½ ,, 6 ,,	**22/-**	28 ,, 17 ,, 8½ ,,	**28/-**
24 ,, 16 ,, 7½ ,,	**24/-**	*30 ,, 17½ ,, 9 ,,	**30/-**

* This case has 2 locks.

No. K. 16B. Week-end Fibre Cases.

For a cheap case this is remarkable value.

Made of genuine fibre, 1 lock and 2 straps, 8 fibre corners, leather handle. Light, Strong, Waterproof.

16in. **4/9** 18in. **5/6** 20in. **6/-** 22in. **6/6** 24in. **7/6**

Made on a light foundation; covered green waterproof canvas, good slide nozzle lock and 2 clips, drill lining, bent wood battens all round which greatly adds to the strength of the case.

20 in. **8/9** 22 in. **9/9** 24 in. **10/9**

26 in. **11/9** 28 in. **12/9**

A smart reliable case at a popular price which has entirely replaced the basket week-end case.

Waterproof, Light and Smart.

ATTACHE CASES.

No. K. 1.

Made of smooth brown hide on a good foundation, two slide nozzle locks, lined leatherine, nickel fittings.

10 x 7 x 2¾	12 x 8 x 3	14 x 9 3½
7/6	**9/6**	**12/6**

16 x 10 x 3½	18 x 11½ x 4
15/6	**16/9**

No. K. 1 quality, 1 in. deeper.

10 in.	12 in.	14 in.	16 in.	18 in.
8/6	**10/6**	**13/6**	**16/6**	**18/6**

No. K. 2.

Better quality, hide Attache, two good slide nozzle locks, nickel fittings, strong handle, lined leather.

12	14	16	18 in.
13/9	**17/6**	**21/6**	**25/6**

Other measurements as above.

No. 2. 1 inch deeper.

15/6	**19/6**	**23/6**	**27/6**

No. K. 3.

Super quality case hide, lined leather, two better locks, well finished.

12	14	16	18 in.
17/6	**20/-**	**23/6**	**27/6**

The "Holborn" Attache Cases.

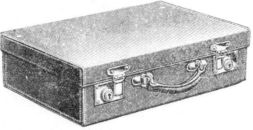

Well selected case hide, on a 3-ply Birch foundation, two nickel slide nozzle locks, well made handle, two patent stays to hold up the lid.

12 in., **18/6**	14 in., **22/6**	16 in., **25/-**
	18 in., **28/6**	

Compressed Fibre Attache Cases.

10 x 7 x 3	12 x 8 x 3½	14 x 9 x 4
3/6	**3/11**	**4/6**

16 x 10 x 4½	8 x 11 x 5
6/6	**6/11**

Leather handle, nickel locks, leather hinge, light and waterproof.
16 in. and 18 in. have 2 locks.

Gamage's "Original" Tennis Attache

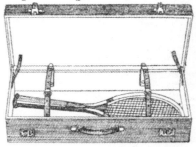

No. K. 1.

Made of good strong brown case hide, linen lined, two good slide nozzle locks, two straps inside for fixing the rackets.

Price **21/9**

No. K. 3.

Made of best selected case hide, hand made throughout, two good brass locks, linen lined, straps inside for rackets.

Price **47/6**

This new "Tennis" Attache has a distinct advantage over the ordinary tennis bag, as it is easier to carry, lighter in weight, and can be used as a week-end case most conveniently. Carriage and initials free.

The "Compartment" Case.

Exceedingly high-class, just the right size to take in the "Compartment." Made of the very finest oak bark tanned case hide, with 8 solid hide corners, 2 bridle leather straps all round, and 1 brass S.N. lock.

26 by 17 by 10 in., **127/6**	28 by 17 by 10 in., **135/-**
30 ,, 17 ,, 10 ,, **145/-**	33 ,, 18 ,, 10 ,, **157/6**

Special Hand Made Attache Case.

Best Quality Hide, lined leather, 2 locks, strong handle, hand-sewn throughout.

14 x 10 x 3½	16 x 10½ x 3½	18½ x 11 x 3½
30/-	**33/-**	**36/-**

20 x 11½ x 4 .. **39/6**

Ditto, ditto, one inch deeper

16 in. .. **36/6**	18 in. .. **39/6**
20 in. .. **43/6**	

Gamage's Week-end Collapsible Top Attache.

No. K. 117.

Made of brown case hide, two nickel locks and fittings, leather handle, visible nickel frame, expanding top, lined leather cloth.

LIGHT. STRONG. NEAT.

14	15	16	17	18	19 in.
23/-	**25/-**	**26/6**	**28/6**	**30/-**	**32/6**

	20	21	22 in.		
	34/-	**35/-**	**37/6**		

Gamage's "Combination" Travelling Case.

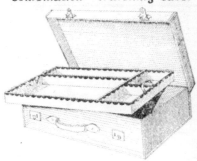

Made of stout case hide on a fibre foundation, two best brass locks, lined superior linen, London steel frame, divided tray for shirts, collars, ties, etc.

Price **107/6**

Gamage's Finest Travelling

Compressed Cane Requisites.

The Gamage Cane Suit Cases.

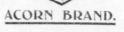

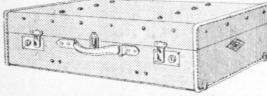

No. A. Made on the finest compressed cane foundation, covered best brown canvas, two best quality brass locks, strong handle, visible steel frame, brass bumpers on the welted ends handsome green striped lining.

Size, 22 by 14½ by 7 in.	.. ..	**35/-**
,, 24 ,, 15 ,, 7½ ,,	.. ..	**37 6**
,, 26 ,, 15½ ,, 7¾ ,,	.. ..	**40/-**
,, 28 by 16 by 8 in.	.. ..	**45/-**
,, 30 ,, 16 ,, 8 ,,	.. ..	**47/6**

VERY SMART, LIGHT, AND STRONG.

The Gamage Shallow Imperial Trunk.

No. F. Gamage's cane trunks are hand sewn throughout, fitted with splendid locks, well protected with battens, and guaranteed to wear for years. No. F. (as illustration) is very popular on account of the shallow shape.

32 x 19½ x 16 in. deep.	34 x 19½ x 16	36 x 20½ x 16
78 6	**85/-**	**97 6**
38 x 20½ x 18	40 x 22 x 18	
107 6	**112 6**	

36, 38, and 40 in. has 4 battens.

LIGHT. SMART. STRONG.

Gamage Cane Cabin Trunks.

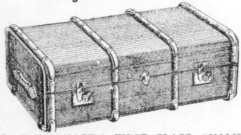

No. G. GAMAGE'S FIRST CLASS QUALITY Cabin Trunks have broken the record for world trotting. They are so compact, yet light.

28 x 20 x 14 in. high	30 x 20 x 14	32 x 20 x 14
62 6	**67 6**	**72 6**
34 x 20½ x 14	36 x 20½ x 14	38 x 20½ x 14
77 6	**85/-**	**95/-**
	40 x 20½ x 14 .. **102 6**	

34, 36, 38, 40 in. have Four Battens.

THE STRONGEST TRUNK IN THE WORLD.

ACORN BRAND.

As strong as an Oak.

Gent's Cane Hat Box.

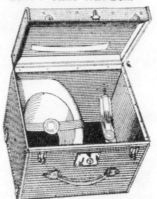

No. C.
To hold Silk, Bowler, Opera, Straw Hat and Cap.
An ideal travelling companion.
Price .. **42/6**

Lady's ane Hat Box.

No. D.
Highest grade finish and style, removable cover for fixing hats, good lock and two clips. The most handsome hat box ever produced.

20 in. ..	**57 6**	24 in. ..	**72 6**
22 in. ..	**66 -**	26 in. ..	**78/6**

Made to take Six Hats.

Cane Compartment Case.

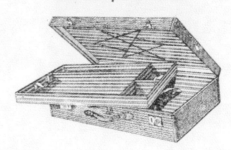

No. B.
Specification as No. A., but fitted with a strong useful tray, divided for ties, shirts, collars, etc. An ideal continental case.

26 in.	..	..	..	**58/6**
28 in.	..	..	..	**62 6**
30 in.	..	..	..	**65/-**

Gamage Cane Deep Imperial Trunks.

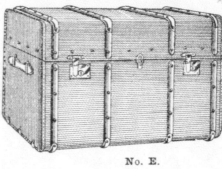

No. E.

Fully recognised as the strongest trunk in the world.

Highest class cane foundations, four strong hoops all round.

Two extra good locks, edges of trunk bound with raw hide.

Foundation covered with good brown canvas.

30 x 18¾ x 19 in.	..	**87/6**
32 x 19½ x 20	..	**92 6**
24 x 20½ x 21	..	**97/6**
36 x 21½ x 21½	..	**112/6**
38 x 23 x 23	..	**118/-**
40 x 23 x 24	..	**126/-**
42 x 23 x 24	..	**139 6**
44 x 23 x 24	..	**142/6**

34, 36, and 38 in. have 4 Battens.

40, 42, and 44 in. have 5 Battens.

36 size and upwards have 2 Trays.

Deep and Shallow Imperial Trunks.

No. K. 60. **Genuine "Flaxite" Fibre Imperial.**

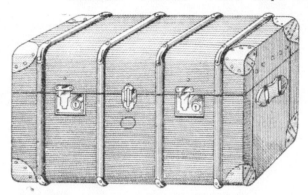

Covered best quality green canvas, visible steel frame, 2 good brass locks, centre clips, 8 solid hide corners, 1 tray inside and lined drill. One of the lightest and strongest trunks in the world.

Sizes : 30 by 19 by 16 in., **54/-** 33 by 20 by 17 in. **59/6**
36 by 21 by 18in. **65/-** 39 by 22 by 19in. **69/6** 42 by 23 by 20in. **75/-**
Sizes 36, 39 and 42 have four battens and two locks.

No. K. 32. **3-Ply Wood Deep Imperial.**

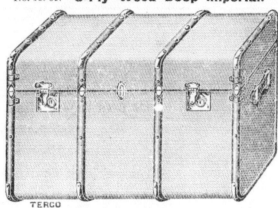

TERCO

Lever Locks.

A thorough good strong trunk at a reasonable price. Made on a strong 3-Ply wood foundation, covered brown canvas. Visible steel frame good slide, nozzle locks, 1 tray, leather handles.

27 in.	30 in.	33 in.	36 in.	38 in.	40 in.	42 in.	44 in.
32/6	**35/-**	**37/6**	**40/-**	**42/6**	**45/-**	**47/6**	**50/-**

36 in upwards have two locks and four battens. Green canvas to order in three days.

No. K. 1. **Compressed Cane Deep Imperial.**

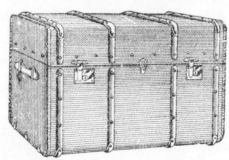

The Original "**Stork Brand**" Compressed Cane Trunk. Covered brown canvas, 2 slide muzzle locks, visible steel frame, good strong hoops all round, lined drill, welted with hide. 28 to 32 in. have 2 battens, 1 lock, 1 tray and collapsible division. 34 inches have 3 battens, and 36 to 38 in. 4 battens and 2 trays. 40 to 42 in., 5 battens.

Length	28 in.	30 in.	32 in.	34 in.	36 in.	38 in.	40 in.	42 in.
Width	17¾in.	18¾in.	19½in.	20½in.	21½in.	23 in.	23 in.	23 in.
Depth	18¼in.	19 in.	20 in.	21 in.	21½in.	23 in.	24 in.	24 in.
Price	**65/-**	**68/6**	**72/-**	**77/-**	**88/-**	**96/-**	**104/-**	**112/-**

No. K. 3.
Compressed Cane, Shallow Imperial Trunk.

The Original "**Stork Brand**" Compressed Cane Trunk.

Specification as K. No. 1.

Welted with Leather. 32 in. has two battens; 34 in., three; 36 in. four, 38 to 42 in. have four battens and two locks; 44 in. has five battens.

Length	32 in.	34 in.	36 in.	38 in.	40 in.	42 in.	44 in.
Width	19½ ,,	19½ ,,	20½ ,,	20½ ,,	22 ,,	22 ,,	22 ,,
Depth	16 ,,	16 ,,	18 ,,	18 ,,	19 ,,	19 ,,	19 ,,
Weight	24 lb.	26 lb.	28 lb.	31 lb.	34 lb.	37 lb.	40 lb.
Price	**64/-**	**68/-**	**76/-**	**84/-**	**88/-**	**92/-**	**96/-**

No. K. 33. **3-Ply Wood Shallow Imperial.**

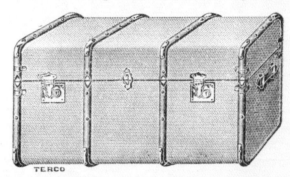

TERCO

Made of best 3 ply birch wood, covered with a good brown canvas, visible steel frame, 2 brass slide nozzle locks, centre clips, 1 tray, lined linen. 36 in and upwards have 4 battons and 2 locks.

27 in.	30 in.	33 in.	36 in.	38 in.	40 in.	42 in.	44 in.
29/6	**32/6**	**35/-**	**37/6**	**40/-**	**42/6**	**45/-**	**47/6**

Gamages Oval Tops 3-Ply Birch Wood Trunks.

No. K. 34. Strong oval top 3-ply birch wood trunk, covered brown canvas, hoops all round, good locks, 1 tray, drill lined, leather handles.

Size 30 in **2** 33 in. **32/6** 36 in. **35/-**

Wood Trunks for use all over the World.

The International Oval Trunk.

No. K. 50. Exceptional Good Value, made of well seasoned wood foundation, covered strong brown canvas, good drop back lock, 2 strong clips, well protected with wood battens and strongly bound with strip iron, 2 leather handles, iron bottom underneath. An Ideal Trunk for the Colonies.

28 by 18¼ by 20in., **20/6** 30 by 17¾ by 20, **22/-** 32 by 18½ by 21, **23/6** 34 by 19¼ by 22, **25/-** 36 by 20 by 22, **26/6**

No. K. 51. Same style as K. 50, but superior quality throughout, lined linen, better lock, covered Willesdon canvas, first class fittings.

28in., **26/-** 30in., **28/-** 32in., **30/-** 34in., **31/6** 36in., **33/-**

The International Trunk. For the hold or general travel.

No. K. 52. Specification and design as K. 50 but with a flat top, lined paper

28 by 18 by 18, **18/9** 30 by 18½ by 18½, **20/6** 32 by 18½ by 19¼, **22/-** 34 by 19¼ by 20, **23/6** 36 by 19¼ by 20, **25/-**

No. K. 53. Specification and design as K. 51, but with a flat top.

Superior quality throughout best quality locks and fittings, covered green Willesden canvas and linen lined.

in.	
30	**27/6**
32	**28/6**
34	**30/-**
35	**31/6**

Wood Trunk.

No. K. 23. For Home or Colonial Use.

 Made of Well Seasoned Wood.

Covered brown waterproof canvas, 1 tray, lined paper, good lock and 2 clips, tin lining underneath, well battened and bound with strip iron.

A Strong Trunk at a Reasonable Price.

26 in., **13/6** 28 in., **14/6** 30 in., **15/6** 32 in., **16/6** 34 in. **18/6** 36 in., **20/-**

Carriage forward.

"The Canadian Traveller."

Gamage's No. M Travelling Trunk, made on a 3-ply best birch foundation covered good brown canvas, brass bumpers, well protected by wooden battens, good lock and clips. A Reliable Trunk to take Abroad.

30 by 19 by 19, **34/-** 32 by 20 by 20, **36/-** 34 by 21 by 21, **38/-** 36 by 22 by 22, **40/-** 38 by 23 by 23, **44/-** 40 by 24 by 24, **48/-**

Popular Travellers at a Popular Price.

Gamage's 'Empire" Wood Cabin Trunks.

No. K. 1. Made of well selected wood, covered brown canvas, lined paper, good lock and 2 clips, tin lined underneath, well bound with strip iron, 1 tray, rollers underneath.

28 in. **12/6** 30 in. **13/9** 32 in. **15/6** 34 in. **16/6** 36 in. long **17/6**

No. K. 2. Selected wood, covered leather, iron bottom, rollers, good lock and 2 clips.

30 in., **18/6** 32 in., **21/6** 34 in., **22/6** 36 in. **25/-**

No K. 3 w. Selected wood covered with Willesden Convas, protected all over with hard wood battens, specially strong lock, clips and furniture.

30 in., **23/6** 32 in., **25/-** 34 in. **27/-** 36 in., **29/-**

Gamage's Drawer Cabin Trunk.

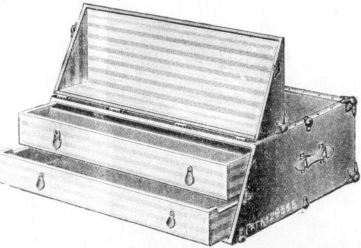

New 1914 pattern. Covered good brown painted canvas, on a best 4-ply wood foundation, lift up front, good locks, 2 pull out drawers, drill lined, trunk well protected with brass bumpers and wood battens.

Size 36 by 22 by 14 in. Gamage's price **39/6**

Oval Top Fibre and Wicker Dress Baskets.

Compressed Fibre Ladies' Dress Trunk.

No. K.46.

Foundation made of real "Flaxite" Fibre, covered best Willesden canvas (green), visible steel frame, slide nozzle lock, 4 solid hide corners, straps over lid, lined drill and fitted with a tray; 2 battens on bottom, complete with rollers. Light and very strong. 30 by 18 by 21 in. .. **45**/- 33 by 19 by 22 in., **47/6** 36 by 20 by 23 in., **55**/- 39 by 21 by 24 in., **59/6**

Ladies' Dress Trunk.

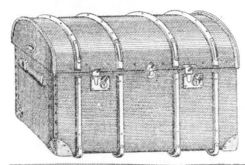

No. K. 66. "Flaxite" Fibre, covered Green Willesden Canvas (or Brown to order), Steel Frame, 8 heavy corners, lever lock, battens all round, fitted with tray and linen lined. 30 in. by 18 in. by 21 in., **54**/- 33 by 19 by 22. **59/6** 36 by 20 by 23, **65**/- 39 by 21 by 24, **69/6**

Compressed Cane Lady's Dress Trunk. (Original Patent.

Welted with Leather. 32 to 36 in., have one lever lock, straps all round and one tray.

38 to 44 in., have two locks and two trays.

42 and 44 in. to order only.

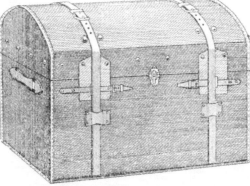

Length	32 in.	34 in.	36 in.	38 in.	40 in.	42 in.	44 in.
Width	19½ ,,	20½ ,,	21½ ,,	22½ ,,	23¼ ,,	23¼ ,,	23¼ ,,
Depth	22 ,,	22½ ,,	24½ ,,	26 ,,	26 ,,	26 ,,	26 ,,
Weight	29 lb.	32 lb.	35 lb.	39 lb.	42 lb.	47 lb.	50 lb.
Price ..	60/9	65/-	73/9	78/-	91/-	95/6	104/-

Ladies' Dress Basket.

No. K. 0. Close Wicker, covered black jappanned canvas, short straps, tray and leather handles.

Length	24 in.,	**18**/-
,,	27 in.,	**20**/-
,,	30 in.,	**22**/-
,,	33 in.,	**24**/-
,,	36 in.,	**26**/-

Ladies' Dress Baskets.

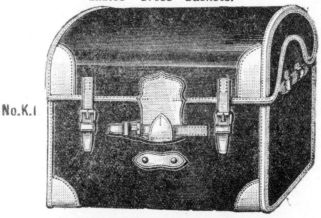

No. K.1

Gamage's Reliable Dress Baskets are made on a close wicker foundations Covered black canvas; 2 short straps in front, flap over lock, 8 hide corners, 1 tray, leather handles, good lock with leather flap, 2 battens underneath, with rollers. Lined drill.

24 in.	27 in.	30 in.	33 in.	36 in.
21/-	**24**/-	**26**/-	**29**/-	**32**/-

No. K.2

All close wicker, covered black twill canvas, 8 solid corners, stout straps all round, hide welting, lock flap, etc., lined linen, and fitted with tray. 27 in., **32**/- 30 in., **35**/- 33 in., **38**/- 36 in., **42**/-

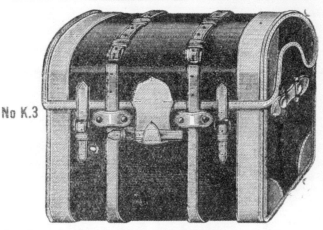

No K.3

Superior quality Dress Basket, covered best black flax canvas, hide corners, heavily welted with a wide hide binding; good slide nozzle lock, 2 good straps all round, well battened, with rollers; best plain drill lining; 1 divided tray, 2 good hide handles.

30 in. .. **42**/- 33 in. .. **45**/- 36 in. .. **50**/-

BEST QUALITY STEEL TRUNKS.

The Deep "Khartoum."

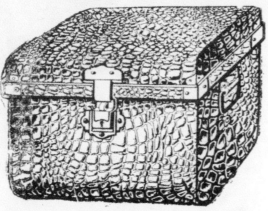

Made of Steel Plates rolled into the very form of Crocodile Hide, making the plates very rigid, and adding immensely to the strength of the trunk without in any way increasing the weight. Japanned Oak.

26 by 16½ by 15½ in.	28 by 18½ by 16½ in.	30 by 20½ by 18¾ in.
12 6	**14/9**	**17/6**

The Patent "Leamington" Steel Trunk.

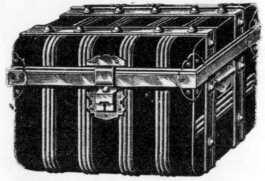

Constructed of Best 24-gauge Steel throughout, fitted with Patent Lever Lock and Duplicate Flat Keys. Protected by Steel Bands all round. Steel Lid Stay and Corner Clips. Japanned Walnut.

26 by 16½ by 15½ in.	28 by 18½ by 16¼ in.	30 by 20½ by 18¼ in.
13 9	**16/6**	**18/6**

The Improved "Atlas" Steel Cabin Trunk.

Made of 24-gauge Steel, fitted with Brass Lever Lock and Duplicate N.P. Keys. Protected by Deep Swages and Steel Corner Clips. Riveted Steel Hinges and Patent Lid Stays. Japanned Grained Oak and Chocolate.

27 by 16 by 9½ in. ..	**11/6**	30 by 18 by 10¾ in. ..	**13/9**
33 by 20 by 12¾ in. ..	**16 6**	36 by 22½ by 14¾ in. ..	**21/6**

The Patent "York" Steel Trunk.

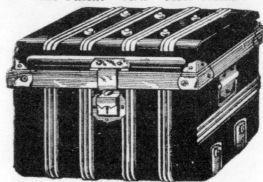

Made of 24-gauge Steel throughout, with Cast Hasp, Brass Lock and Body protected by Steel Mouldings, and Corners, Steel Rivetted Hinges and Strapped the whole length of bottom. Jappanned Oak and Chocolate.

26 by 16½ by 15½ in.	28 by 18½ by 16¾ in.	30 by 20½ by 18¾ in.
9/9	**11/6**	**13 6**

The Improved "Dunbovne" Steel Trunk.

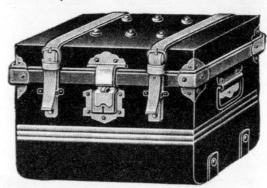

Made throughout of best 24-gauge Steel, Patent Corrugated Steel Block Steel Pockets, heavily Strapped full length of bottom, Rivetted Steel Hinges, with Heavy Leather Straps, Wide Cast Hasp Brass Lock and Duplicate N.P. Flat Keys. Japanned Black.

26 by 16½ by 15 in.	28 by 18½ by 16¼ in.	30 by 20½ by 18¼ in.
15/6	**16/6**	**19/6**

The "Khartoum" Steel Cabin Trunk.

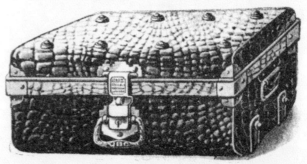

Made of Best Steel Plates and rolled into the very form of Crocodile Hide, which adds immensely to the strength of the trunk. Fitted with Brass Lever Lock and Duplicate Flat N.P. Keys.

27 by 16 by 9½ in. ..	**12/6**	30 by 18 by 10¾ in. ..	**15/6**
33 by 20 by 12¾ in. ..	**17/6**	36 by 22½ by 14¾ in. ..	**22/6**

G 2

RELIABLE STEEL CABIN TRUNKS AND UNIFORM CASES.

The Patent Steel "Traveller" Cabin Trunk.

Made of best steel, fitted with brass lever lock and packing flat, N.P. keys. lid protected by wood bands and steel corner clips, body protected by riveted clips. Japanned grained oak and chocolate.

Long	27	..	30	..	33	..	36 in.
Wide	16	..	18	..	20	..	22½ ,,
Deep	9½	..	10¾	..	12¾	..	14¾ ,,
Price	**13 6**		**16 6**		**19 6**		**28 6**

The New "Orient" Steel Cabin Trunk.

Made of best steel, fitted with patent 3 lever lock and duplicate nickel plated keys. Protected on lid by patent steel wood bands. Body fitted with patent steel wood bands and rollers. Japanned Ebonite.

Length to nest.	Width outside.	Depth outside.	Price.
27 in.	16 in.	8¾ in.	**21/6**
30 ,,	18 ,,	10½ ,,	**25 6**
33 .,	20 ,,	12½ ,,	**29 6**
36 .	22½ ,,	14¾ ,,	**32/6**

The "War Office" Steel Cabin Trunk.

High Grade Trunk Class A. Specially manufactured for travelling in the Colonies, whether by ship, Rail, Mule, or Camel. Japanned black & scarlet bands.

Long	..	27	..	30	..	33	..	36 in.
Wide	..	16	..	18	..	20	..	22½ ,,
Deep	..	8¾	..	10½	..	12½	..	14¾ ,,
Price		**27/6**		**33 6**		**37/6**		**47/6**

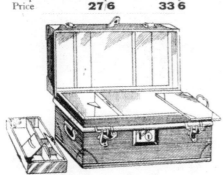

The "Shackleton"

Air-tight Uniform Case and Despatch Boxes.

Size inside, 25 by 16 by 10½ in.

With hardwood bottom, patent clips, and eight extra steel corner plates. Documents and cash tray to lock up separately.

Price .. **55/-**

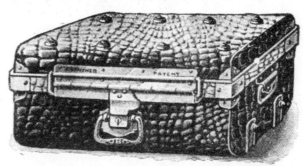

The Patent "Rhandolf" Cabin Trunk.

Made of the Best Steel, rolled into the form of Crocodile Hide, making the plates very rigid, and adding immensely to the strength of the Trunk without in any way increasing the weight. Japanned oak.

28 in. by 16½ in. by 10½ in., **17/6**		30 in. by 18½ in. by 11 in., **20/-**
33 in. by 20 in. by 12 in., **22/6**		36 in. by 22 in. by 13½ in., **26/-**

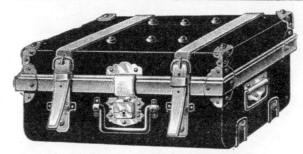

The "Adjutant" Steel Cabin Trunk..

24 gauge steel plates, japanned ebonite strongly clipped. corners well protected strong hide straps, brass lock and flat H.P. keys.

Long	27	..	30	..	34	..	36 in.
Wide	16	..	18	..	20	..	22½ ,,
Deep	8¾	..	10½	..	12½	..	14¾ ,,
Price	**19/6**		**22/6**		**25 6**		**35/-**

The "Emperor of India" Cabin Trunk.

This splendid Trunk enjoys a well deserved reputation in India and can be highly recommended for good and hard wear. Japanned dark green, with nickel lock and two keys.

27 by 17 by 10 in. **17/6** 30 by 18 by 11 in. **21/6** 33 by 20 by 13 in. **26/6**

The Army "Regulation" Sword and Helmet Case.

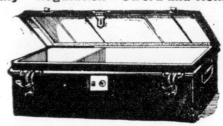

Made of best steel plates, japanned black, good lock and two clips, sliding division for helmet, rings to take web for sword and clothes, absolutely air-tight and insect proof. Used by Officers and Travellers all over the world

Size 43 by 14 by 9 inches **47/6**

Deed and Despatch Boxes.

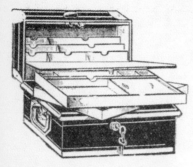

The "Clement" Despatch Box.

Best steel, japanned polished ebonite and fillet, best 3-lever Lock, two Trays and lock-up Cash Box.

Size	14	16	18 in.
Price	**37/6**	**40/-**	**45/-**

Despatch Boxes.
No. D B 11.

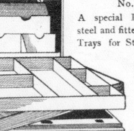

A special Line of very best steel and fitted with two divided Trays for Stationery, &c., with Rack in Lid fitted with Patent Triple Lock and Two Keys.

14 in. ..	**33/6**
16 in. ..	**37/6**
18 in. ..	**39/6**

Japanned polished Ebonite and Gold.

No. D B 26.

This is a specially cheap line. Made of strong steel, fitted with stationery rack in lid with hinged flap. The tray is divided, and has lock-up recess for money, &c., with patent triple lock by which the box is secured in three places by one turn of the key.

14 in. ..	**26/6**
16 in. ..	**30/-**
18 in. ..	**33/6**

Japanned polished Ebonite and Gold.

The "Bombay." No. D. B. 80.

Fitted with Tray with Partitions for pens, penholders, inks, stationery and ruler, with Brass Lever Lock and Duplicate Keys, and Strong Leather Strap all round.

14 in. ..	**19/6**
16 in. ..	**22/6**
18 in. ..	**27/6**

Japanned Polished Ebonite and Gold.

Safety Deed or Cash Box, fitted with Lock, fixed permanently to desk or counter, receives the cash box each day and locks on to the bottom when key locks the lid. It is then impossible to remove it. The boxes are pressed in one piece out of steel plates, and are fitted with double bolt four-lever locks and two keys.

No. K. 3. 8 by 6 by 3½ in.
24/-
No. K. 4. 9½ by 7 by 4 in.
26/-
No. K. 5. 12 by 8 by 4½ in.
30/-

B K. 11010.

Masonic Regalia Air-tight Case.

Made of BEST STEEL, with leather fitted round top to keep air-tight, japanned outside, polished ebonite and inside a nice light colour, polished brass lever lock, two brass bolts, and brass name-plate on top.

Size 18½ by 10½ by 2⅜ in.
Price **14/6** each

"C. O." Best Steel Air tight Despatch Box.

Size 18 in. long by 13 in. wide by 6 in. deep, with two patent Holdfast Clips and Combination Lever Locks. Two Trays, the top one fitted with divisions for pens and inks and with separate lock-up compartments for money drafts, etc.
Price **49/6**

Date Case.

No. K. 5.

3½ in. ..	**1/3**
4½ in. ..	**1/6**
5½ in. ..	**2/-**
8½ in. bank size	**3/6**

Postage 2d. and 4d.

The Mail Letter Cage.

Strong Steel Case, japanned black, and gilt lettered and lined.
Price .. **2/-**

The Regd. Handy Set of Cash Drawers or Jewel Case.

No. K. 1. Japanned Black. Complete with cards & drawer.
Price .. **5/6**

B K. 11006.

This set of Cash Drawer is designed to meet a long felt want in all countries where a silver currency predominates. The ordinary Cash Box is too small to hold the cash which a business man must of necessity have by him. The bottom of the gold and silver drawers are **rounded to facilitate the removal of the coin**, thus preventing the nuisance of the small coin sticking in the corners and defying removal; there is a place for a Bank Book.

It can be used as a Jewel Case.

Fitted with a good brass lock and duplicate keys, nicely japanned and polished black, with neat fillet.

B 11006. No. 1. 9 by 7 by 5 in. Price **21/-** each
No. 2. 10 by 8 by 5½ in. Price **27/6** each

The "Superbe."

The Latest Designed Landau Carriage for one or two children.

DESCRIPTION.

Body—Coach-built, roomy and comfortable. Deep convex sides conceal well. Panels on sides formed by raised mouldings. Measurements: Top (outside), 41 in. by 19 in. ; seat level (inside), 31 in. by 15 in.

Springs—Best quality Steel Strap Cee, fitted with strong leather suspension and steadying strap, electro-plated levers of oval iron, patent balancing axle, unbreakable steel axles, extended celluloid cross-handle.

Upholstering—Superior Sanitary Leather Cloth, loose cushions, piped arms, carpeted foot-well, divided well cover, over-end apron of black Gamsoo non-crackable rubber cloth, one registered Safety waist strap (cloth-lined),

Hood—Reversible, Steel-framed (padded rims), black non-crackable rubber cloth covering, and wool cashmere lining, edged round with deep frilling lace. Electro-plated lever adjustable joints.

Wheels—Ball-bearing (electro-plated) Hubs, tangent spokes, full $\frac{7}{8}$ in. Best Grey rubber wired-on tyres, 23 in. and 18 in. diam. Guaranteed for one year.

Stock Colours—Dark Green Paintwork with suede grey interior (as illustration) or Dark Blue throughout. (Other colours in about eight days.)

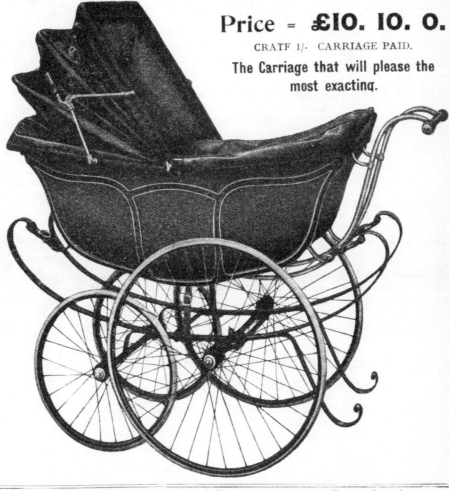

Price = £10. 10. 0.

CRATE 1/- CARRIAGE PAID.

The Carriage that will please the most exacting.

For full range, Accessories, and Special Notes on Baby Carriages, see Special 72 page Booklet Post free.

The "Marmet"
BABY CARRIAGE.

The Greatest Invention of the day in Baby Carriage Construction.

A TUBULAR & BOLTLESS FRAME.

Body—High grade, of three-ply Timber, extra large ; deep sides and high backs. Measurements: Top (outside), $40\frac{1}{2}$ in. by 18 in. ; seat level (inside), 31 in. by 13 in.

Springs—Patent Tubular Undercarriage (no bolts used), very light and strong. Body suspended by eight coil springs.

Upholstering—Superior Sanitary Leather Cloth, piped arms, loose cushions, well cover and one wide registered Safety waist strap (cloth-lined). Long (over-end non-crack) Apron 10/6.

Stock Colours—Dark Blue Paintwork with suede grey interior (as illustrated), or Dark Green throughout. (Other colours in about ten days.)

Wheels—Ball-bearing (Plated) Hubs, tangent spokes, $1\frac{3}{4}$ in. White rubber wired-on tyres. Guaranteed for one year.

Hood Joints—Lever adjustable pattern. All brasswork plated.

Hood—Covered in black Gamsoo non-crackable rubber cloth, reversible.

COMPLETE with Gamsoo Non-crackable Hood and Apron, and Tangent Spokes, Ball-bearing Wheels.

Price = £9. 9. 0.

CRATE, 1/- CARRIAGE PAID.

The "Burlington."

Landau Carriage.

DESCRIPTION.

Body.—Canoe-shaped, of Selected Three-ply Timber, light and strong, Bent Panel Ends. Measurements: Top (outside), 36 in. by 17 in.; seat level (inside), 26 in. by 12½ in. Deep sides, Concealed Well.

Springs.—Cee-shaped, Steel, Leather Suspension and Steadying Straps. Oval-handle Levers. Polished Wood Cross Handle.

Upholstering.—Sanitary Leather Cloth, Fixed Cushions, Well Cover, and one Registered Safety Waist Strap. Long (over-end) Apron (as illustration).

Hood.—Reversible, Steel Framed, Leather Cloth Covering, and Colour-fast Lining. Adjustable Brass Joints, by means of which the Hood can be kept open at various positions.

Wheels.—23 in. and 16 in. diameter, with ½ in. Wired-on Rubber Tyres.

Stock Colours.—Dark Blue, Dark Green. Other Colours in about seven days.

Price ... **£3 3 0**

Crate 1/-   Carriage paid.

EXTRAS.

Ball-bearing Wheels, Wired-on Tyres, Direct Spokes, **16/6**

SUITABLE FOR ONE OR TWO CHILDREN.

THE "NEWMARKET"

Landau for one or two Children.

'B' GRADE as illustration.

DESCRIPTION

Body.—Canoe-shaped, of Selected Three-ply Timber, Bent Panel Ends, Bevelled Moulding Design on Sides, Concealed Well, Deep Sides. Measurements: Top (outside), 36 by 17 in.; seat level (inside), 27 by 13 in.

Springs.—Steel Strap Cee with Strong Suspension and Steadying Straps. Fitted with Patent Levers which can be instantly adjusted to various heights or folded under carriage. Celluloid Cross Handle.

Upholstering.—Sanitary Leather Cloth, Piped Arms, Loose Cushions, Well Cover and one Registered Safety Waist Strap. Short (centre) Apron, 2/- extra; Long (Over-end) Apron, 4/6 extra.

Hood.—Reversible, Steel-framed, neatly Lined with Colour-fast Cloth, and fitted with Adjustable Brass Joints, by means of which the Hood can be kept open at various positions.

Wheels.—23 by 16 in. diameter, with ½ in. Best Grey Rubber Wired-on Tyres. Guaranteed for one year.

Stock Colours.—Dark Blue Paint-work with Grey Interior (*as illus.*), or Dark Green throughout. (Other Colours in about eight days.)

Price .. **£3 12 6**

Crate 1/-   Carriage paid.

A' GRADE, as 'B' Grade except—

Wheels.—Ball-Bearing (plated) Hubs, Tangent Spokes, and ⅝ in. special quality Wired-on Tyres, Guaranteed for one year.

Hood.—Black Non-cracking Rubber Cloth Hood Covering, Joints and other Brasswork Plated.

Price .. **£5 15 0**

Crate 1/-   Carriage Paid.

The "Wonder"
Landau Carriage
The Most Wonderful Value ever offered.

THE "WONDER"
DEFIES COMPETITION.

DESCRIPTION

Body—Of three-ply timber, with sides deep enough to conceal well. Measurements: Top (outside), 35 in. by 16 in.; Seat level (inside), 26 in. by 12 in.

Springs—Steel Strap Cee, curved to follow shape of body fitted with strong Leather Suspension and Steadying Straps. Extended Wood Handle.

Upholstering—Crockett's Leather Cloth, fixed Cushions, Well Cover and Waist Straps. Short (centre) Apron, 1/6 extra; Long (over-end) Apron, 4/6 extra.

Hood—Reversible, neatly lined with colour-fast Cloth and fitted with Brass Joints.

Wheels—Good ½ in. Grey Rubber Wired-on Tyres, 23 in. and 16 in. diameter.

Stock Colours—Dark Green or Dark Blue (other colours in about seven days).

   Price **£2 2 0**   Crate 1/-   Carriage Paid.

Can be supplied to order only with Cemented Tyres, **39/6**

   The above Carriage is also supplied in a better quality with loose Cushions, fitted Registered Safety Waist Strap and superior finish throughout.

   Price **£2 15 0**   Crate 1/-   Carriage Paid.

The "New Sterling"
Landau Carriage. with Patent Folding Levers.

DESCRIPTION.

Body—Convex-shaped sides, cane beaded. Measurements: Top (outside) 35 in. by 17 in.; seat level (inside), 26¾ in. by 13 in.

Springs—Reliable Steel Cee with Strong Suspension and Steadying Straps, fitted with Registered Folding Levers. Handle is perfectly rigid when in use, and effects a great saving of house room when folded.

Upholstering—Sanitary Leather Cloth, Fixed Cushions, Well Cover, and one Registered Safety Waist Strap. Short (centre) Apron, 1/9 extra; Long (overend) Apron, 4/- extra.

Hood—Reversible Steel-framed, neatly lined with Colour-fast Cloth, and fitted with Adjustable Brass Joints, by means of which the Hood can be kept open at various positions.

Wheels—23 in. and 16 in. diameter by ½-in. Special Quality Wired-on Tyres.

Stock Colour—Paintwork: Dark Green with Black Vertical Stripes, with interior in Grey (as illustrated).

   (Other Colours in about eight days).

   Price **£3 5 0**

   Crate 1/-   Carriage paid.

   EXTRAS to order only.   Time required about seven days.

Direct Spoke Ball Bearing Wheels with 9/16 in. Wired-on Tyres, **16/6** extra.

   A New design invaluable for those living in flats.

For Full Range and Special Notes see Baby Carriage List post free on application.

— THE —
"CLOVELLY"
Cane Carette.

THE "SOUTHWOLD."
Cane Carette.

Description.

Reedwork painted Cream, Strap-hung Springs, upholstered throughout, Reclining Back and Hood, Waist Strap.

Wheels - 14 in. and 10 in. by ½ in.

Stock Colour—Reedwork Cream, Upholstering and Hood, Art Green

Price—

£2 5 6

Crate 1/-

Carriage paid.

Description.
For one child to sit up.

Body—Pretty design in Raffia Cane, Swelled Reed Sides.
Springs—Steel Cee Strap Suspension.
Upholstering—Sanitary Leather Cloth, if fitted with Waterproof Apron, **4/6** extra.
Wheels—12 in. by 10 in. by ½ in. Wired-on Tyres.
Stock Colours—Cane-work painted Cream, Upholstery Dark Blue or Green

PRICE **£2 15 6**   Crate 1/-

— THE —
"EMPRESS"
Cane Carette.

THE —
"CHERTSEY"
Cane Carette.

Price—

£2 10 0

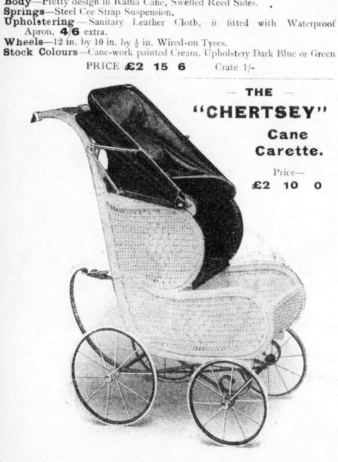

Description.
Smart new design, Cane Carette.

Dainty yet Strong, Enamelled Cream, Upholstered in Dark Blue or Dark Green Sanitary Leather Cloth. Detachable Hood of same material with Brass joints. Cee Strap Suspension Springs, 12 by 10 by ½ in. Wired-on Tyred Wheels. Crate 1/-

Description.

Body.—New Design in Raffia Cane, with Bulged Panels, Enamelled Cream, Dark Blue or Dark Green. Upholsterings to match. A good roomy Car.
Springs.—Mounted on Steel Cee Strap Springs, with Wired-on Tyred Wheels.
Hood.—Complete with Hood and Apron, Strong, Light, Handsome and comfortable.

Price ..   .. **£2 11 6**   Crate 1/-

For Canopies and parts see Special 72 page Booklet, post free on application.

The New "Swan" Collapsible Gamcah.

The most Comfortable Draught-proof Folding Car made.

The New 'Swan' Folding Car.

Improved and Beautified.

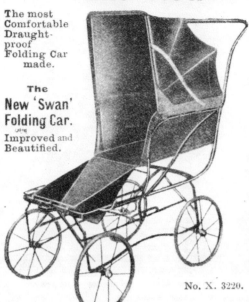

No. X. 3220.

A four-position Car—Sitting, Reclining & Bed position.

Framework—All Steel with our new double strut gear, which is improved on last year's model, simpler and stronger. Tubular handle. Enamelled black and fine lined bronze. Upholstered in strong leather cloth, and so constructed that it is also draught-proof. **The Seat** when in bed position is perfectly flat, and has a length about 30 in. Large detachable hood, lined colour-fast material. Long lined apron. **Wheels**—10 in. with ½ in. tyres. **Stock Colours**—Dark Green and Dark Blue.

British Made Throughout.

No. X. 3220 .. .. price **35 6** Packing 1/-

The "Swan" Gamcah with a man and three children in it, the wheels do NOT spread.

Ball-bearing Wheels can be fitted to any of these Models.

Direct Spokes, **12/9** extra.
Tangent Spokes, **27/6** extra.

No. X. 3225. Fitted with Self-compensating Automatic Springs, which enable the Car to be pushed over rough roads with ease, and the child is free from any vibration. Each wheel is sprung separately, and the Car is self-rising over low kerbs. We strongly recommend this spring. **Wheels**—12 in. and 8 in. with ½ in. wired-on tyres. Otherwise as **No. X. 3220.**

No. X. 3225 .. price **45/-** Packing 1/-

Note how the Car with all the comforts still folds perfectly flat.

All the above 1/- extra for packing, but sent Carriage paid.

The "Swan" Gamcah

The Car with the X Strut.

Made like a Motor Car.

Strong Wheel Base.
Absolute Comfort.

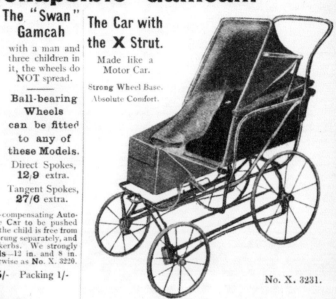

No. X. 3231.

No. X. 3231.—A four-position Car, similar to No. X. 3225, but with nickel-plated tubular handle, joints and foot-gear. Upholstered in superior leather duck. **Wheels**—14 in. and 10 in. with ½ in. wired-on tyres. **Stock Colours** - Framework black enamel, fine lined in gold. Upholstering and hood dark green or dark blue. No. X. 3231 price **55/6** Packing 1/-

No. X. 3236.—Similar to No. 3231, but the framework nickel-plated throughout except the wheel rims, if these are plated the cost is **7/-** extra.

No. X. 3236 .. .. price **75/-**

The New GAMCAH, which enables the person who is wheeling it to see the Child in the Car.

No. X. 3241.

Tubular handle, fine lined bronze. Upholstered in strong leather cloth. "Hemco" body and detachable hood, lined apron. **Wheels**—10 in. with ½ in. wired-on tyres.

No. X. 4241 .. price **39/6** Packing 1/- Carriage paid.

No. X. 3246. A three-position Vis-à-vis Folder, as specified above, but fitted with our remarkable Spring, as described with car No. X. 3225. These springs have now large diameter coil spring, which gives a wonderful resilience and strength.

Wheels—12 in. and 8 in. with ½ in. wired-on tyres. Price **45/6** Packing 1/-

Note how compact the Vis-a-vis is when folded. 👉
The Car that has come to stay.
Invaluable for the Holidays.
omfort, Strength and Utility combined.

No. X. 3421. This is a four-position Vis-à-vis Folder, as illustrated. Made on the same lines as our other folders, but giving the advantage that the child can be seen and amused by the person in charge of the car. The child faces the handle. The wheels are kept in position with our Patent Struts, which is the strongest method known for this class of work. The Cars are built up on scientific principles, and the "Swan" Folders are the only ones with this new method.

X. 3251.

A vis-à-vis four position folder.

Framework— All steel, with Patent Struts. Nickel-plated tubular handle, joints and foot gear. Upholstered in superior leather duck. "Hemco" seat, which is constructed to provide a 30-in. draught-proof bed. Detachable steel frame hood in leather duck and colour-fast lining. Long lined apron. Each wheel sprung separately with our remarkable Patent Spring.

Patent Nos. 17394/11, 21673/11, 23455/11.

No. X. 3251.

Wheels—14 in. and 10 in. with ½ in. wired-on tyres. Ball-bearing wheels with tangent spokes (as illustrated), **27/6** extra.

No. X. 3251 .. .. price **58/6** Packing 1/-

No. X. 3256.—Similar to No. X. 3251, but with the framework nickel-plated throughout except the wheel rims which are black; if these are supplied plated the cost is **7/-** extra, to order only.

No. X. 3256 .. price **£4 4 0** Packing 1/- Carriage paid.

Ball-bearing Wheels can be fitted to any of the above Models as follows—

Direct Spokes	**12/9** extra
Tangent Spokes ..	**27/6** „

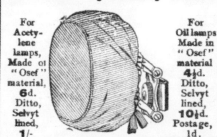

MILLER'S LAMPS.
ACETYLENE.

Cetolite, No. 3.

Fitted with lens, patent burner and bracket. Detachable glass covered reflector. One opening for cleaning purposes. Capacity 4 hours.
Price, plated .. **12/6** each.

Cetolite, No. 1.

Fitted with lens, patent burner and bracket, detachable glass covered reflector. Price .. **8/6** each.
Cetolite, No. 2, similar lamp, but larger size. Capacity 4 hours.
Price, plated .. **10/6** each.

The Monarch.

Large capacity lamp, similar to Cetolite No. 2.
Fitted with handle and detachable bell front. Dome glass. Plated **7/6** each.
Price, Plated with Lens .. **8/-**

Regalite Duplex.

Shows white head light and red rear light. Supplied complete with bracket for front fork.
Price, plated .. **6/9** each.

Regalite.

Dome glass, 3⅛ in. Patent burner, side screw bracket. Capacity 2½ hours. Detachable bell front.

Price, plated .. **5/6** each.

Mito.

Dome glass, 3⅛ in., side screw bracket, detachable bell front. Capacity 2½ hrs.
Price, plated .. **4/9** each.
If fitted with self-lighter, price, plated, **6/3**

Beto.

Dome glass, 3⅛ in. Made of brass. Capacity 2½ hours.
Price, plated .. .. **3/3** each.
If fitted with self-lighter **4/9** ,,

The Carbo.

Dome Lens, Glass Covered Aluminium Reflector, Fishtail Burner.
2½ hours Carbide Capacity.
Price plated, **6/6**

MILLER'S OIL LAMPS.

Edlite.

Made of brass throughout.
D.C. lens, 2½ in.
Wind and rain proof top.
One opening for cleaning.
Eight hours oil capacity.
Price, plated .. **9/6** each.

Bell Rock.

Made of brass.
D.C. lens, 2½ in. Burner, ⅞ in.
One opening for cleaning.
Oil capacity 6 hours.
Price, plated, **7/6** each.

Excelite.

Made of brass throughout.
D.C. lens, 2½ in. Burner, ¾ in.
Opens for cleaning.
Capacity 6 hours.
Price, plated .. **5/9** each.

Raylite.

Fitted with 2½ in. lens.
Opens for cleaning.
Oil capacity 6 hours.
Price, plated .. **4/-** each.

CANDLE LAMP.
The Raylite

Similar to the Raylite Lamp.

ADAPTED FOR BURNING CANDLES.

Price, plated .. **5/-** each.

Lito.

D.C. lens, 2⅜ in.
Burner, ⅞ in.
Side screw bracket.

Price, plated .. **3/-** each.

Jupiter No. 2.

A very strong pattern for every day use.

Lens, 2⅜ in. Burner, ⅞ in.

Price, plated .. **5/-** each.
Japanned .. **4/-** ,,

Millo.

D.C. lens, 2¼ in. Burner, ⅞ in.
Price, plated, **2/3** each.

Millerette, similar pattern, but with dome glass, 2½ in., **2/-** each.
Millo Duplex, shows white head and red rear lights, **2/9** each
Millo Tail, shows red rear light, Price ... **2/3** each.

Lumolite.

D.C. lens, 2¼ in. Side screw bracket, prism side glasses.
Plated, **2/3** Japanned **1/10½**
Lumo. Similar lamp, but with dome glass, spring bracket and plain side glasses.
Plated .. **1/6** each.
Japanned .. **1/3** ,,
Cyclight, a similar pattern, Japanned .. **1/-**

LUCAS LAMPS.

ALL POST FREE.   ALL POST FREE.

The Lucas "Kora."

No. 262 E.

Burns

No.	Ht. in.	Wt. oz.	Lns. in.	abt. hrs.	Finish.	Price.
Cy.262E	7	32	3¼	3¼	Plated	**13/6**
Cy.262EB	7	32	3¼	3¼	Ebony blk.	**13/6**
Cy.264E	7½	34	3¼	3¼	Plated	**14/6**
Cy.264EB	7½	34	3¼	3¼	Ebony blk.	**14/6**

Lucas "Radia"

No. 313. RADIA.

Plated or Ebony Black.

Burns

No.	Ht.	Wt.	Glass.	abt.	Finish
Cy.313	7½in.	24 oz.	3½in.	3½ hrs.	Plated
Cy.313B	ditto	ditto			Ebony blk.

Price ... **8/9**

The "Holophote."

No. Cy 307. Height, 5½in. Weight, 20oz.
Lens, 3 in. Burner, 1 in.
Finish, Plated ... **12/6**
No. Cy.307B. Do., finish, Ebony Blk. **12/6**

Lucas "Kinglet."

No. 210.

No. Cy. 210. Height, 5in. Weight, 12oz.
Lens, 2¼ in. Burner, ⅝ in.
Finish, Japanned ... **4/-**
No Cy. 211. Do.. Plated ... **5/-**

The Lucas "Acetyphote"

No. 317.
ACETYPHOTE.

Plated or Ebony Black.

No.	Height.	Weight.	Lens.	Burns about.
Cy. 317.	7½in.	34 oz.	3½ in.	4½ hours.

Price ... **12/6**

Lucas "Lustra."

No. 256
LUSTRA

Plated or Ebony Black.

No.	Height.	Weight.	Glass.	Burns about.
Cy. 256.	6in.	16 oz.	3½ in.	3 hours.

Price ... **7/6**

Lucas "Aceta."

No.	Height.	Weight.	Glass.	Burns abt.
Cy. 316.	5¾ in.	14 oz.	2⅝ in.	3 hours.

Price ... **5/-**

Lucas Pathfinder.

No. Cy. 216.	Height, 4½ in.	Weight, 11 oz.
	Lens, 2¼ in.	Burner, ⅝ in.
	Finish, Japanned	... **2/9**
No. Cy. 218.	Do. Plated	... **3/-**

Lucas "Leader."

No. Cy. 206. Height, 5½ in. Weight, 11 oz.
Lens, 3½ in. Burner, ⅝ in.
Nickel-plated **3/9**

Lucas "Colonia"

LUCAS

Plated or Ebony Black.

Burns.

No.	Height.	Weight.	Lens.	about.
Cy. 260E.	7 in.	30 oz.	3¼ in.	3½ hrs.

Price ... **11/6**

"Aceta Major."

No. 314.
ACETA MAJOR.

Cy. 314. Plated or Ebony Black.

Height.	Weight.	Glass.	Burns about.
6¼ in.	19 oz.	3½ in.	3½ hours.

Price ... **7/6**

"King of the Road."

A similar Lamp to the "Silver King,"
but japanned.

No. Cy. 305.	Height, 4½ in.	Weight, 16½ oz.
	Lens, 2¾ in.	Burner, ⅝ in.
	Finish, Japanned	... **8/6**

Lucas "Lucen"

No. Cy. 212.	Height, 4½ in.	Weight, 9 oz.
	Glass, 2¾ in.	Burner, ⅝ in.
	Finish, Japanned	... **2/-**
No Cy. 214.	Do. Plated	... **2/3**

Lucas "Captain"

No. Cy. 320. Height, 4¾ in. Weight, 12 oz.
Lens, 2¼ in. Burner, ⅝ in.
Price **5/-**

"Calcia King."

No. 318 E.

Plated or Ebony Black.

Burns abt.

No.	Height.	Weight.	Lens.	
Cy. 318E.	7 in.	30 oz.	3 in.	3½ hrs.

Price ... **10/6**

Lucas "Lucia."

No. 250

Plated or Ebony Black.

No.	Height.	Weight.	Glass.	Burns abt.
Cy. 250.	5½ in.	16 oz.	3½ in.	3 hrs.

Price ... **6/6**

Lucas "Silver King."

No. Cy. 306.	Height, 4½ in.	Weight, 16½ oz.
	Lens, 2¾ in.	Burner, ⅝ in.
	Finish, Plated	... **10/-**
No. Cy. 306B.	Do. Finish, Ebony Blk.	**10/-**

Petroleum "Silver King."

No. Cy. 306. Finish, Nickel-plated.
Burner, ⅝ in. petroleum **10/6**

Lucas "Toura."

No. Cy. 324. Height, 5 in. Weight, 14 oz.
Lens, 2¼ in. Burner, ⅝ in.
Price **6/-**

Genuine Lucas Burners for Gas Lamps, 3½d. each

POWELL & HANMER'S LAMPS. Acetylene and Oil.

The P. & H. Lamp.

Nickel-plated **8/-**

The Vulture.

Nickel-plated on brass **6/9**

The Sultan.

Nickel-plated,
on brass, **5/9**

The Sultan Self-Lighter.
Nickel-plated on Brass **7/3**

The Panther.

Nickel-plated
3/6

The Panther Self-Lighter.
Nickel-plated .. **5/-**

The Revenge.

Nickel-plated **4/9**

P. & H. Duplex.

Nickel-plated **5/-**

The Horoscope.

Nickel-plated **6/9**

The Zephyr.

Nkl.-plated, **5/6** Petro Zephyr, **6/9**

The Kingfisher.

Nickel-plated **4/6**

The Dictator.

Nickel-plated **3/3**

The Citadel.

Japanned, **2/6** Nickel-plated, **3/-**

The Referee.

Japanned, **2/-** Nickel-plated, **2/6**

The Corsair.

Nickel-plated **2/3**

The Demon.

Japanned, **1/-** Nickel-plated, **1/6**

CARRIAGE PAID ON ALL POWELL & HANMER LAMPS.

ACETYLENE LAMPS.

The Excelsior.

Nickel-plated Acetylene Gas Lamp .. **1/9**
Post 3d.

The Dreadnought.

A powerful light-giver—divided front glass with lens mirror reflector, with handle or carrying.
4/9
Post 3d.

Do. with hood over front glass
5/3

The Prince of Wales.

Separate Generator Gas Lamp.

No. Cy, 106/568. Large size.
Price **6 9** Post 3d.
Hood only **3/6**
Generator only .. **3/9**

The Queen.

Acetylene Lamp Price .. **2/6**
Ditto, fitted with condensing lens **2/11** Post 3d.

The New Torpedo Lamp.

This lamp is entirely made of brass. Stylish shape, burns splendidly, easily cleaned and polished, nickel-plated.

Price .. **6/6**
Post 3d.

The Prince of Wales.

No. Cy. 88.
Lens Mirror Reflector.
Price .. **6/6**

No. Cy. 130.
Cheaper quality,
4/11
Post 3d.

Royal Calcide Gas Lamp.

This is a well-known Lamp, many thousands of which have been sold. Always gives satisfaction.

Price .. **3/9**
Post 3d.

P & H Pattern Lamp. (ROSEBERY.)

Guaranteed brass throughout, nickel-plated, extra strong back, detachable convex curved glass detachable reflector, Brays burner, unbreakable bottom screws, 4½in. front fitted with handle, jewelled side glasses.

Price .. **5/6**

Ditto, ditto, oxydized finish,
5/11 Post 3d.

The Dreadnought Separate Generator Gas Lamp.

Very brilliant, lens mirror reflector, divided front glass.
5/9

Hood only **2/6**
Generator only .. **3/6**
Post 3d.
Dreadnought with Hood over front glass, **6/3**

CANDLE LAMPS.

New Oracle. Candle Lamp.

Nickel-plated .. **6/6** Post free.

The Original ASP CANDLE LAMP.

We are re-introducing this lamp, at the request of many customers who consider it is still the best candle lamp.

Price **4/6** Post 2d.

The Asp Candle Lamp.

With lens front.

Price **6/-**
Postage 2d.

Asp candles for do., **9d.** per doz.

The Aerolite Candle Lamp.

Nickel-plated .. **4/-** Post free.

Candles.

Price ... ... **9d.** per dox.

TABLE LAMPS.

Carriage and Packing extra.

Complete Oil Lamp Catalogue on application.

No. 7.
Polished Brass
Reading Lamp,
With 7½ in. White Shade
Price **3/9** complete.

Ir. 9631. Polished Brass.
15 line **Wizard**
Burner and 9¼ in. opal
shade **7/6** each.

No. 12.
Special Line.
Polished Brass, with
Duplex Burner and
Tinted Globe.
Price **15/11** complete.

No. 389.
Table Lamp.
Polished Brass with
Oxidized Silver Finish.
4 Columns, 50-candle
Power, Veritas Burner.
Complete with Globe and
Chimney. Price **25/6**

Ir. 9418. Polished Brass,
50-candle power
'Lampe Veritas'
with tinted manography
globe.
14/11 each.

No. 83.
Table Lamp.
Polished Brass, with
Veritas Burner and
Tinted Shade.
Price **16/3** complete.

Ir. 10235. Polished Cast Brass
Stand, Brass Front, 30 candle
power. **'Wizard'** Burner.
Tinted Manography Shade.
Price .. **29/6** each.

No. 84.
Reading Lamp.
Polished Brass, with 7½ in.
Opal Shade.
Price .. **4/9** Complete.

No. 24.
Good Value
Reading Lamp.
Polished Brass, with
7¼ in. Opal Shade.
Price **2/6** complete.

Ir. 8987. Polished
Brass with II. quality
Duplex Burner.
5/6 each.

No 20 **Table Lamp.**
Handsome design.
Oxidized Copper finish
Stand, with 50-candle
power Veritas Burner.
Price **23/6** complete.

No. 9.
Table Lamp.
Polished Brass, with
Duplex Burner.
Price **3/9**
Complete with Globe.

No. 15.
Special Line.
Table Lamp.
Polished Brass, with
Duplex Burner and
tinted Globe.
Price **7/11** complete.

Ir. 9417. Polished
Brass, I. quality Duplex
Burner. Without globe.
Price .. **7/11** each.

Bracket and Hand Lamps, etc.

**No. Ir. 2.
Electric Brassed Bracket Lamp.**
Fitted with Duplex burner. Complete with globe and chimney, **8/9**

No. Ir. 49524. Oxidized Copper with 15-line "Wizard" burner and tinted man-graphy shade. **10/6** each.
No Ir. 49525. Scratched Brass, fitted as above. **10/6** each.

No. Ir. 49524a. Oxidized Copper, with II qual' Duplex Burner. No glass. **9/-** each.
No. Ir. 49525a. Scratched Brass, fitted as above. **9/3** each.

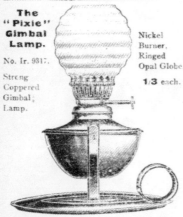

The "Pixie" Gimbal Lamp.
No. Ir. 9317.
Strong Coppered Gimbal Lamp.

Nickel Burner, Ringed Opal Globe. **1/3** each.

No. Ir. 8818. Brassed ditto. **1/-** each. Each lamp boxed complete.

The "Empress" Night Light
with Art Green Shade. For the Writing Table, Sideboard or Bedside.
Decorative night or small Reading Lamp.
Burns Ordinary Paraffin.
Quite odourless.
Height—11½ in. over all.
Polished Brass **2/3** each.
Nickel plated **2/9** each.

Brass Fount with side filler, 15-line "Wizard" burner and tinted manography shade.

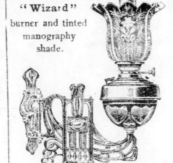

No. Ir. 49534. Bronzed finish, **8/6** ea.
„ 49535. Polished electro brassed finish. **9/9** e ch.

No. Ir. 9278. With 50-candle power "Lampe Veritas." **25/-** each.
No. Ir. 9278a. With I. qual. Duplex burner. **21/-** each.

The Vicereine Bed Room Lamp.
Brass, with Bead Fringe Shade.
Price .. **2/3**
Stock Colours—
Cardinal, Yellow or Green.
Postage 6d.

Complete Lamp List on Application.

**No. Ir. 1.
Electric Brassed Bracket Lamp.**

With round burner. Special Value .. **5/11** Complete with globe.

No. Ir. 9566. Polished brass with 50 candle power "Lampe Veritas." **21/-** each.
No. Ir. 9566a. Ditto, with I. qual. Duplex burner. **16/6** each.

No. Ir. 9196. Polished Brass, with III. qual. 6-line Kosmos burner, polished chimney and wick, **1/6** each.

No. Ir. 303 **Hand Lamp.** With ½ in. Burner. Polished Brass. Price **1/11** complete with Chimney.

No. Ir. 9279. Ormolu Gilt finish. 5-candle power "Lampe Veritas." **27/6** each.
No. Ir. 9279a. With I. qual. Duplex burner. **22/6** each.

No. Ir. 26. **Bracket Lamp** Stiff, bronzed, with brass fount Round burner, globe & chimney **2/11** each.

No. Ir. 9120. Polished Brass with Gem burner, polished chimney and wick. **10½**d. each.

No. Ir. 8986.
The "Viceroy" Night Light.

For Nurseries, Bedrooms, and Corridors.
Burns ordinary Paraffin.
With Celadon Coloured Globe and Lilliput Burner.
Quite Odourless.
Height 9 in.
Price **1/-** each.
Post 3d.

Carriage Extra on all Lamps.

Hanging Lamps for Oil.

Carriage extra on all Lamps and Gas Fittings.

11 in. Opal Shade.

No. Ir. 9295. With 30-candle power " Wizard " Burner.

15/11 each.

No. Ir. 9295a. With medium quality **Duplex** Burner.

15/3 each.

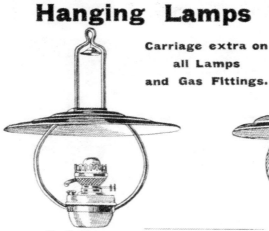

No. Ir. 11.

Hanging Lamp.

With 18 in. japanned Reflector, fitted with brass fount and duplex burner.

Price **6/3**

Including chimney.

No. 12.

Hanging Lamp.

With 18 in. japanned Reflector, 50-candle power burner.

Price .. **9/3**

Do., with 22 in. Reflector and 100-candle power burner.

Price .. **12/9**

No. 13.

Harp Hanging Lamp,

Twisted brass tube, with opal shade, brass container, and duplex burner.

Price .. **8/6**

12 in. Opal Shade.

No. Ir. 9091. With 50-candle power " **Lampe Veritas.**"

34/- each.

No. Ir. 9091a. With 20 line **Helios** Lamp.

29/6 each.

No. Ir. 9091b. With II. quality **Duplex** Burner.

25/- each.

With 11 in. Opal Shade.

No. Ir. 9233. 20 line **Helios** Lamp.

17/6 each.

No Ir. 9233a. 50-candle power " **Lampe Veritas.**"

21/- each.

No. Ir. 9233b. 20 line **Invicta** Lamp.

18/6 each

Finished Oxidized Copper.

6/9 each extra.

Screwless Fitting.

Two-arm Stiff Suspension, with 9¼ inch Opal Shade.

No. Ir. 9217.

With Glass Fount and III. quality **Duplex** Burner.

5 11 each.

No. Ir. 9217a.

Ditto, with 1 inch English **Slip** Burner.

5/3 each.

No. Ir. 9243.

With Glass Fount and 15 line **Mikado** Burner.

6/- each.

No. Ir. 9243a.

With Large Brass Fount and 15 line **Mikado** Burner.

7/6 each.

No. Ir. 9244,

With Large Brass Fount and 30-candle power **Wizard** Burner.

8/3 each.

No. Ir. 9244a.

Ditto, with 16 line **Odin** Burner.

8/6 each.

No. Ir. 22.

Hanging Lamp.

Cast iron bronzed finish, with 50 - candle power burner, and 12 in. opal shade.

Price .. **17/6** complete.

No. Ir. 25.

Hanging Lamp.

Cast iron electro brassed. Can be fitted together witho screws or nuts.

With 50-candle power burner

Price **23/9** complete.

Oil Lamp Catalogue on Application.

Floor Lamps.

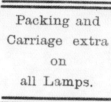

Packing and
Carriage extra
on
all Lamps.

Complete List of
OIL LAMPS
sent on application.

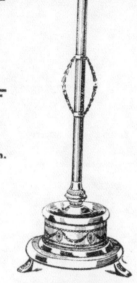

No. 89. Floor Lamp.
Polished Brass, with Duplex Burner.
Price .. **79/6** each.
Ditto, with 50 c.p. Central Draught
Burner. Price .. **82/-** each.

No. 49. Floor Lamp.
Polished Brass, with Duplex
Burner. Price **60/-** each.
Ditto, with 50 c.p. central
Draught Burner, **65/-** each.

No. 72. Floor Lamp.
Polished Brass, with Duplex
Burner. Price **42/-** each.
Ditto, with 50 c.p. central
draught Burner.
Price **45/-** each.

No. 11. New Design **Floor Lamp.**
Wrought Iron and Copper, with Duplex
Burner. Price .. **31/-**

Ditto, with 50 c.p. Central Draught
Burner. Price .. **39/6** each.

All the
Latest
Patterns
to be seen
in our
Showrooms

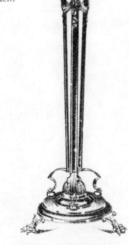

No. Ir. 49563. Cast
brass ornaments, enrich-
ments and feet, 50 candle
power "Lampe Veritas"
Price .. **119/-** each.

No. 1r. 49563a. With
Superior Lever Raiser
Duplex Burner.
Price .. **117/-** each

Handsome
and
Serviceable
LAMPS
at Minimum
Prices.

No. 551. Floor Lamp.
Wrought Iron with Coppered
Stamped Metal Scroll and
50 C.P. Veritas Burner.
Price .. **21/-**

No. 552. Floor Lamp
Polished Brass. Special Value, **29 6**

No. 39. Polished Brass, with Duplex
Burner. Price .. **69 9**
Ditto, with 50 c.p. Central Draught
Burner. Price .. **75/-**
Shade Extra.

No. 75 Floor Lamp.
Wrought Iron with Copper Table
and Duplex Burner. **60/-** each.
Ditto with 50 C.P. Central Draught
Burner. Price .. **63/-**
Shade extra.

LAMP AND CANDLE SHADES.

No. Ir. 4243.
Special Cheap Florentine Handkerchief Shade.
with 1½ in. Silver Bead Fringe.
18 in. diameter.   **12/6** each.

No. Ir. 467.
Silk Handkerchief
Candle
Shade.
2/3 each.
Post 2d.

No. Ir. 2896.
Candle Shade.
Chintz Goffered Linen.
Pink Flowers on White
Ground.
2/3 each.
Post 2d.

No. Ir. 2786.
Candle Shade.
Goffered Linen.
Fancy Bead
Fringe.
1/4½ each.
Post 1d.

No. Ir. 2787.
Candle Shade.
Goffered Linen.
Fancy Silver
Bead Fringe.
1/9 each.
Post 1d.

**Complete List of
Lamp and Candle
Shades
on application.**

No. Ir. 2595.
Candle Shade.
Goffered Linen Chenille
Trimming. Vandyked
Fancy Green Bead Fringe.
1/4½ each.
Post 1d.

No. Ir. 2440.
Candle Shade.
Silk Gimp and Ribbon Bow.
Gold or Silver Bead Fringe.
10½d. each.
Post 1d.

No. Ir. 4301.   Lamp Shade.
Best Silk, Tinsel Gimp Trimming, Gold or Silver
Bead Fringe.   18 in. diameter.   **21/-** each.

No. Ir. 2737.
Candle Shade.
9½d. each.
Post 1d.

No. Ir. 2778
1/- each.
Candle Shade.
Post 1d.

No. Ir. 2890.
Candle Shade.   **4½d.** each.
Post 1d.

No. Ir. 2762.
Candle Shade.
4½d. each.
Post 1d.

No. Ir. 2744.
Candle Shade.
7½d. each.
Post 1d.

No. Ir. 4261.   Lamp Shade.
Florentine, Pleated Top, Cords and Tassels.
2 in. Gold or Silver Fringe. 18 in. diameter. **18/6** each.

No. Ir. 2690.
Candle Shade.
Gimp Top and Base, 1 in.
Gold or Silver Bead Fringe.
9d. each. Post 1d.

PLEASE STATE COLOUR OF SHADE REQUIRED WHEN ORDERING.

PERFUMERY DEPARTMENT.

Lavender Water
Potter & Moor's
Mitcham
Lavender Water.
In bottles—
**1/6 2/6 3/9 6/6
12/6**
Postage extra.

French Lavender Water
GIRAUD'S
Superior Quality.
In bottles –
**1/3 2/3 3/3
4/11 8/6**
Postage extra.

Cachous in Great Variety.
Jockey Club, Parma Violet, Wallflower,
White Rose, **4**d. per oz. **5**/- per lb.

Phul-Nana Cachous, **3**d. per box.
Postage 1d.

Grossmith's Floral Perfumes.

Parma Violets,
Wallflowers,
Sweet Pea, Violet
Blanche,
Lily of the Valley.
6d. bottles **5**d.
1/- bottles **9**d.
Postage 2d.

"Ciola" Hygienic Tooth Powder.
In the past Tooth Powders have been highly coloured, so as to render them attractive to the eye; but this has been produced by introducing harmful dyes. The antiseptics employed are mostly poisonous, such as Carbolic Acid, Salycylic Salol, Sublimates, &c. Both are very injurious, their habitual use being frequently the unsuspected cause of ill-health.

"CIOLA" TOOTH POWDER is guaranteed free from poisonous matter of any description, and to be perfectly harmless.

Its active principle, the aromatic essences extracted from Flowers and Herbs possessing antiseptic properties to a higher degree than any poisons, and constituting at once an Ideal and Charming Dentifrice, antigermic, deodorising, of great fragrance, and wonderfully refreshing.

6d. and **1**/- per box. Postage 1d. and 2d.

Roger and Gallet's Perfumes.
Violette de Parme, 1/11 2/6 3/10 5/6 10/9 13/3 26/0

Alsatian Clover	Indian Hay	Lilas Blanc
Chypre	Iris Blanc	New Mown Hay
Giroflee	Jasmin	Peau d'Espagne
Heather	Lily of the Valley	Vera Rosa
Heliotrope Blanc		

Per bot., 3/0 4/6 6/9 11/6

Vera Violetta	..	per bot., 3/3 4/6 6/9
Violette Ambree	..	.. per bot. 4/3 5/9
Fiorenta	..	.. .. 4/6
Extrait Splendor	..	.. ,, 4/9
Violette Merveille	..	.. ,, 11/3
White Rose	..	.. ,, 6/9
Amberose ..	..	.. ,, 11/3

Postage extra.

Atkinson's Perfumes.
Per bot. .. 1/9, 2/9, 4/10, 11/6

Chypre	Lily of the Valley	Stephanotis
Ess Bouquet	Moss Rose	Tea Rose
Frangipanni	Musk	Violette de Parme
Heliotrope	New-Mown Hay	White Lilac
Jasmin	Opoponax	Wood Violet
Jockey Club	Peau d'Espagne	Ylang Ylang

Atkinson's White Rose Perfume.
1 oz. size.	2 oz.	4 oz.	8 oz.
2/-	**3**/6	**6**/-	**10**/6

Atkinson's Rose Cold Cream.
1/- **1**/6 **2**/6 per pot.

Mousse-Diane, a newly invented natural Perfume, peculiarly distinctive in odour and of fragrance delightful and exquisite, highest concentration .. per bot. 3/6
Postage extra.

Atkinson's Newest "Eonia" Perfumery.
VERY POWERFUL AND LASTING.
Phlox-Eonia	..	..	..	.. 2/9
Violette-Eonia, in silk lined case			..	.. 4/0
Jasmin-Eonia	,,	,,	..	.. 3/10
Californian Poppy	,,	,,	..	.. 3/3

Postage 3d.

Perfumes in Fancy Cases.

Courvoisier's latest production
Rose Royale, a new and delicious odour of Rose. Very lasting. **3/6** Post 3d.

Courvoisier's **Trefleurs** The new and lasting Trefle Perfume in handsome cases.
Price ... **3**/- Postage 3d.

Courvoisiers' well-known Perfumes.
Havanita and Viotto.

Havanita.
Latest creation in fashionable Perfumes.
2/3 4/3 7/6 14/6
per bottle.

Viotto.
Otto of Violets Perfume.
**1/8 3/2 6/- 11/9
22/6** per bottle.

Postage extra.

Concentrated Perfumes without Spirit.

Courvoisiers' Viotto, Lily of the Valley and Havanita.

One drop is equal to a teaspoonful of the finest perfume. In handsome presentation cases **3/9** each. Postage 1d.

Grossmiths Gold Medal Perfumery.
Phul-Nana, Hasu-no-Hana, and the latest production, Shem-el-Nessim.

2/3 4/- 7/9

2/3 4/- 7/9

2/6 4/6 8/6

Postage 2d., 3d. 4d.

Colgate's American Perfumes
Caprice	.. .. 2/0	Italian Violet	.. 2/0
Cashmere Bouquet	2/0	La France Rose	.. 2/0
,, ,,	3/3	White Heliotrope	.. 2/0
Dactylis ..	2/0 and 3/3		

Colgate's Satchets.
Alba Rose, Cashmere Bouquet, Caprice, Heliotrope, La France Rose, Peau d'Espagne, Violet, Vioris, Satchet Envelopes, **5**d. each.

PERFUMERY DEPARTMENT—*continued.*

Oriental Perfume.

The well-known Trefle Rosat Oriental perfume of Giraud Fils of Grasse and Paris. Each bottle packed in a fancy box. The case is about 5 in. long by 2¼ in. broad The bottle holds about 16 drachms.

Price, complete in case, **2/9**

Sachet Powders. Grossmith's Floral Powders. **5**d. Postage 1d. For perfuming the Wardrobe, Cabinet, Gloves, etc., also for preventing the moth.

White Rose, Heliotrope, Parma Violet, Wallflower, Millefleurs, Phul-Nana. Hasu-No-Hana, Florodora, etc.

A full 2-oz. bottle of triple perfume in Jockey Club, Parma Violet, Wood Violet, White Rose, Lily of the Valley, Wallflower, etc.

Packed in fancy Gold Lined Case, beautifully blocked and embossed. Price complete, **2/9** Post free.

Grasse les Fleurs Series. "Jn. Giraud Fils"

No. D. 182 In Violet de Parme only.

Flat bottle **2/3**
3/-
4/6

The Case stands 5½ in. long by 2½ in. wide. The Bottle is a handsome glass stoppered one, holding about 20 drams. of first quality French perfume in assorted odours, Violet, Jockey Club, White Rose.

3/3 and **3/9** in case complete. Post free.

Piver's French Perfumery.

We stock a range of the most popular odours in this make, viz.:—

Piver's Le Trefle Incarnat, Azurea, Rosiris, Safranor, Floramye, Vivitz, Pompeia.

Prices, **4/3**, **6/9**, **12/-** per bottle.

Piver's Sachets in the above odours.
In paper envelopes, **1/-** and **1/9**

Piver's Face Powders.
Azurea, Trefle, Safranor (Blanche, Rachel, Rosée).
2/9 per box.

Piver's Toilet Soaps.
Savon Trefle, Savon Floramye, Savon Azurea.
6/- per box of 3 tablets.

Houbigant's Perfumery.

Cœur de Jeannette	per bot.	**8/9**	**28/7**
Violette Ideal	,,	—	**5/9**
,, Russe	,,	—	**4/3**
Houbigant's Le Perfum Ideal	,,	—	**11/6**

Postage extra on all above.

The Genuine Giraud Fils.

No. D. 53. Full 5 oz. glass stoppered bottle.

In Lily of Valley, Jockey Club, Parma Violet, Wood Violet, Opopanax, Wall Flower, Stephanotis, White Rose.
4/6

No. D. 1 (as illust.) In Jockey Club, Heliotrope, White Rose, Violet, Opopanax, Lily of the Valley, 1 oz. bottle, **1/-**, 2 oz. ,, **1/10**

Any Perfume not already in stock or listed can be obtained if desired. Post us your orders no matter what they are for and we will endeavour to procure your wants.

Sachet Powder.

GIRAUD FILS, in Parma Violet, Wood Violet, Jockey Club, Lily of Valley.

½ lb. bottles, square, stoppered per bottle	..	**5/-**
¼ lb. ditto	,, ..	**2/9**

No. D. 860, ½ lb. bottles, square, stoppered, superior quality, per bottle, **5/-** Post extra.

Roger and Gallet Sachets.

Violette de Parme Sachets, **11½**d.

Sachet de Corsage, Peau d'Espagne, Violette de Parme, White Rose, **10½**d.

We carry an immense stock of all the well known Perfumes: Atkinson's, Giraud Fils, Roger and Gallet, Piver, Grossmith, &c., &c. The articles illustrated here convey but a slight idea of the variety we display in this department. Where "assorted" odours are mentioned, the following are stocked—White Rose, Oppoponax, Violet, Lily of the Valley, Jockey Club.

We make a speciality of supplying **Perfume in Bulk**, so that customers can fill their own bottles. In the case where a fancy bottle is not wanted, it will be found a considerable saving to buy in this way. In all well-known odours guaranteed full strength.

10d. per oz., bottle free

Eau de Cologne. "No. 4711."

2 oz. bottle **1/1**
4 oz. ,, ... **2/2**

Wicker-covered Bottles.
3/6 6/6 13/-
Postage extra.

Eau de Cologne.

GUARANTEED BEST QUALITY. IMPORTED DIRECT.

JOHANN MARIA FARINA,

Gegenuber dem Elogius Platz.

GENUINE AND VERY BEST.

Prices—2 oz. bottle, **1/-** 4 oz. bottle, **1/10½** 8 oz. bottle, **3/6**
Original case of ½ doz. 4 oz. bottles, **10/9**
In wicker-covered bottles. Small, **3/-** Medium, **5/9** Large, **11/-**

Eau de Cologne.

Gegenuber dem Julichs Platz.
2 oz. .. **1/1** 4 oz. .. **2/2**
In wicker-covered bottles.
3/3 6/6 and **13/-**

Johann Maria Farina. Genuine.

2 oz., **10½**d. 4 oz., **1/8** 8 oz. **3/-**
Wickers, **2/7 5/-** and **9/6**

Atkinson's "Eonia" Lavender Water.

In Bottles at **2/- 3/- 4/6**
Post extra.

Luce's "Jersey" Eau de Cologne.

1/- 2/- 4/-

In Wicker-covered Bottles,
3/3 6/6 12/6
Post extra.

Crown Perfumery Company Celebrated Perfumes, etc.

Iroma Perfume, **2/6** and **4/9** per bottle. Crab Apple Blossom, **2/- 3/10** & **5/-**
Crown Lavender Smelling Salts, **1/- 1/6** and **3/-**
Crown Natural Violets .. **4/6** per bottle.
Iroma Face Powder, **1/6** per box. Iroma Toilet Soap, **2/6** per box.
Post extra.

Atkinson's POINSETTA Perfume.

4/6 and **8/6** per bottle.

Post extra.

Strops, Stropping Devices, Hair Clippers, etc.

THE IMPROVED ROCKIT.

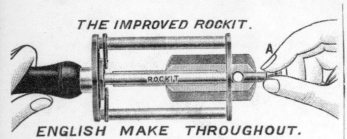

ENGLISH MAKE THROUGHOUT.

For double edge.   Thin blades.   Illustration shews Gillette Blade held in position.   Price **2/11½**
Good quality Strop for above, **1/-** extra.

The **"Carlton"** Stropping Machine for Safety Razor Blades of all kinds.   With special clip for "Gillette" style.   Price **2/11½**
Good quality Strops for above, **1/-** each extra

Fine quality Graduating Strop.
FOR HOLLOW-GROUND RAZORS.   Price **5/6**

Fine quality Leather and Canvas Hanging Strops with nickel finish fittings.
1/6   2/-   2/6   3/6 and **5/-**

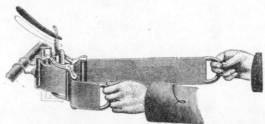

The **"Universal,"** Wilkinson's Patent Double Action Stropping Machine, for ordinary Razors.
Price **12/6**   Adapter for taking Safety Razor Blades, **1/-** ea. extra

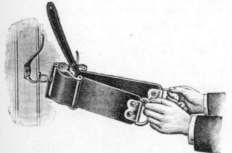

The **'Presto' Automatic Stropping Machine** for Ordinary Razors or The **"Mikado"** for Safety Razor Blades.
5/6 each

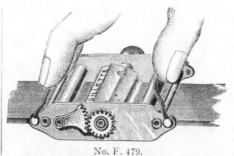

No. F. 479.
Wilkinson's Patent Machine
For stropping Gillette and other double edge Safety Razor Blades.   **6 6** each.
Special Horse-hide Strops for above Machine, **1/-** ea

Twin Plex.   The Finest Machine offered.
For Gillette Blades. **Strops both edges at once.**
It is guaranteed to last and give perfect service for 10 years.   Full directions sent with each.   Price **15/-**

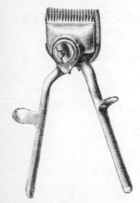

The **"Leopold" Hair Clipper.**
3/6
A cheaper quality Clipper at **2/-** and **2/11**

The **"Pall Mall"** Cushion Strop.   Price **2/-**
Other prices and qualities in Cushion Strops:—
1/-   1/6   2/6   3/6 and **5/6**

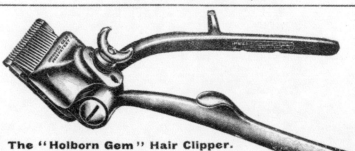

The **"Holborn Gem"** Hair Clipper.
Fitted with stamped steel cap and improved spring washers
Supplied in the following sizes.
To cut $\frac{1}{16}$ in. **5/11** $\frac{1}{8}$ in. **5/11** $\frac{1}{4}$ in. **6/6** $\frac{3}{8}$ in. **7/6**

The **"Trimmer"**
Neck and Beard Clipper.
4/6

Fretwork Machines. Of British Manufacture Throughout.

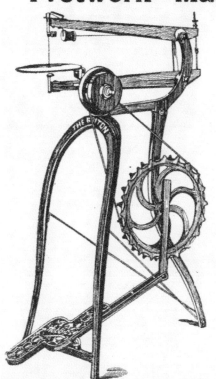

No. 1. Briton Fretsaw .. **14/6**

No. 2. Ditto, with Nickel Plated Tilting Table and Emery Wheel 17/-

The "BRITON" Machine is one of the cheapest reliable Treadle Fretsaws on the market. The arms will take 18 in. work, and the height to the Table is 32 in. The Machine is fitted with Hobbies Patent Lever Steel Clamps with new patent screws and shackles. There is also an improved Dust Blower, and the end of the Balance-Wheel Spindle is pierced for holding a Drill. A Drill Bit, Wrench, Oil Can, Saws, and two Designs are sent out with each Machine.

Young Briton, 13/6

The Young Briton is a new model this season and is a cheap and reliable Fretsaw. The frame of the Machine is made entirely of iron finished in cycle enamel. The Balance-Wheel Pulley and Table are the same as used on our "Briton" Machine. The Saw Clamps are our Patent Spring Open pattern. A Wrench, one dozen Saws and Design are sent with each machine.

The "Companion" Lathe and Fretsaw.

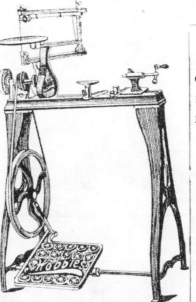

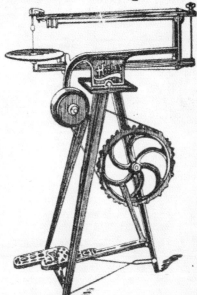

No. 1. A1 Treadle Fretsaw. 21/-
No. 2. With Nickle-Plated Table and Emery Wheel **23 6**

Considering its low price of one guinea, the Hobbies A1 Fretsaw is acknowledged to be un-surpassed. The Machine is fitted with Hobbies Patent Lever Clamps. These will securely grip the finest Saw Blades, and they are so made that the Lever cannot fly back and loosen the tension of the Saw.

The end of Balance-Wheel Spindle is arranged to hold a Drill, and there is also an improved Dust Blower.

A Drill Bit, Oil Can, Screwdriver, Spanner, one dozen Saws, and two Designs are sent with each Machine.

Hobbies 6/- Fretwork Outfit.

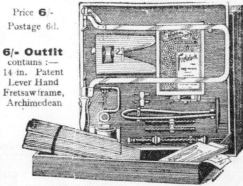

Price **6/-**
Postage 6d.

6/- Outfit contains :—
14 in. Patent Lever Hand Fretsaw frame, Archimedean

Drill with 2 Bits, Pressed Steel Cutting Table with Iron Cramp, Fretwork Saw Blades, 2 dozen, Liquid Glue in Collapsible Tube, Fretwork Hammer, Sandpapering Block, Illustrated Handbook, Parcel of "Gem" Designs, with sufficient Fretwork for making six articles.

Larger size **Boxed Outfits.**

Price .. .. **8/6** Postage 7d.
.. .. .. **11/6** .. 8d

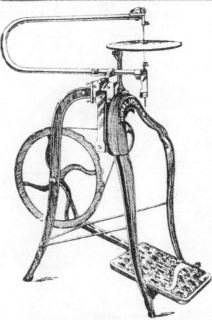

Royal Hobbies Fretsaw.

No. 1 As illustrated, with Dulled Nickelled Table and
Japanned Saw Frame **32/-**
Ditto, with Plated Table **34/-**
No. 2. With all Bright Parts Plated, including
Table and Saw Frame **37/-**

This "Companion" Machine forms a useful Amateur's Lathe and Fretsaw. The large Driving Wheel has two groves of varying depths to give a change of speed. The Lathe head is provided with a 2-in. Face Plate, a Spur Centre, and a Screw Centre for turning Cups It has also a solid Emery Wheel and a Drill Spindle. The Tail Stock has a Screw Feed Centre. The Lathe is provided with two Rests. three Turning Tools, Wrench and Screwdriver, and for the Fretsawing Attachment, Designs, Saws, Drill Points. &c. Swing of Lathe, 5 in. Length of Bed 24 in. Distance between Centres, 14 in. A Circular Saw Attachment with Nickel-plated and polished Table can be fitted to the "**Companion**" Lathe. The Fretsawing Attachment is secured to the Lathe Bed by one bolt, and can be put on and taken off at leisure. It is fitted with 19-in. arms, with Trusses to prevent bending, Dust Blower. nickel-plated Tilting Table, and Hobbies Patent Lever Saw Clamps.

Lathe and Fretsaw. **35/-** Lathe and Tools. **27/6** Fretsaw Attachment. **8/6** Circular Saw Attachment, **5/6**

All Machines are carefully tested before being despatched, packed in crates in complete working order, and ready for immediate use. Direct from Works. Machines are sent by Rail at the Railway Company's risk. The purchaser pays carriage on delivery.

Write for our Complete Tool List.

Travelling Watches, Carriage Clocks, &c.

Travelling Watch.

Fold-up Leather Case. 30 hour Lever Movement.
Price.. .. .. .. **18/9**

8-day Lever Movement Price **39/6**

A Small Size Travelling Watch in Folding Case.
Lever Movement. Price .. **12/9**

No. F. 4035. **Travelling Watch.**
Leather Case. Folds Flat. Radium Dial.
Time distinctly seen in the dark.
30-hour Movement. Price .. **25/-**
8-day Movement. Price .. **40/-**

Travelling Alarm Watch.
Folds Flat. 30-hour Lever Movement. Leather Case.
Price .. **39/6**

8-day Carriage Clock.

Gilt Finish.

Complete in Leatherette Case.

Price .. **14/9**

Lever Movement.

Price **21/-**

No. F. 1150. **8-day Carriage Clock.**
Reliable Timekeeper. Polished Gilt Mounts.
Complete in Leather Case. Price .. **23/6**
Lever Movement **29/6**

No. F. 1149. **8-Day Carriage Clock.**
Oval Shape. Polished Gilt Mounts.
Complete in Leather Case. Price .. **33/9**

8-day Office Dial.

Strikes Hours and Half-hours.
12 in. diameter.
Polished Wood Rims.
Price **16/9**

Timepiece only. Price .. **13/6**

8-day Striking Clock.

Strikes Hours and Half-hours.
12 in. bold Dial. Polished Wood Rims.
Length of clock . Price .. **19/6**

8-day Office Dial.
Best Quality and Finish. Reliable Timekeeper.
Polished Wood Rim. Size 8 in. Price .. **24/6**
,, 10 in. ,, .. **27/6**
,, 12 in. ,, .. **30/-**

R 2

Best Possible Value in Watches and Pedometers.

The "Enigma" Watch.

Finest value offered at the price. Oxydized steel or nickel silver case. Price .. **4/6**

Or with luminous dial; time easily seen in the dark. Price **9/6**

100-Mile Adjustable Pedometer

As illustrated, **4/11** Superior quality & finish. No. F 113. ¼-Mile to 12 Miles. Best nickel case, glass back showing mechanism .. **10/6**
80 Yards to 1,000 Miles **15/6**

The "Finalo" Lever. Non-magnetic.
Jewelled movement.   Neat in appearance. Nickel silver or oxydised steel case .. **8/6**

The "Railway" Dial Lever.
RELIABLE TIMEKEEPER,
Nickel silver case.   Price .. **10/6**

No F. 1852. Race Timer.
Accurate a'justment; timing events to ⅕ of a second. Price .. **14/6**
Lever movement **18/6**

The "Hexameter" Lever. Jewelled movement, compensation balance. Exceptional Value.
Oxydized steel or nickel silver cases.   Price **12/6**
Sterling silver English Hall-marked cases ... **21/-**
Rolled Gold (10-year) cases **25/-**

The "Reco" Flat Lever.
Jewelled movement.   Very fine timekeepers.
Nickel silver or oxydized steel cases. Price **11/6**
Sterling silver cases **21/6**
☞ Made in two sizes—FOR BOYS or MEN.

8-day Watch. Really good timekeepers.
Nickel silver or oxydized steel case .. **8/11**
Sterling silver case **15/6**

Calendar Watch. Very simple mechanism
Self-changing every 24 hrs. Lever movement. Nickel silver or oxydized steel case **15/6**
Cheaper quality **11/6**

High Grade Watches FOR ALL AT COMPETITIVE PRICES.

The Smart Dress Watch.
Lever Movement. Exceptionally Flat.
Sterling Silver, **38 6** Solid Gold, **85 -**
Heavy Case.

Gamage's "Holborn" Lever.
Jewelled Movement. Thoroughly Reliable. No
Better Value Offered at the Price.
Oxydized Steel Cases, **10/-** Or in Sterling Silver
Case, **18 6** Equal to any watch offered at 21/-

**Independent
Fly-back
Chronograph
Watch.**

Eight Day Lever. Fine Quality.
15 Jewelled Movement, Breguet Hairspring. Accurately Timed
and Adjusted. Sterling Silver Case, **47/6** Rolled Gold.
(10 year) **50/-** Do. (20 year) **65/-** Solid Gold, 9ct. **£6 6 0**
Solid Gold, 18ct. **£13 13 0**

**The Billiard Player's Pocket
Watch.** Strong Hunter Case.
Made to withstand any pressure, extra strong
lever movement, oxydized steel case, **18 6**
Sterling Silver Case .. **30,-**
Rolled Gold Case, (10 year) .. **35/-**
Solid Gold Case **£6 5 0**

Non-magnetic Lever Movement. Expressly made for
timing important sporting events. Accurately
Adjusted, registering to 30 min. Oxydised steel case.
Price **37/6** Sterling Silver, **47/6** Best quality
Silver Case, price **70/-**

High Grade Lever. Jewelled Movement,
Half Hunter Cases, Sterling Silver **29 6**
Rolled Gold (10 year) **39 6** Solid Gold. **98 6**

**Repeater
Watch.**

The "Gramma" High Grade Lever.
Fully Jewelled Movement, Non-magnetic Hair Spring.
Sterling Silver English Hall-marked Case **23 6**
Rolled Gold (10 year) **30/-** Solid Gold **85/-**

High Grade Movement, Striking Hours and Quarters
on Beautifully Toned Gong. Oxydized Steel Case,
59/6 Sterling Silver **69/6** Solid Gold **£10 10 0**

POCKET ALARM ROUSER. Very Convenient
for Tourists. Thoroughly Reliable Movement.
Oxydized Steel Case, **23/6** Cheaper Quality, **14/6**
Also with RADIUM DIAL VISIBLE AT NIGHT, **30**
Best Quality Only

NAUMANN'S CELEBRATED SEWING MACHINES

THE BEST MACHINES on the Market AT THE LOWEST PRICES.

Beautifully Finished in the Best possible manner, and all wearing parts case-hardened.

The NAUMANN Machines are made to go right. They cannot get out of order if properly handled according to Instruction Book. They are the cheapest in the long run, as they last longer than any other make. Over 3,000,000 have been sold, all have given satisfaction. The Naumann Machines are practically noiseless, work very quickly, and run easily owing to the simplicity of the mechanism.

Square Cover and One Drawer Treadle Machine only.
No. X. 26 Boat Shape Shuttle £3 13 6
No. X. 111 Vibrating ,, ... 4 10 0

Hand and Treadle Machine (as illustrated.)
No. X. 11 Boat Shape Shuttle 3 16 0
No. X. 115 Vibrating ,, ... 4 14 6
All complete with a full list of Accessories.

**The NAUMANN
Vibr.-Shuttle Drop Head Machine**

Is the ideal of a highly ornamental and useful Sewing Machine. When closed, the roller shutter top forms a perfectly even table.

X. 114. 4 drawers (as illustrated) **£5 17 0**
X. 124. 4 do. (Hand & Treadle) **6 15 0**

All complete with full set of Accessories.

The Naumann Machines make a beautiful pearl lock-stitch. They have a large space under the arm, a high presser, leaving plenty of room for thick materials, and are provided with an improved tension releaser, an automatic bobbin winder, and have a full set of attachments for seaming, cording, hemming, quilting, binding, braiding, gathering, felling, etc., and an instruction book dealing very exhaustively with the different points.

All Machines on this page sent Carriage Paid to any Goods Station in the United Kingdom.

Ornamental Cover and Two Drawers Treadle Machine only (as illustrated.)
No. X. 113 Vibrating Shuttle Treadle Machine **£5 0 0**

Hand and Treadle Machine.
No. X. 117 Vibrating Shuttle Machine ... 5 15 0
Foot Rest 3/- extra.
All complete with full set of Accessories.

NAUMANN No. X. 9 "SPECIAL."

A perfect Hand Machine for the Home, suitable for all kind of work.

Price **£2 16 0**

Complete with cover and full set of Accessories.

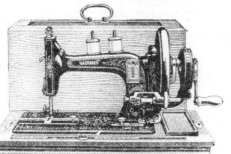

NAUMANN No. X. 101.

Vibrating Shuttle Hand Machine

Most up-to-date and specially strong, with extra large space under arm.

Price **£3 7 6**

Complete with cover and full set of Accessories.

Ornamental Cover and Five Drawers Treadle Machine only.
No. X. 122 Vibrating Shuttle and Drop Leaf **£6 6**

Hand and Treadle Machine (as illustrated.)
No. X. 118 Vibrating Shuttle and Drop Leaf **£6 16**
All complete with full set of Accessories.

For full Range see Departmental List, sent Post Free anywhere.

VACUUM CLEANERS of Repute. For Home and Office use.

Replace Broom, Dustpan and Brush, and are Light, Simple, Effective and Labour Saving. The latest and best appliances for Cleaning Carpets and Upholstered Furniture. Further List gratis and post free with pleasure.

The WINDSOR Hand Models

The Dustaw Windsor No. X. 2.

THE WINDSOR No. 2

£3 3 0

Height .. 19 in.
Width .. 10½ in.
Length .. 19 in.
Weight.. 25 lb.

Issued complete with 6ft. of 1 in. Flexible Metallic Tubing, 1 Carpet and 1 Upholstery Nozzle, 1 Extension Tube. Built of selected white-wood, mahogany finish, or otherwise to order.

The Dustaw Windsor No. X. 1.

THE WINDSOR No. X. 1

£4 4 0

We Strongly Recommend this Model.

The most powerful Vacuum Cleaner ever built on the hand-lever principle.

Has a greater traverse of the bellows than any other machine of this class, and thus displaces a larger volume of air with an equal amount of labour. Light, portable, and strongly built, with a suction of sufficient intensity to clean the heaviest grades of carpet. The Dustaw Knee Rest (Registered Design) gives the user increased control over the machine, and greatly facilitates its operation.
Height 20in. Width 12in. Length 20in. Weight 32lb.
Supplied complete with 6 ft. of 1 in. Metallic Tubing, 1 Carpet, 1 Upholstery, and 1 Brush Nozzle, 1 Extension Tube.

The Special Zorst Vacuum Cleaner.

Size 22 by 10 by 16 in. The most powerful and easiest small machine, made complete with carpet and upholstering nozzles, 5 ft. length of metallic taking substantial bellows Very portable. Special price **39/6** Carr. paid.

The Zorst Portable Rotary Vacuum Cleaner.
(Regd.) Model X. 15. Weighs only 25 lbs. without flywheel (9lbs) approx. Size 1 ft. by 1 ft. by 2 ft. 9 in. high, approx.
£5 5 0 complete with 6 ft. flexible tubing, target nozzle, upholstery nozzle, extension tube, and instructions for use.

Many other Vacuum Cleaners stocked.

New X.L. Vacuum Cleaners.
Leaflet on application.
No. X. 1 **£2 10** X. 1A. **£3 3** X. 1B **£4 4**
" X. 2A. **£4 10** X. 2B **£5 5**
" X. 3. **£6 6** X. 10. **£7 7**

The "Boreas" Hand Pneumatic Sweeper. **28/6**
"Daisy" Vacuum Cleaner. From **42/-**

DEMONSTRATIONS DAILY.
Special Leaflets with full Particulars, FREE on Application

The Windsor Rotary Models

The Dustaw Rotary Windsor.

THE ROTARY WINDSOR.
No. X. 1.. **£5 10 0**
No. X. 2.. **£6 15 0**
The No. X. 2 Model has Quadruple Bellows giving Continuous Suction.

Supplied complete with 6 ft. of 1 in. Metallic Tubing. 1 Carpet, 1 Upholstery, and 1 Brush Nozzle, 1 Extension Tube.

The Cabinet Dustaws.

Both patterns are enclosed in handsomely polished Cabinets of Fumed oak fitted with India rubber tyred wheels and carrying handles. They are issued complete with 9 ft. of 1 in. Flexible Metallic Tubing, 1 Carpet, 1 Upholstery and 1 Brush Nozzle. 1 Extension Tube.
The C2 Model has quadruple bellows giving Continuous Suction.

THE DUSTAW C1. **£6 6 0** Made in
THE DUSTAW C2. **£7 7 0** Figured Oak.

BRITISH VACUUM CLEANERS.

Model G.B.
Price **£2 5s.**
Weight less equipment 23lb.
Height 16 in. Width 9 in.
Length 15 in.
EQUIPMENT.—Extension Arm in two parts, Carpet Cleaner, Upholstery Cleaner, 4 ft. Flexible Metallic Hose.
DESCRIPTION
Although very moderate in price it is quite an efficient article, well suited for use in small households.

It is constructed of well-seasoned white wood, beautifully polished. The cleaning implements are polished aluminium, die castings of superior quality. It is very easy to work. At the price this Cleaner is listed at we cannot fit our "bridge" operating lever. This will be found on all our higher priced models.

Model G.K.
Price **£3 3s.**
Weight less equipment 28 lb.
Height 16 in. Width 10 in.
Length 18 in.
EQUIPMENT.— Extension Arm in two parts, Carpet Cleaner, Upholstery Cleaner Brush to slide on same and 6 ft. Flexible Rubber Hose.
DESCRIPTION.— This is our lowest-priced Cleaner having our unique "bridge" operating lever, which enables a large capacity cleaner to be operated with the minimum of effort, and is a proved success. The construction is solid oak, highly polished, best quality leather bellows. Cleaning implements of die cast aluminium, polished.

Model G.G.

	closed 12 in.
	open 12 in.
	closed 12 in.

Weight less equipment 44 lb. Width
Height open or closed 20 in. Length
Width open 12 in.
EQUIPMENT.—Extension Arm, Carpet Cleaner, Upholstery Cleaner, Combined Cleaner, consisting of Brush for cornices, &c., and special Narrow Arm for corners of chairs, &c., 6 ft., Flexible Rubber Hose.
DESCRIPTION.—This Model is the last word in Lever-operated Hand Vacuum Cleaners. The whole machine folds up into a very small space. It has the largest capacity of all our Lever Hand Machine Models, and our special "bridge" operating lever is fitted, ensuring utmost ease in working. It is fitted with a cupboard where hose can be kept, and wheels are fitted to the front of the machine, so that by slightly tilting it can be easily wheeled from place to place. A "DE LUXE" BRITISH VACUUM CLEANER of incomparable quality and efficiency .. .. Price **£6 6s.**

The NEW RUN-ABOUT Vacuum Sweeper.

No More Brooms Wanted. Revolving Bristle Sweepers Superseded.
Made in Figured oak. Nickel-plated Parts. Detachable Handle.
£1 19 6
A First class Machine at a Reasonable price.
The only Machine with Quadruple Bellows. Continuous Suction.

Can be used by anyone without undue exertion either as a Vacuum Cleaner, or as a Carpet Sweeper after Meals, etc., without circulating a particle of Dust in the Atmosphere.

The ELECTRIC Dustaws.

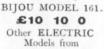

BIJOU MODEL 161.
£10 10 0
Other ELECTRIC Models from
£12 12 0 to
£21 0 0
Built in Figured oak Fumed finish, or to order. The prices include all necessary switches, flexible Wire, 1 in. flexible metallic Tubing, 1 Carpet, 1 Upholstery, 1 Brush, and 1 Crevice Nozzle, 1 Extension Tube.

All Vacuum Cleaners sent Carriage Paid.

A PAGE OF LABOUR SAVING DEVICES.

The O-Cedar Polish Mop.

Gathers all the dust from everywhere and holds it.

The O-Cedar Polish Mop puts an end for ever to the constant getting down on your knees, also the back-breaking stoop to clean, dust, and polish your Lino and Stained floors.

The Mop is impregnated with O-Cedar Polish, padded to protect furniture, and when very dirty can be cleansed by washing with soap and water, and made new by adding a few drops of O-Cedar Polish.

Price **5/11** Carriage paid.

O-Cedar Polish.

THE DIFFERENT POLISH.

The O-Cedar is unlike any of the so-called Furniture Polishes. It is different in composition as well as in results, containing no grease, mineral by products or benzine.

4 oz.. **1/-** 12 oz., **2/-**
Quart-cans, **4/6**
Half-gallon cans, **6/9**
One-gallon cans, **10/6**
Always get the large sizes, it is cheaper.

The last word in VACUUM SWEEPERS

The "Rapid" Dust Extractor.

A Vacuum Cleaner and Sweeper combined.

Brooms and Bristle Carpet Sweepers entirely superseded Has a Wonderful Suction created by Twin-Bellows, connected with rubber-tyred wheels, and by simply running to and fro, sucks up all dirt and dust into the Filter.

Worked with one hand.

The Flexible Nozzle ensures efficiency at whatever position the machine is operated.

Made in solid oak, highly finished and polished metal fittings.

Hygienic Homes for all.

British made throughout.

Price **33/-** each complete. Carriage paid.

The Lino Rub.

Best for Linoleum and all Polished Floors.

A hard wooden core, japanned black, is covered with soft durable rubber, fluted " herring bone " pattern. The core has three flat faces, one for the application of the polish and the other two for polishing and finishing off. The " key " of the polisher (to enable the polishing cloth to be adjusted or changed) is a hardwood strip, extending lengthway along a groove on one of the three faces of the core.

No. 1.
Medium Size,
4 6

No. 2.
Large Size,
6/11

No. 3.
Medium Size
(Special Cheap Line)
1/6

The Solopulvo.

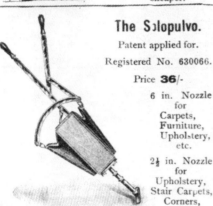

Patent applied for.

Registered No. 630066.

Price **36/-**

6 in. Nozzle for Carpets, Furniture, Upholstery, etc.

2½ in. Nozzle for Upholstery, Stair Carpets, Corners, etc.

Whitfield's Patent Carpet Nozzle .. **10/-** extra
Suction Brush for Linoleum.. .. **3/4** "

For use by one person.

A genuine vacuum cleaner, with suction on both forward and back strokes.

Very even working and regular suction.

Double bellows of special Pulvo fabric.

No loss of power. Simple to use. Weight 10 lbs.

Particularly useful for Stair Carpets.

THE "Star" Vacuum Cleaner.

The "STAR" is a single-handed Vacuum Cleaner. It is used like a broom. Light as a broom. It takes up no more room than a broom. Instead of pushing the dust about, it absorbs it. Draws it all into a bag without making a dust. Draws dust right through carpets.

Cleans carpets, stairs, Bedding, Furniture. It is very simple, no loose parts to lose.
30/- complete with plated tube and extra stair piece. Carr. paid.

All Vacuum Cleaners sent carriage paid.

The "Star" is a hand vacuum cleaner of simple construction and great draught, it is built by an old firm of ironfounders entirely of metal and is very strong. In form it is like a broom and the action in using is the same as a broom. It has a long piece for the floor sweeping and a short extra powerful piece for furniture, stairs, etc. There are no loose parts at all and nothing to get out of order. It is entirely of British origin and manufacture.
The Incorporated Institute of Hygiene, London, has granted their CERTICATE for the 'STAR' Vacuum Cleaner which is of the highest evidence of merit.

The Lever Pulvo Vacuum Cleaner.

Reg. No. 570385.

For the household there is no Vacuum Cleaner to equal the Lever Pulvo. It is strong, handy and inexpensive, being in fact specially designed for effective work combined with extreme portability.

This is the only machine of this type which has a separate and detachable dust box that can be carried away and emptied without the necessity of opening it in the room.

Price
£3 18 0

Carriage paid.

Including 6 in. Carpet, Curtain, Upholstery, etc., Nozzle, 2½ in. Upholstery, Stair Carpet, Corner Nozzle, 1 length Armoured and Canvas covered Hose, Long Hand Tube in two parts.

Whitfield's Patent Nozzle, 10/- extra. Suction Brush for Linoleum, 3/4 extra. Angle Suction Brush, 3/- extra. Extra Lengths, Hose, 1/6 per foot.

Liquid Veneer is not a varnish, nor a varnish stain, nor a colouring, but a scientifically prepared liquid food, cleaner and polish for all varnished or enamelled surfaces to which it is applied. It is a splendid preservative of the finish of furniture and woodwork, causing it to retain its brightness and beauty indefinitely. This makes it of great economical value to the housewife.

Furniture and Woodwork.

Liquid Veneer instantly removes scratches, stains, dirt, and dullness, destroys disease germs, and leaves a smooth, polished surface. If you have furniture with stains of any kind, even ink stains, or such stains as those frequently appearing on gold or gilt picture frames, chairs or cabinets, etc., it will be a revelation to you to see how effectually Liquid Veneer will remove them. It is of great value when used on the lower and medium qualities of furniture, as well as on mahogany, rosewood, ebony, golden-oak, white enamel, gilt, silver, brass and other finishes. Liquid Veneer is highly beneficial to any varnished, enamelled or painted surface, and is unexcelled for use on any polished woodwork or furniture.

It is not a varnish and no brush is needed—nothing but a piece of cotton cloth. There is no drying to wait for, and it leaves no streaks, gum or stickiness. It imparts a beautiful gloss and also acts as a perfect disinfectant, cleansing and purifying everything it touches.

For Cleaning.

Liquid Veneer will instantly remove every bit of grease from all surfaces to which it is applied. On that account it is well suited to renovating kitchen tables, sinks of all kinds, kitchen woodwork and enamelled and lacquered surfaces. Sewing machines may be so thoroughly and beautifully redressed as to defy anyone to distinguish them from new. Not only this, but dust will not adhere to them so quickly as before.

Liquid Veneer is put up in several sizes. The 1/- and 2/- packages are the popular sizes, but many people are purchasing the preparation in larger packages and using it not only for interior work, but for motor car, bicycles, carriages, etc. Below is the description and price list of the various packages:—

Four-ounce Bottle .. **1/-**   Twelve-ounce Bottle .. **2/-**   Quarts .. **4/-**   Half-Gallons .. **7/-**   Gallons .. **12/-** each.

CARPET SWEEPERS.

THE WORLD'S FINEST SELECTION AND LARGEST STOCK.

THE GREAT GROWTH

the use of Carpet Sweepers during recent years, has caused us to make a distinct feature of the **best brands** on the market. The following is believed to be the best selection of patterns known in the trade.

A Carpet Sweeper has now become a necessity in every household.

THE BENEFIT OF A CARPET SWEEPER

Arises from the ease and speed with which it does the work. It causes neither stooping nor backache, and does not permit any dust to escape into the room. The sweeping is done more thoroughly than that done by a broom under the most favourable conditions; and it is less troublesome, inasmuch as the sweepings are taken right out of the carpet into the machine, and so carried completely away.

Bissell's Ball Bearing 'Parlour Queen.'

Bissell's "Parlour Queen" Carpet Sweeper is all its name implies, and is one of our most highly finished carpet Sweepers. The case of the "Parlour Queen" is made of Rosewood, beautifully figured and given the highest quality piano polish. All the metal parts are of original design, and well finished in nickel plate.

Price .. **21/-**
Carriage Paid.

Bissell's Ball Bearing "Elite."

The "Elite" is a new design in carpet sweepers and combines elegance and richness in style. The case is entirely new in shape, being oval, thus securing artistic effect and at the same time giving the sweeper unusual solidity. The woods used in making the case of the "Elite" are of the choicest, being made in Hungarian Ash, Curly Birch Mahoganized, Brazilian Rosewood and Curly Maple in Seal Brown. The bail and metal ends are also specially designed to harmonize with the artistic lines of the case, all the trimmings being nickelled.

Price .. **20/-**
Carriage Paid.

TOY SIZES.

These are delightfully instructive Toys, which sweep in a miniature way, and retain the sweepings like the real machine.

Practically a bye-product of the Bissell factory, and on that account offered at very low prices.

Baby .... 11½d.
The Child's, 1/5½
The Little Queen, 1/11½
The Little Jewel 2/7½

Carriage Forward.

**New Brushes, 3/- New Tyres, 6d. each
New Tyre-wheel** complete ... ... **"**

Domestic de Luxe.

(SPECIAL).

A Perfect Combined Cleaner and Sweeper.

The finest all-round cleaning device on the market. Has the largest vacuum slot made. Ball bearing throughout, patented roller adjustment in front, carpet sweeper brush attachment to throw in or out which works perfectly on any carpet or rug, complete hose attachments for cleaning everything in the home. The ideal machine for cleaning efficiently and getting every bit of dust on every article from cellar to roof.

PRICES.

Complete with Sweeper and Attachments	£5	0 0
With Sweeper, but no Attachments	4	5 0
,, Attachments, but no Sweeper	4	5 0
Without Sweepers or Attachments	3	10 0

Model F.

This is a smaller and lighter machine than the de Luxe, carpet sweeper attachment underneath same as in the de Luxe, only smaller, gets all the dirt and litter whether on the carpet or in it.

PRICES.

With Sweeper	£2	2 0
Without Sweeper	1	12 0

HOTEL SIZES.

These sweepers are especially designed for sweeping large surfaces in Hotels, Halls, Corridors, etc. Being wider than the ordinary sweepers they do the work in much less time. The cases are made of oak.

Bissell's Ball Bearing "Grand."

Width over all, 17 in.   Width of Brush, 13½ in.
Price .. **23/9**

Bissell's "Cyco" Bearing "Club."

Width over all, 25 in.   Width of Brush, 21 in.
Price .. **33/3**

Bissell's "Cyco" Bearing "Hall."

Width over all, 28 in.   Width of Brush, 24½ in.
Price .. **40/-**
Carriage paid.

Carpet Sweepers of any make are promptly REPAIRED by experts at very moderate charges.

Bissell's Ball Bearing "Grand Rapids."

The most Popular Sweeper in the World

The "Grand Rapids" Sweeper is now fitted with ball bearings. It runs so easily, a mere touch propels it, and its efficiency as a dust extractor is greatly increased. This sweeper is fitted with new pressed steel wheels and improved dust proof axle tube, which ensure free and easy working. The case is made in six assorted choice cabinet woods.

No. 1.   With ball bearings and japanned fittings—
Price .. **15/-**
No. 2.   With ball bearings and nickel fittings—
Price .. **16/6**
Carriage Paid.

Bissell's "Cyco" Bearing "Universal."

An old Sweeper under a new name.

Formerly known as our regular "Grand Rapids."
Supplied only with "Cyco" Bearings and Japanned Fittings in eight varieties of handsome hardwood. This sweeper combines the best mechanical equipment with the least expensive quality of finish.
Price .. **14/-**
Carriage Paid.

Bissell's "Cyco" Bearing "Superior."

Nickelled Fittings.

The "Superior" has a single automatic dump for each pan, and contains all improvements such as "Cyco" bearings, dust-proof axle tubes, anti-raveler, reversible bail spring, etc.
Price .. **15/6**
Carriage Paid.

The "Standard." Popular Model

A Strong and Durable Sweeper

The patterns shown on this page have ample power for medium carpets, but like all non cyco sweepers they cannot tackle the heavy piles for which the cyco-bearing movement was created. They are well built, with brushes of pure bristle, and are fully guaranteed.
Price .. **11/3**
Carriage Paid.

The "Crown Jewels" Sweeper

Similar to above, price **10/6**

A. W. G.'s Celebrated Mangling and Wringing Machines.

The "Gamage."

No. X. 18.

Rollers, 20 in. by 6 in., Brass Caps	£2	5	6
,, 21 in. by 6 in. ,,		2 7 0
,, 22 in. by 6 in. ,,		2 8 3
,, 24 in. by 6 in. ,,		2 10 6
,, 27 in. by 6 in. ,,		2 16 9

Superior Quality. Fine Polished Rollers.

Extra Powerful Springs.

NO BETTER MANGLE MADE AT ANY PRICE.

Broken in Transit.—Should any Machine be broken by the Railway Company or Carriers, it should be returned to us at once, marked "Carriage Free, Broken in Transit," and an advice forwarded by Post.

The "Gamage" Improved Table Mangle.

The "Gamage" is the most cleverly designed Table Mangle in existence. Being small, compact, and light, it can easily be stowed away after use; yet is in every way an absolutely efficient machine, and so strong as to be almost unbreakable. Every part is carefully made and thoroughly tested. The New Lever Handle in place of a balance wheel—saves space, and works with the greatest ease.

When reversed, it is not only out of the way, but also forms a Safety Lock to prevent the cogs and rollers from turning. The "Gamage" is, in fact, the Ideal Machine for every house where space is valuable.

Sizes and Prices—Best Quality Rollers:

16 in. by 3½ in. **19 11**   18 in. by 3½ in. **21 9**   20 in. by 3½ in. **22/9**

Delivered Free within London Radius.

Country and Abroad Carriage Forward.

Every part of this little Machine is strong and durable. The framework is made of wrought iron combined with cast iron. There are four steel spiral springs, and three powerful clamps.

The "City."

No. X. 11.

Best Value ever offered.

Rollers, 18 in. by 5¼ in. ..	..	**36 9**
,, 20 in. by 5¼ in. ..	..	**37 9**
,, 21 in. by 5¼ in. ..	..	**38 9**
,, 22 in. by 5¼ in. ..	..	**39 3**
,, 24 in. by 5¼ in. ..	..	**40 9**

Equal quality. Cannot be bought elsewhere except at 25 per cent. over these prices.

BEST LONDON MAKE.

Selected Maple Rollers.

Every Machine Guaranteed.

The "New Era" Wringer.

On Ball Bearings.

Standard high grade Rollers.

Steel Springs.

Wheel Pressure Screws.

Extra Large Folding Apron.

Size of Rollers—

10 in.   12 in.   14 in.

	Usual price	Gamage price
10 in.	20/6 ..	**15/11**
12 in.	25/6 ..	**18/11**
14 in.	36/6 ..	**21 6**

All Mangles and Wringers delivered Carriage Free in London.

Outside London carrier radius Carriage forward.

OUR SPECIAL LEADING LINE.

The "Beatorl" Mangle.

Remarkable Value. Guaranteed throughout. This Mangle has been placed on the Market to meet the demand for a cheap but serviceable Mangle, and we are confident of its giving every satisfaction.

Made in One Size only, 18 in. by 5 in. Selected Rollers.

Price	..	..	..	..	**30/9**

BEST LONDON MAKE.

With Brass Caps, 1/6 extra.

Absolutely the Cheapest Mangle on the Market.

Free delivery in London District.

Country and Abroad carriage forward.

The "Tweenie" (Regd.)

The design of the "Tweenie" which is quite new is something between an Ordinary and a Table Mangle. Like the former it stands on the floor, but the pressure and gear arrangements are similar to those of a Table Machine. As the "Tweenie" however does not need to be lifted, we have been able to fit it with extra strong gear wheels and 4-in. rollers, a course we do not adopt with Table Mangles because the extra weight would make them troublesome for a woman to lift. The "Tweenie" is a very capable and practical little machine and its price is remarkably low.

Made in 2 sizes : Rollers 18 by 4in., **26/11**

20 by 4 ,, **29/11**

If fitted with Brass Caps, 1/6 extra.

STERLING.

The "STOWAWAY." The Latest Speciality.

Is an easy-running and reliable Mangle which can be used as a Table when not required for mangling or wringing. It is so cleverly designed and nicely balanced that the change can be made in a moment and without effort. Just one easy movement and the thing is done. It is undoubtedly the best machine of its kind on the market, the easiest to manage, the safest and the most efficient, and we strongly recommend it for all houses and flats in which space is limited.

The rollers are of selected maple, and are usually made 20 in. by 4 in., a very suitable size for the work of small households. The pressure arrangements are excellent, four steel spiral springs being provided.

18 in. by 4 in. Rollers, **37/9**   20 in. by 4 in. Rollers, **41/-**

The larger size is recommended.

PATENT

STERLING.

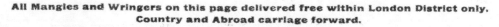

All Mangles and Wringers on this page delivered free within London District only. Country and Abroad carriage forward.

The Gamage Magic Table.

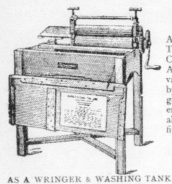

An ingenious but simple combination of Mangle, Wringer, Washing Tank and Table, eminently suitable for flats and small houses, where space is limited. Can be converted into a table, mangle or washing tank in a very few moments. As a **Table**, sides and legs of very strong American maple wood, neatly varnished, whitewood top; really looks like a table. Dimensions 31½ in. height by 34 by 23½ in. As a **Washing Tank**, the tank is constructed of strong galvanised iron, fitted with outlet, plug, &c. As **Mangle** and **Wringer**, entirely new design, compact and practically unbreakable. The tank catches all the drips. Constructed of wrought iron bars embeded in cast iron and fitted with 4 spiral steel springs. Rollers of selected American maple.

Size of rollers, 18 by 3½ in. Price .. **42/6**

Carriage forward outside London district.

AS A WRINGER & WASHING TANK. AS A TABLE.

"UNEEDA" Washing Machine.

The "UNEEDA" is the best of all washers, the simplest in construction, the easiest to use, the kindest to clothes. Clothes are worn out faster by rubbing than by wear. The washboard and the brush work havoc with fine laces, and make ragged seams and edges. The "UNEEDA" washer does not injure the most delicate fabric; it is steam and water tight, and makes no sloppy floors. The tub is made of white cedar and will not leak. The inside of the tub is corrugated. The fly-wheel turns in either direction and gives a reversing motion to the dolly. The ball-bearing mechanism enables the machine to be worked with the greatest ease. Every washer warranted. Satisfaction guaranteed.

The "President" Wringer.

This Machine has best tempered steel spring, iron fixing screws, and ACME Rubber Rollers with Cogs on both ends.

Guaranteed for one year— Fair wear and tear excepted.

To fix on Round or Square Tub or Table.

Order No.	Size of Rollers.	Price
X. 10	12 in.	**19/11**
X. 11	14 in.	**21/-**
X. 13	16 in.	**25/6**

Free Delivery in London District. Country, Carriage forward.

Prices—"Uneeda" Washer with fly-wheel **39/6**

12 in. "Uneeda" Wringer with ball-bearings **24/9**

We also supply a cheaper pattern Washer on same principle but operated by a lever instead of fly-wheel. Price .. **26/6**

SPECIAL NOTICE.—Prices of Rubber Wringers are apt to fluctuate according to the state of the markets.

THE WASHING PROBLEM SOLVED.

No more worry about Washing Day,

THE SUNRISE PATENT WASHING MACHINE

has proved its claim to popularity as a public benefactor because

It Lightens Labour, Saves Time, and Washes Clothes as if Washed by Hand.

A Child using the Sunrise Washer can do a woman's work in quarter the time. DO IT BETTER & ENJOY DOING IT.

The "SUNRISE" Washing Machine gets through all the hard work of Washing Days, the actual cleaning of the clothes, in a way which will simply delight you.

The "SUNRISE" Washing Machine has a capacity of holding either 10-15 Shirts, or 30-40 Towels, 4 Sheets or 2 Blankets.

Price 42/- only. Complete with Brass Tap. Wooden Table Top.

The Sunrise is useful for other purposes. By taking out the rocker which can be hung up on a wall, you can convert the tank into a convenient table by putting a wooden lid on the top. It also makes useful Tank for washing up dishes. It can be used as a Bath for children.

Delivery Free in London. Country Carriage Forward.

The "SUN" Washer.
(Improved Pattern.)

Not only a useful Washer, but a Piece of Furniture

In placing before our numerous Customers the above Washer (which is now considered to be one of the most useful and compact Washers ever placed on the market), we wish to point out the principal improvements:—

The depth of Tub has been increased from 1 ft. 2 in. to 1 ft. 4 in., thereby increasing the holding capacity considerably. The length of Table Top has been increased from 3 ft. 1 in. to 3 ft. 8 in. The Lid to prevent the water from splashing out on to the operator, when washing, can be utilised for a Scrubbing Board. An arrangement is fixed at back of Tub which acts as a Splash Board and Soap Tray.

Besides the above there are a number of minor improvements, all of which will, we hope, help to make the Washer a success. The manipulation of the Washer is very easy, and can be accomplished by any ordinary strong girl. There is an outlet at the side by which the water can be readily drained off. A Wood Plug is supplied with each Machine, but a Brass Tap can be fitted, if required, at a slight extra cost.

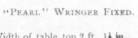

SHOWING WASHER CONVERTED INTO A TABLE.

X. 1. "Sun" Washer, fitted with 15 by 3½ in. Pearl Wringer, with Wood Rollers, and fitted with Brass Tap.

SHOWING WASHER WITH 18 in "PEARL" WRINGER FIXED.

Price .. .. **£3 18 9** Width of table top 1 ft. 9 in.

X. 2. "Sun" Washer, fitted with 18 by 3½ in. "Pearl" Wringer, with Wood Rollers. Price **£4 5 0** Width of table top 2 ft. 1½ in.

Brass Tap 3/- extra. SENT DIRECT FROM FACTORY. CARRIAGE FREE IN ENGLAND.

Write for Full Departmental List sent post free anywhere.

I 1

GAMAGES OF HOLBORN. — 145 — **BENETFINKS OF CHEAPSIDE.**

THE FINEST SELECTION OF **WRITING CASES** IN THE . . BRITISH ISLES.

No. F. 6.
The "Popular" Writing Case.
Straight grain leather, nickel fittings.

Size.	Price.
8½ in.	**26**
9½ in.	**3/9**

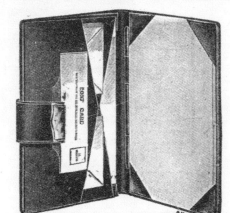

No. F. 3. Useful **Writing Case.** Straight grain leather. Nickel fittings.
Size 8¾ in. .. **1/6**   Size 9¾ in. .. **1/11½**

No. F. 7.
The 'Favourite' Writing Case.
Seal Grain Leather.

8¼ in. .. **3/3**
9½ in. .. **4/6**

Nickel fittings. Calendar, Paper Knife, Folding Blotter.

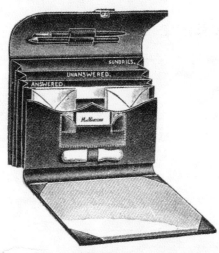

No. F. 29.
The "Compact" Writing Case.
Straight grain leather, nickel fittings.
Capacious pockets, as illustration.
Size 10 in. Price **6/11**

No. F. 37827½.
The "Holborn" Writing Case.
Long grain roan leather. Fitted with Nickel Safety Ink Bottle, Calendar, Paper Knife. Mounted with two Sterling Silver Corners.
Size 8½ in. .. **8/6**   Size 10 in. .. **10 6**

No. F. 27.
The "Special" Writing Case.
Crocodile Grained Leather.

Fitted with Nickel safety Ink Bottle. Nickel Fittings.

Size 8½ in. .. **7/6**   Size 10 in. .. **9,6**

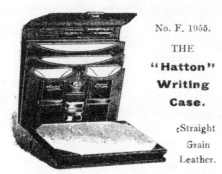

No. F. 1955.
THE "Hatton" Writing Case.
Straight Grain Leather.

Lined throughout in straight grain leather.
Fitted with Journal and Address Book, Nickel Ink Bottle, Nickel Fittings.
Size, 8½ in. .. **9/11**   10 in. .. **13/9**

No. F. 17.
The "Tourist" Writing Case.
Seal grain leather. Loose Blotter. Roomy pockets, nickel fittings.
Size 8½ in. .. **8/3**   Size 10 in. .. **10/6**

No. F. 34121.
The "Viaduct" Writing Case.
Grained roan leather. Lined throughout in straight grain leather. Fitted with Nickel safety Ink bottle. Nickel fittings. Size 10½ in. **15/9**

WRITING ATTACHE CASES.

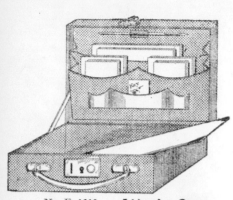

No. F. 1610. **Attache Case.**
Grained leather top. Loose Blotting Pad.
Stationery and Stamp Pockets.
Size 10 in. by 7 in. by 3 in. Price **5/9**
AN EXCEPTIONALLY FINE VALUE.
Size 13¾ by 8½ by 3½ in. Price **8/11**

No. F. 622. **Attache Case.** Solid Hide.
Extra deep. Lined straight grain leather.
Pockets for stationery Loose Blotter.
Memo and Address Book. Nickel Safety Ink.
Size 12 in., **24/6** 14 in., **30/-**

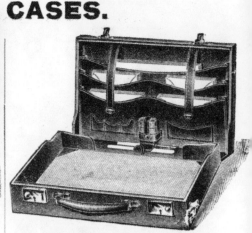

No. F. 6005. **Attache Case.**
Long grain leather with deep back cover.
Fitted with Stationery Pockets. 2 strap fastenings.
Gilt Safety Ink. Penholder and Paper Knife.
Size 14 in., **34/9** 12 in. with 1 lock only, **28/6**

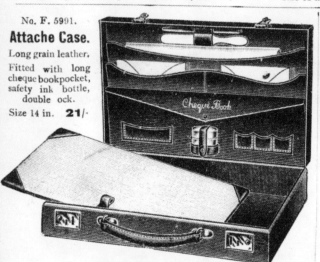

No. F. 5991.

Attache Case.

Long grain leather.

Fitted with long
cheque book pocket,
safety ink bottle,
double ock.

Size 14 in. **21/-**

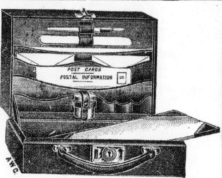

No. F. 34753. **Attache Case.**
Straight grain leather top.
Fitted with Stationery and Stamp Pockets.
Nickel Safety Ink Bottle. Nickel Fittings.
Size 10 in., **7/9** 12 in., **9/9** 14 in., **12/9**
No F. 5987. Similar to above. Superior quality
and finish. Prices **10/11 13/11** and **16/11**

No. F. 1755A. EXCEPTIONAL VALUE.
Attache Case Solid leather.
Hide colour. Fitted with Stationery Pockets,
Memo and Address Books, Blotting Pad,
Safety Ink, Paper Knife, Strong Handle,
2 Nickel Locks. Size 14 by 9½ by 3½ in. **17/6**

No. F. 1742. Style as above. Fitted with
full length Cheque Book Pocket, **19/9**

No. F. 6002. **Attache Case.** Long grain leather.
Fitted with Blotter, Safety Ink, Memo and Address Books, Scissors,
Paper Knife, etc. Gilt Fittings. Size 14 in. Price **37/6**
No. F. 6012. Above style. Best quality HIDE. Lined long grain leather.
Price .. **63/-**

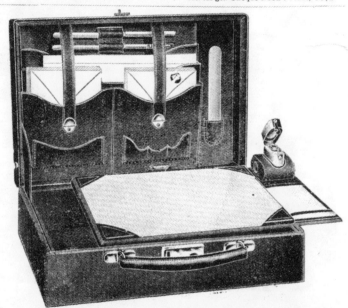

No. F. 6000. **Attache Case.** Long grain leather. Fitted Stationery
Pockets, Safety Ink, Blotting Pad fits top of well, leaving space for papers,
etc., underneath. Size 12 in., **29/6** Size 14 in., fitted with 2 locks, **36/6**

Stationery Department.

PENS OF EVERY MAKE IN STOCK.

Firefly Pen.

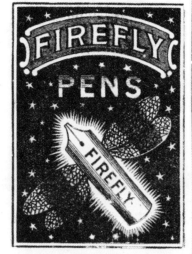

This pen has been specially designed to suit those writers requiring a smooth rapid nib done up in boxes of 18 and 1 gross. Firefly Pens, specially recommended, are heavily gilt, which prevents tarnishing, and also renders them much more durable. 6d. size, **4½d.** Gross boxes, **3/-**

Easterbrook's Relief Pen.
No. N.314. In boxes, 6d. size, **4½d.** Per gross, **2/6** Postage 2d.

Macniven & Cameron's Pens.
"Pickwick," "Owl," "Waverley," "Hindoo" (Nos. 1, 2, 3), and "Big Waverley," or Assorted. 6d. size, **4½d.** Gross Boxes, **2/8** 1/- size, **9d.**

Hewitt's Patent Ball-pointed.
Ball-pointed Pens have been specially manufactured to suit those who desire a perfectly smooth writing pen. The nib having a small ball at the point prevents scratching or spurting.

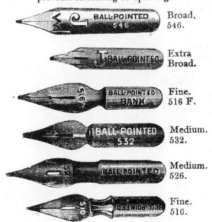

Broad, 546.

Extra Broad.

Fine. 516 F.

Medium. 532.

Medium. 526.

Fine. 510.

In boxes of 18 .. 6d. size, **4½d.**

Gamage's School Pens.
The Federation Pen.
1 gross pens in box . **10½d.** Postage 2d, Fine and medium points.

The New Pen for Rapid Writing.
The Regina Pen in Silver or Gilt.
Suitable for any writer or paper.
Sample Box of Silver and Gilt, assorted, **4½d.** Post 1d.

The "Horseshoe" Pen.

(An oblique pointed Reservoir Pen. Specially adapted for quick writers.
Treble Gilt. Contains sufficient ink to write a whole letter. Boxes containing 18 pens, **11d.** per box. Boxes containing half gross, **3/6** per box.

New Metal Pens.
These pens are specially made to resist the acids of all inks, and are the nearest approach to the action of gold pens.

No.

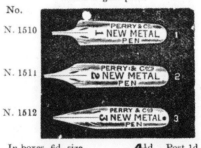

N. 1510

N. 1511

N. 1512

In boxes, 6d. size .. .. **4½d.** Post 1d.
1 gross boxes .. **3/4** ,, 2d.

PERRY'S PENS.
The Lady Pen.
In fine, medium and broad points.

No 24.

1 doz. box, 6d. size .. .. **4½d.**

All Perry's Pens supplied to order.

William Mitchell's Pens.
Mitchell's Black **J**, 2 doz. box, 6d. size, **4½d.**
" " " " " **4½d.**
" **G** Pen, for Fine Writing.
2 doz. box. 6d. size .. .. **4½d.**
Postage 1d.
Also supplied in gross boxes at **2/3** Postage 2d.

BRANDAUER S Circular-pointed Pens.
The Review Pen

6d. size, **4½d.** .. .. Gross boxes, **2/-**
Strong and moderately fine pointed, best gilt.

Baltic Pen, 6d. size, **4½d.** Gross boxes, **2/11**

Gilt, Broad-pointed Pen, with beautiful quill-like action.

Mail Pen, 6d. size, **4½d.** Gross box, **2/7**

Strong pen, with coarse fine points—also in extra fine and medium points. 18 pens in box.

Times Pen, 6d. size, **4½d.** Gross box, **2/-**

Strong Pen, moderately fine and flexible—also in extra fine and medium points.

Punch Pen, 6d. size, **4½d.** Gross box, **1/10**

Moderately flexible, with coarse fine points—also in extra fine and medium points. 24 in box.

Oriental Pen, 6d. size, **4½d.** Gross box, **1/4**

Extra fine pointed and extremely flexible, fo correspondence—also in fine points. 36 in box.

Herald Pen, 6d. size, **4½d.** Gross, **1/4**

Extra fine and hard, for ladies' use—also in medium points. 36 in box.

Arctic Pen, 6d. size, **4½d.** Gross, **1/11**

Extra fine and very flexible, for foreign correspondence—also in fine points. 24 pens in box.

Brandauer's celebrated J Nibs

J Pen—a very superior pen in F., M., B. points.

N.B.—The Silver Steel J Pen is made rather rounder in the point than the regular J pen and in the B points only. 6d. boxes, 2 doz., **4½d.** Gross boxes, gilt, **2/-**
Large J Pen—a splendid pen for bold and professional writing, in B points.

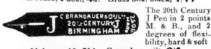

6d. boxes, 2 doz., **4d.** Gross box, black, **1/11**

The 20th Century J Pen in 2 points M. & B., and 2 degrees of flexibility, hard & soft

6d. boxes, 18, **4½d.** Gross box, gilt, **2/4**
Sample Boxes containing an assortment of the two points and flexibilities.
All Brandauer's Pens not listed can be supplied to order
Post extra—6d. boxes, 1d. Gross boxes, 3d.

The Gamage 1914 Improved Folding Pocket and Film Camera.

Model P. I.
1914 Pattern Superb Camera.

The No. P. 1. Model is the best and cheapest ¼-plate Camera offered. costing less than 20/- The body is made of seasoned wood, covered in morocco-grained leatherette, all metal parts are polished black or nickel-plated. The front is the new U pattern, very rigid. This is adjusted for rising or cross movement. Hooded focussing and 2 single metal slides are included with outfit. The lens is of good quality, being an R.R. working at F/8. in

New Model time and instantaneous shutter, giving time bulb and instantaneous exposures.

Prices—

Camera and 2 Plate Holders, 3½ by 2½	..	..	**18/9**
Do. do. ¼-plate	..	..	**19/11**
Do. do. Post-card, 5½ by 3½		..	**35/-**
Extra Slides, 3½ by 2½, each	..	..	**9½d.**
Do. ¼-plate, each ..	..	..	**10½d.**
Do. Post-card, each ..	..	..	**1/2½**
Film Pack Adapters, 3½ by 2½, each	..	..	**4/3**
Do. ¼-plate, each	..	..	**4/6**
Do. Post-card, each ..	..	..	**5/9**

Post free.

Model P. 2.
1914 Pattern Superb Camera.

No. P. 2 Model, similar to No. P. 1, but very much better finish. Body covered with leather. It has double extension and is fitted with superior lens and shutter. The lens is an Aplanat working at F7/·7, and the shutter gives exposures from 1/25, 1/50, 1/100th part of second.

Prices—

Camera and 2 Plate Holders, 3½ by 2½	..	..	..	**42/3**
Do. do. ¼-plate	..	..	..	**45/-**
Do. do Post-card, 5½ by 3½	..	..	..	**61/9**
Extra Slides, 3½ by 2½, each	..	..	..	**9½d.**
Do. ¼-plate, each ..	..	..	..	**10½d.**
Do. Post-card, 5½ by 3½	..	..	..	**1/2½**
Film Pack Adapters, 3½ by 2½ ..	..	..	..	**4/3**
Do. ¼-plate..	..	..	..	**4/6**
Do. Post-card	..	..	..	**5/9**

Post free.

New Model
1914 Superb Film or Plate Camera.

Daylight Loading.

Best Value ever offered.

Made in ¼-plate and Post-card Sizes.

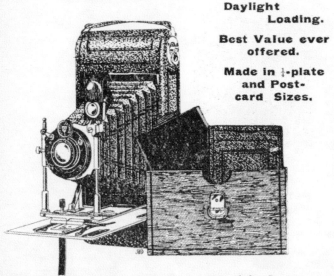

Fitted with rising and cross front, double brilliant finder, Leonar automatic shutter with antinous release giving time and instantaneous exposures 1/25, 1/50, 1/100th seconds. Extra rapid aplanat lens of good quality working at f/8 aperture, has aluminium base and covered in good quality leatherette complete with three dark slides and focussing screen in wallet.

PRICES.

¼-plate size..	..	..	..	**£2 1 9**
Post-card size	..	..		**2 5 3**

THE GAMCAM.

A ¼-plate Double Extending-Roll-film Camera,
With Rapid Rectilinear Lens f/7.7, Ibso Shutter, &c.

GAMAGE'S SPECIAL OFFER.

A well-made and well-finished Roll-film Camera, complete with every movement and all the best fittings. The Specification includes the following :—

Double Extension.

Rack Focussing.

Solid Cast Front.

Rack Rising Movement.

Cross Movement.

F/7.7 Rectilinear Lens.

Ibso Shutter, Speeds 1 to 1/100th second.

Antinous Release.

Brilliant View Finder.

Fitted with Plate Back.

Three Slides. Focussing Screen.

Film-pack Adapter.

A complete Outfit for Roll-films, Film-packs, or Plates.

Gamage's Price	..	..	**£3 19 6**

No better Value obtainable under £5.

Your Old Camera taken in Part Payment for a New One.

Model I.

Models VI. and VII.

45/- Watch Pocket Carbine

"The Perfect Miniature Camera."

The Watch-pocket Carbine is a day-light loading roll film Camera made in two sizes, taking standard size films that are obtainable in every part of the world.

This is the original Model Watch pocket Carbine. It has been perfected in many details; is provided with rising front and reversing finder. Covered in Morocco Leatherette and fitted with Lukos II. shutter, having adjustable speeds $\frac{2}{5}$, $\frac{1}{50}$ and $\frac{1}{100}$ secs.

The Cameras are of absolute minimum dimensions, thoroughly well constructed in every part, and although complete with every movement for all classes of photography, are so small that either size can be carried in the pocket all day without the least inconvenience.

Model III. ($2\frac{1}{4}$ by $2\frac{1}{4}$).

This model is similar in every respect to Model II. Fitted with compound shutter, but arranged to take plates $2\frac{1}{4}$ by $1\frac{3}{4}$ in dark slides, as well as the $2\frac{1}{4}$ by $2\frac{1}{4}$ roll films.

It is fitted with a direct vision view-meter so that it can be used at eye level, in addition to the ordinary type finder. Prices include two dark slides.

Takes $2\frac{1}{4}$ B 6-exposure Spools.

This is an entirely new model, manufactured on the latest and most approved principles, and now offered with every confidence of a huge success as a perfect Roll Film Camera. Although it takes a picture $2\frac{1}{4}$ by $3\frac{1}{4}$, it is very little bigger than the $2\frac{1}{4}$ by $2\frac{1}{4}$ Cameras. When closed it is most compact; it is free from any form of projection; opens instantly, and is as "ever ready" as a Magazine Camera, with the advantage of being twice as useful.

IT IS the Standard C.D.V. size.
IT IS of absolute minimum dimensions.
IT IS made entirely of metal.
IT IS of rock-steady construction.
IT IS a perfect miniature Camera.

Model I Prices.

		£	s	d
With Aldis Uno Anastigmat, f/7·7..		**£2**	**5**	**0**
,, Zeiss Triotar .. f 6·3..		**4**	**10**	**0**
Release Flexo **2/6** extra.				

Model II.

This model is similar to Model I. in all respects except that it is covered in real fine grain Morocco Leather, and is fitted with a compound shutter having speeds from 1 second to $\frac{1}{250}$ second.

Model II. Prices.

		£	s	d
Aldis Uno Anastigmat f/7·7 ..	..	**£3**	**7**	**6**
Beck Mutar do. f/4·9 ..	..	**4**	**17**	**6**
Zeiss Triotar do. f/6·3 ..	..	**5**	**12**	**6**
Dallmeyer IV. do. f/6·3 ..	..	**6**	**5**	**0**
Cooke IV. do. f/5·6 ..	..	**6**	**7**	**6**
Ross Homo do. f/6·8 ..	..	**6**	**17**	**6**
Zeiss Tessar do. f/6·3 ..	..	**7**	**2**	**6**
Zeiss Tessar do f/4·7 ..	..	**7**	**12**	**6**
Flexo Release	**2/6** extra.			

Model III Prices.

		£	s	d
Aldis Uno Anastigmat f/7·7..	..	**£4**	**4**	**0**
Beck Mutar do. f/4·9 ..	..	**5**	**14**	**0**
Zeiss Triotar do. f/6·3 ..	..	**6**	**10**	**0**
Dallmeyer IV. do. f/6·3 ..	..	**7**	**2**	**6**
Cooke IV. do. f/5·6 ..	..	**7**	**5**	**0**
Ross Homo. do. f/6·8 ..	..	**7**	**15**	**0**
Zeiss Tessar do. f/6·3 ..	..	**8**	**0**	**0**
Zeiss Tessar do. f/4·7 ..	..	**8**	**10**	**0**

Extra Dk. Slides, **1 6** ea.   Focussing Screen with Hood, **5/-**

Models VI. & VII. Prices.

			Model VI. Lukos II. Shutter.	Model VII. Compound Shutter.
Aldis Uno Anastigmat f/7·7..		**£3 5 0**	**£4 10 0**
Beck Mutar do. f/6		**3 15 0**	**5 0 0**
Beck Mutar do. f/4·9		**5 0 0**	**6 6 0**
Zeiss Triotar do. f/6·3..		**5 10 0**	**6 15 0**
Cooke Series III. do. f/6·5..		**—**	**7 15 0**
Ross Homocentric do. f/6·3..		**—**	**7 15 0**
Zeiss Tessar No. 3 do. f/6·3		**—**	**8 10 0**
Zeiss Tessar ,, 13 do. f/4·5..		**—**	**9 0 0**
Flexo Shutter Release	...		**2/6** extra.

The Watch-pocket "Klimax."

Model I. with Lukos Sector Shutter.

Model II. with Compound Sector Shutter.

Size ..	.	$3\frac{1}{4}$ by $2\frac{3}{8}$ by $1\frac{1}{4}$.
Weight	..	12 oz.

For Plates $2\frac{5}{16}$ by $1\frac{3}{4}$ (4·5 by 6 c/m.) or Film Pack.

The Watch-pocket "Klimax" is a Miniature Model of the well-known "Klimax" series of Cameras. It is a beautifully finished little instrument, has every desirable movement, and is so compact that it can be carried in the watch-pocket without inconvenience.

Prices (including two Dark Slides and Sling Shoulder Strap).

Model I. with Lukos II. Sector Shutter.

				£	s	d
Aldis Uno Anastigmat f/7·7	..	..	..	**£2**	**5**	**0**
Zeiss Triotar do. f/6·3	..	..	..	**4**	**10**	**0**

Model II. with Compound Sector Shutter.

					£	s	d
Aldis Uno Anastigmat f/7·7	..	..	..	..	**£3**	**7**	**6**
Beck Mutar do. f/4·9	..	..	..		**4**	**17**	**6**
Zeiss Triotar do. f/6·3	..	..	..		**5**	**12**	**6**
Zeiss Tessar do. f/4·7	..	..			**7**	**12**	**6**
Dark Slides, Single Metal ..	..					**1**	**6**
Film Pack Adapter	..					**7**	**6**
Daylight Enlarger, 10/1, for enlarging to $\frac{1}{2}$-plate	..				**8**	**6**
Case, Morocco, to carry Camera, six slides	..				**8**	**6**
Flexo Release						**2**	**6**

The "Klimax."

Model III.

SPECIAL FOR F/4·5 LENSES

For $3\frac{1}{4}$ by $4\frac{1}{4}$ inches, and

9 by 12 c/m. plates.

This Special Model "Klimax" is a Camera of superlative quality; every possible advantage has been introduced to make it perfect and to fulfil the requirements of the most exacting photographer. It is similar in construction to the Model II., but has an extra large body and large and massive front, in order that it may accommodate large-size shutters and lenses, and allow every possible movement.

Prices (including three Dark Slides).

					£	s	d
Aldis Butcher Anastigmat 6 in. f/4·5	..	..		**£10**	**15**	**0**
Cooke II. do. $5\frac{1}{2}$, f/4·5	..	..		**13**	**0**	**0**
Zeiss Tessar Ic. do. $5\frac{3}{8}$,, f/4·5	..	..		**13**	**7**	**0**
Ross Homocentric do. $5\frac{1}{2}$,, f/4·5	..	..		**13**	**10**	**0**
Goerz Dogmar do. $5\frac{1}{4}$,, f/4·5	..	..		**13**	**10**	**0**
Camera without Lens and Shutter	..				**5**	**5**	**0**

Accessories—

						£	s	d
Extra Dark Slides ..	..	..	..	..			**2**	**6**
Solid Leather Case	..	..	..	..			**10**	**6**

A Series of British-made Folding Plate Cameras

OF EXCELLENT DESIGN AND FINISH.

Small in Size, Practical and Reliable. Fitted with the "Stirrup" Shape Front.

Nos. P. 000 and P. 00.

Folding Klito.

A Camera with a **Stirrup front** for **21/**
Wood body, polished baseboard, nickelled fittings, well covered, leather bellows, reversible finder.

Junior Auto Shutter and one metal slide

No. P.	Lens.	¼-plate.	Post-card
000.	Rapid Achromatic ..	1 1 0	—
000A.	Rectimat Symmetrical ..	1 5 0	—

Ensign Simplex Auto Shutter,
With Speeds, two Slides and Antinous Release.

No. P.			
0.	Rapid Achromatic ..	1 5 0	—
00.	Rectimat Symmetrical ..	1 11 6	2 10 0
00K.	Ensign Anastigmat, F. 7·7	2 2 0	3 5 0
00N.	,, ,, F. 6	2 15 0	3 17 6
00D.	Aldis Plano ,, F. 6·8	2 15 0	3 17 6
00S.	Zeiss Triotar ,, F. 6·3	4 12 0	6 7 6

Nos. P. 3 and P. 4.

Folding Klito.

RACK AND PINION FOCUSSING.

A superior Model of Folding Klito, with all necessary movements and latest improvements.

Ensign Simplex Auto Shutter,
With Speeds, two Slides and Antinous Release.

No. P.	Lens.		¼-plate
3.	Rectimat Symmetrical ..	..	£2 2 0
3K.	Ensign Anastigmat, F. 7·7	..	2 12 6
3N.	,, ,, F. 6	..	3 5 0
3D.	Aldis Plano ,, F. 6·8	..	3 5 0
3S.	Zeiss Triotar ,, F. 6·3	..	5 5 0

Ensign Sector Shutter.

No P.	Speeds 1 sec. to 1/100 sec.		
4.	Rectimat Symmetrical ..	..	£2 10 0
4K.	Ensign Anastigmat, F. 7·7	..	3 0 0
4N.	,, ,, F. 6	..	3 12 6
4D.	Aldis Plano ,, F. 6·8	..	3 12 6
4S.	Zeiss Triotar ,, F. 6·3	..	5 12 6

Extra Single Metal Slides.
¼-plate, A, 2/-, B, 1/6 Post-card, A, 2/6, B, 1/6
Solid Leather Case .. 7/6 and 9/-

No. P. 3, P. 5 and P. 6.

Folding Klito.

Double Extension Cameras, for ¼-plate and Post-card sizes.

A new and improved series of Double Extension Cameras with Stirrup Front, wood body, polished baseboard, nickelled fittings, leather bellows & finder.

Ensign Sector Shutter, with speeds 1 sec. to 1/100 sec., two Slides and Antinous Release.

No. 5.—¼-plate.

With Rapid Aplanat Lens, f/8	£2 15 0
,, Ensign Anastigmat, f/7·7	3 5 0
,, ,, ,, f/5·5 (3 foci)	5 2 6
,, Aldis-Plano ,, f/6·8	3 15 0
,, Cooke-Luxor ,, f/6·8	4 12 6
,, Zeiss-Triotar ,, f/6·3	5 15 0
,, Zeiss-Tessar ,, f/6·3	7 10 0
,, Zeiss Double Amatar Lens, f/6·8	7 15 0
,, Goerz-Dagor Anastigmat, f 6·8	8 0 0

Koilos or Compound Shutter fitted for 15/- extra.

No. 6.—Post-card.

With Rapid Aplanat Lens, f/8	£3 5 0
,, Ensign Anastigmat, f/7·7	3 15 0
,, ,, ,, f/5·5 (3 foci)	5 15 0
,, Aldis-Plano ,, f/6·8	4 7 6
,, Cooke-Luxor ,, f/6·8	5 5 0
,, Zeiss-Triotar ,, f/6·3	6 17 6
,, Zeiss-Tessar ,, f/6·3	8 2 6
,, Zeiss Double Amatar Lens, f/6·8	8 12 6
,, Goerz-Dagor Anastigmat, f/6·8	9 7 6

Koilos or Compound Shutter fitted for 15/- extra.

Extra Single Metal Slides.
¼-plate, A, 2/-, B, 1/6 Post-card, A, 2/6, B, 2/-
Solid Leather Cases, 7/6 and 9/- each.

Folding Klito Junior.

The Folding Klito Juniors are entirely new. In use they are exceptionally simple. Every movement for good work is included, whilst the construction and finish are excellent in every way.

A very effective, automatic locking infinity catch is fitted. The lens front is particularly strong and rigid. The view finder reverses for upright or oblong pictures. An automatic opening Focussing Hood is supplied, which folds compactly when not in use. Bulb, Time as well as Instantaneous Exposures can be made, and there are "stops" of f/11, f/16, f/22 and f/32.

The Nos. 1, 2 and 2 PC. Cameras are fitted with Single Achromatic Lenses and Ensign Junior Auto Shutters, and the No. 1 a, with a Rapid Aplanat Lens, f/8, and an Ensign Simplex-Auto Shutter with varying speeds.

No. 1.	Folding Klito Junior	(3¼ by 2¼)	17/6
,, 1a.	,, ,, ,,	(3¼ ,, 2¼)	25/-
,, 2.	,, ,, ,,	(4¼ ,, 3¼)	18/6
,, 2PC.	,, ,, ,,	(5½ ,, 3½)	37/6

No. P. 9.

Folding Klito de Luxe.

¼-plate.

The Folding Klito de Luxe is a triumph for British Workmanship. Nothing at once so perfect in design, so strong and rigid in action, or so excellent in its construction has ever been offered at anything like the price.

Constructed in the best possible manner throughout and fitted with the rigid Stirrup Front and hinged travelling carriage; wood body covered in leather, with leather bellows and nickelled fittings throughout. Lever rising and falling front and simple cross front; focussing hood, large brilliant finder and level.

Ensign Sector Shutter.

With Speeds from 1 sec. to 1/100 sec. and two "A" quality Metal Slides.

No. P. 8. Single Extension.

WITH RACK AND PINION.

Folding Klito De Luxe with Ensign Anastigmat Lens, f/7·7 ..	£3 7 6
Folding Klito De Luxe with Aldis-Plano Anastigmat Lens, f/6·8 ..	3 17 6
Folding Klito De Luxe with Cooke-Luxor Anastigmat Lens, f/6·8 ..	4 15 0
Folding Klito De Luxe with Zeiss-Triotar Anastigmat Lens, f/6·3 ..	5 17 6
Folding Klito De Luxe with Zeiss-Tessar Anastigmat Lens, f/6·3 ..	7 12 6
Folding Klito De Luxe with Goerz Dagor Anastigmat Lens, f/6·8 ..	8 2 6

No. P. 9. Double Extension.

WITH RACK AND PINION. ¼-plate.

In addition to all features described in the SINGLE EXTENSION, this Model enables the back combinations of most of the lenses listed to be used. A special spring Infinity Catch is also fitted, which ensures the Front being drawn forward to the correct position for general views when the Camera is opened. Metal bellows Extenders are also fitted and come into action automatically when the front is racked out, bringing the larger folds of the bellows forward and preventing any of the picture from being cut off.

With Ensign Anastigmat Lens f/7·7	£4 12 6
,, Aldis-Plano ,, ,, f/6·8	5 2 6
,, Cooke-Luxor ,, ,, f/6·8	6 0 0
,, Zeiss-Triotar ,, ,, f/6·3	7 2 6
,, Zeiss-Tessar ,, ,, f/6·3	8 17 6
,, Zeiss Double Amatar Lens, f/6·8	9 2 6
,, Zeiss Double Protar Lens, f/7	11 7 6
,, Goerz-Dagor Anastigmat Lens f/6·8	9 7 6

Koilos or Compound Shutter in place of Shutter as listed	15/-
Single Metal Slides, 'A' quality .. each	2/-
Best Leather Case, velvet-lined, for Camera and 12 slides	9/-
Klito Plate Pack Adapter	5/-

All Cameras on this Page sent Post Free.

"Pilot."

Sizes—

3½ by 2½ and

¼-plate.

Specification.

CAMERA.—Thoroughly well made in seasoned wood, covered in Morocco-grained leatherette, strong solid leather handle.

LENS.—Rapid achromatic of fine covering power.

MAGNIFIERS.—Revolving by outside lever for objects at 4 and 8 feet.

DIAPHRAGMS.—Revolving f/11, f/16, f/22, f/32 operated from outside.

SHUTTER. Adjustable for time and instantaneous exposures, with catch for long time exposures.

FINDERS.—Ground-glass or horizontal and vertical pictures.

PLATE CHANGING.—Absolutely reliable; plates inserted in any order.

RECORDER.—Showing number of plates or films expos d.

Prices.

No. P. 1. Complete for 6 plates, 3½ by 2½ **7/6**
,, P. 2. ,, 6 ,, 4¼ ,, 3¼ **10/6**
,, P. 3. ,, 12 ,, 4¼ ,, 3¼ **12/6**

The Beck-Pilot."

For 6 plates

3¼ by 2¼

Specification.

CAMERA.—Thoroughly well made in seasoned wood, covered in Morocco-grained leatherette, strong solid leather handle.

LENS.—Beck Rapid Rectilinear.

MAGNIFIERS.—Revolving by outside lever for objects at 4 and 8 feet.

DIAPHRAGMS.—Revolving between lens, f/11, f/16, f/22, f/32.

SHUTTER.—Adjustable for time and instantaneous exposures, with catch for long time exposures.

FINDERS.—Ground-glass for horizontal and vertical pictures.

PLATE CHANGING.—Absolutely reliable; plates inserted in any order.

RECORDER.—Showing number of plates or films exposed.

EXPOSURE SIGNAL.—For preventing two exposures on one plate.

Prices.

No. P. 4. Complete for 6 plates, 3¼ by 2¼ **13/6**

The "Clincher."

Sizes—3¼ by 2¼ and ¼-plate

Specification.

CAMERA.—Thoroughly well made in seasoned wood, covered in real Morocco-grained leatherette and with strong solid leather handle.

LENS.—Rapid landscape of fine covering power.

DIAPHRAGMS.—Revolving, f/11, f/16, f/22, f/32, operated outside.

SHUTTER.—Adjustable for time and instantaneous exposures with catch for long time exposures.

FINDERS.—Ground-glass for horizontal and vertical pictures.

PLATE CHANGING.—Absolutely reliable; plates inserted in any order.

Prices.

No. P. 1. Complete for 6 plates, 3½ by 2½ **5/6**
,, P. 2. ,, 5 ,, 4¼ ,, 3¼ **7/6**
,, P. 3. ,, 12 ,, 4¼ ,, 3¼ **10/6**

"Nipper" Cameras.

The Improved "Little Nipper" Camera.

Holds 6 plates. Takes pictures 2 5/16ths by 1⅞.

A perfect Magazine Camera, Time and Instantaneous Shutter. Well finished and thoroughly practicable.

Price 2/10½

Specification.

CAMERA.—Thoroughly well made in seasoned wood, covered inmorocco-grained leatherette, withstrong carrying handle

LENS.—Rapid Landscape of good covering power.

DIAPHRAGMS.—Revolving, f/11, f/16, f/22.

SHUTTER.—Adjustable for time and instantaneous exposures.

FINDERS.—Gunrod-glass for horizontal and vertical pictures.

PLATE CHANGING.—Veryreliable, plates inserted in any order.

Developing and Printing Outfit

Price ... 2/10½

The DANDYCAM Automatic Camera.

For Photo-Button Photography.

Photography with Dandycam is simplicity itself. Even a child can work it successfully. No dark room or outfit is required. The Camera is complete. After exposure the plates are developed and fixed in the Camera—a finished photograph being ready three minutes after exposure. The Dandycam can be loaded in daylight.

This photograph shows the actual size and style of photo-buttons taken in a Dandycam.

Outstanding Features

Body is of wood.
Covered in Morocco leatherette.
Lens of great rapidity.
Finder shows a full-sized image.
Shutter is opened by the milled head at side of Camera.
Developing box is fittted in the back of Camera.
Magazine holds 12 plates.
Loaded in daylight.
No dark room necessary.

Price complete .. **7/6**

Accessories.

Spare Developing Tanks **6**d. Dandycam Developer, bt **6**d.
Dandycam Plates, doz, **6**d. Ditto, in powders **6**d.
Dandycam Brooches, per dozen, **2**/-

The "STEREOLETTE."

A MINIATURE STEREOSCOPIC CAMERA.

For Plates 4¼ by 1¾ in. (45 by 107 m/m).

The "Stereolette" is a dainty little camera taking stereoscopic pictures on plates 4¼ by 1¾ in. (45 by 107 m/m). It is so small and compact that the camera and 6 slides can be comfortably carried in a jacket pocket. The size is "International" and the plates and film packs can be purchased all over the world.

The "Stereolette" Camera is made of metal and is leather-covered. The front is a solid U casting, unrivalled for strength and rigidity, the lens and shutter is made to rise by means of a rack. Focussing is by rack and pinion. There is a bush for tripod and a hooded focussing screen is supplied. A large brilliant finder is fitted as well as a spirit-leve. The shutter fitted to the standard model is an Everset Sector, but the Compound Sector is fitted as an extra. Aldis "Uno" Anastigmat lenses f/7.7 are fitted, and the negatives produced are needle sharp.

PRICES (including two dark slides).

No 1. Aldis "Uno" Anastigmat, f/7·7	..	**£4**	**4**	**0**
,, 2. ,, Compound Shutter	..		**6**	**0**	**0**
3. Zeiss Tessar, f 6·3 ,,	..		**13**	**0**	**0**
,, 4. ,, f/4·5 ,,	..		**14**	**0**	**0**

Accessories.

Dark Slides, numbered ... **2**/- Film Pack Adapter ... **8/6**
,, for Autochrome Plates **3/6** "Flexo" release ... **2/6**
Morocco Leather Case .. **10**/-

The New "Sanderson" Regular Popular Camera.

The "Regular Popular" Sanderson Cameras posses all the well known "Sanderson" movements including all the recent improvements.

A special feature of this Camera is the great range of extensive obtainable, the ½-plate size extending to 21 inches, and yet, even when raised to the fullest, the Lens may be set back to within 2¾ in. of the focal plane without cutting off any portion of the image.

The "Sanderson" Camera has a greater range of movement between the lens and the plate than is found in any other Camera on the market, which make it not only suitable for the most difficult architectural work, but also the most practical instrument for all ordinary and general work it is possible to obtain.

The "Regular Popular" Sets include Camera, Double Dark Slide, Lens, Shutter, Turntable and Three-fold Tripod Stand.

Price of Complete Sets.

The "Regular" and "Tropical" Popular Models.

No.		Model.	4¼ by 3¼ £ s. d.	6½ by 4¾ £ s. d.	8½ by 6½ £ s. d.
P. 1.	Camera, complete with "Ensign" Symmetrical Lens f/8, "Thornton-Pickard" Time and Instantaueous Shutter, 1 double Book-form Slide, 3-fold Ash Tripod Stand	Regular ...	4 15 0	5 10 0	8 0 0
		Tropical ...	5 17 6	6 15 0	9 15 0
P. 3.	Do. with "Beck" Symmetrical Lens, f/8, do. ...	Regular ...	5 0 0	5 15 0	8 7 6
		Tropical ...	6 2 6	7 0 0	10 2 6
P. 2.	Do. with "Busch" Symmetrical Lens, f/8, do. ...	Regular ...	—	5 17 6	8 10 0
		Tropical ...	—	7 2 6	10 5 0
P. 1v.	Do. with "Ensign" Anastigmat Lens, f/7·7, do. ...	Regular ...	6 5 0	7 10 0	10 12 6
		Tropical ...	7 7 6	8 15 0	12 17 6
P. 1x.	Do. with "Ensign" Anastigmat Lens, f/5·8, do....	Regular ...	7 0 0	8 12 6	—
		Tropical ...	8 2 6	9 17 6	—
Extra Double Slides ... each		Regular ...	0 8 6	0 8 6	0 14 6
		Tropical ...	0 12 6	0 12 6	0 18 6

The "Junior" Popular Model.

Camera complete with Lens, "Thornton-Pickard" Time and Instantaneous Behind Lens, Shutter, Double Book form Slide and Three-sold Tripod Stand.

		½-plate.
No. P. 1.	With "Ensign" Symmetrical Lens, f/8	£4 10 0
P. 3.	With "Beck" Symmetrical Lens, f/8...	4 15 0
P. 1v	With "Ensign" Anastigmat Lens, f/7·7	5 5 0
P. 1x.	With "Ensign" Anastigmat Lens, f/6	6 17 6
P. 4a.	With "Aldis-Plano" Anastigmat Lens, f/7·5	6 12 0
Extra Double Slides. each ... —		0 8 6

The "TRIPLE VICTO."

Specification.—CAMERA: Polished mahogany, triple extension (21 in.), actuated by two racks and pinions, highly finished lacquered brass fittings. Automatic self-erecting swing front and back with extreme rising, falling, and cross front (rigid in any position), wide angle movement, double swing back, reversing frame, real leather truncated bellows, plumb indicator, and beautifully finished flushed turntable with clamp. DOUBLE DARK SLIDE—Feather pattern of superior make, book form, with superior light-tight joints, spring catches, and hinged metal partitions. LENS—"Ensign" Rapid Symmetrical f/8, or "Ensign" Aplanat f/7·7, or "Busch" or "Beck" Rapid Symmetrical f/8. SHUTTER—"Thornton-Pickard" time and instantaneous behind lens pattern, with speed indicator and pneumatic release. TRIPOD STAND—Three-fold, with fittings, straps and handle.

Set complete with one Double Slide.				½-plate. £ s. d.	1/1-plate. £ s. d.
No. P. 1.	"Triple-Victo" Set complete with "Ensign" Rapid Symmetrical Lens, f/8, and "Thornton-Pickard" Shutter, &c.			3 17 6	6 0 0
No. P. 3.	Ditto	ditto	"Beck" Rapid Symmetrical Lens, f/8, ditto...	4 2 6	6 7 6
No. P. 1k.	Ditto	ditto	"Ensign" Anastigmat Lens, f/7·7...	4 10 0	7 7 6
No. P. 1s.	Ditto	ditto	"Aldis-Plano" Anastigmat Lens, f/5·8	6 0 0	—
No. P. 1t.	Ditto	ditto	"Ensign" Anastigmat Lens, f/6 ...	6 5 0	—
No. P. 1z.	Ditto	ditto	"Zeiss" Tessar Lens, f/6·3	10 12 6	22 10 0
No. P. 7.	Ditto	ditto	"Goerz" Dagor Lens, f/6·8	10 17 6	16 0 0
No. P. 8.	Ditto	ditto	"Cooke" Anastigmat Series, f/6.5...	9 4 6	14 4 0
Extra Double Slides, each				0 8 6	0 14 6
Extra for "Houghton" Envelope Adapter, Model B, with Self-Contained Focussing Screen for Plates or Films...				1 5 0	—

SPECIAL OFFER. ½-PLATE CAMERA.

FITTED WITH "ALDIS" ANASTIGMAT LENS, F/7·7.

COMPLETE OUTFIT 72/6 USUALLY SOLD FOR 80/-

Specification of Half-Plate Outfit.

CAMERA.—Mahogany polished, very substantial, best leather bellows, with truncated corners, reversing and swing back, uuiversal rising, falling and extendiug front, double extension with swing extending front, rack and pinion.

DARK SLIDE.—Mahogany polished, book-form, double rabbeted, with spring catches to the shutters, and hinged metal division.

SHUTTER.—"Swift" time and instantaneous roller blind, fitted behind the lens, with speed indicator and pneumatic release, with adjustments for time, instantaneous and bulb exposures.

LENS.—Aldis Anastigmat, working at f/7.7.

STAND.—¼-plate 2-fold ash, ½-plate 3-fold polished with slidinp leg.

TURNTABLE.—Solid cast brass, fitted flush in baseboard with fixing screw.

Prices, with "Aldis" Anastigmat, f/7·7, **72/6**

Extra Slides, **7/9** each. Carriage paid.

All Cameras on this Page sent Post Free.

Developing Tanks and Sundries.

Premo Film Tank

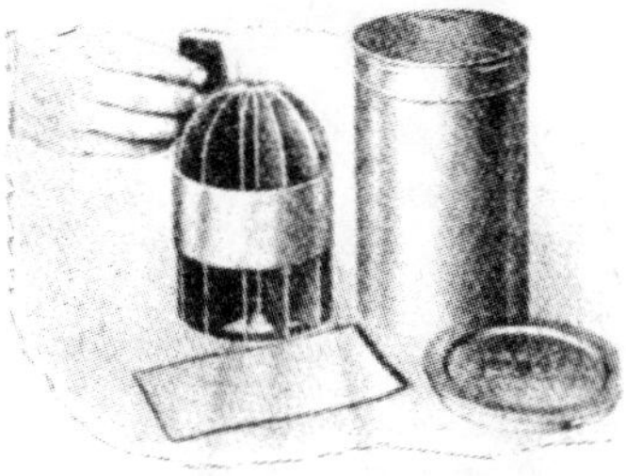

For developing 12 or less Film Pack Films at one time. Simple and inexpensive, it places the absolute novice on a level with the expert. The Premo Film Tank is loaded and unloaded in the dark room by the light of a ruby lamp.

PRICES.

No. P. 1. For 3¼ by 2¼ in. Films, takes 12 exposures .. **6**/-

No. P. 2. For 3¼ by 2¼, 4¼ by 2½, 4¼ by 3¼, 5½ by 3¼, 5 by 4 in. Films, takes 12 exposures, **16**/-

No. P. 3. For 7 by 5 or 6½ by 5¾ Films, takes 12 exposures, **18/6**

Developing Powders.

No. P. 1. **1**/- No. P. 2, **1/6** No. P. 3, **1/9**

Post free.

"Klimax" Daylight Developing Tank.

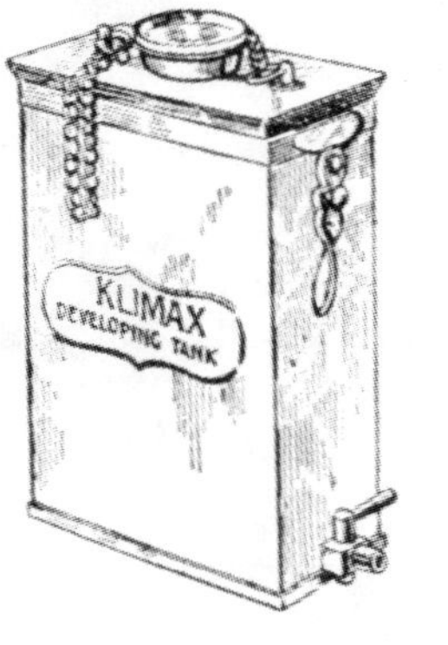

The 'Klimax' Developing Tank is the very last word in daylight developing apparatus, and with its aid the whole process of Developing, Fixing and Washing can be carried out without making use of an organized dark-room. Its use also ensures the production of clean, crisp negatives perfectly free from light fog.

The "Klimax" Tank is made of stout brass, heavily nickel-plated and takes 6 plates. The lid is fitted with a soft rubber pad into which the Tank is pressed when the two clamps are brought into use. An inlet is fitted on the top, through which the various solutions can be poured; a tap is fitted at the bottom for emtying, and a chain for hanging the tank on the water supply when washing.

Miniature Selfix,	(4·5 by 6 cm.)	**7/6**
Stereolette, 4¼ by 1¾	(4·5 ,, 10·7 ,,)	**8/6**
3¼ by 2¼	(6·5 ,, 9 ,,)	**8/6**
Quarter-plate	(10·7 ,, 8·5 ,,)	**8/6**
9 by 12 cm.	—	**8/6**
6 by 13 cm.	—	**10/-**
Post-card, 5½ by 3½	(14 ,, 9 ,,)	**10/6**
5 by 4	(10·2 ,, 12·7 ,,)	**10/6**
Half-plate	(12 ,, 16·5 ,,)	**13/6**
Stereoscopic, 6¾ by 3¼	(8·3 ,, 17 ,,)	**12/6**
13 by 18 cm.	—	**15/-**

Each Tank is sent out with full instruction Booklet. Post Paid.

The "Klimax" Flat Film Daylight Developing Tank.

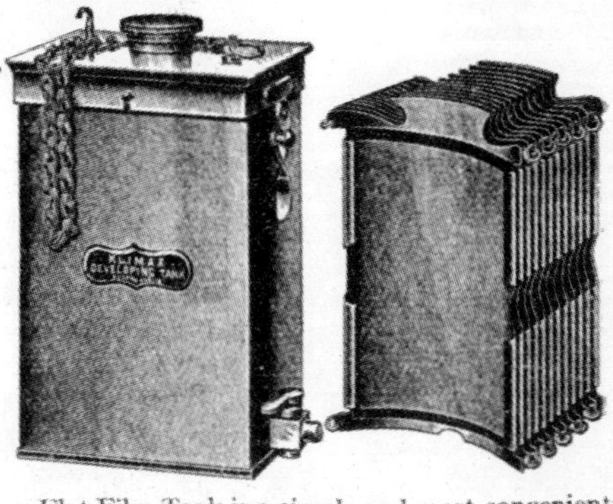

The Klimax Flat Film Tank is a simple and most convenient means of employing the time and temperature method to the developing of cut films and has many features which will recommend it to the expert worker.

Like the Klimax Plate Tank it is constructed so that the complete process, developing, fixing and washing can be performed without exposing the films to light in any way. For this purpose it is provided with inlet and outlet plugs perfectly light trapped. The films are each held seperately in a "chain" which is slightly concave. This has the effect of bending the film, and preventing any tendency to buckle, and, consequently, sticking against the opposite support. There is ample clearance between each holder, premitting the free flow of the solutions and ensuring even action This apparatus holds 12 flat films, is made of brass in a most substantial manner, and is heavily nickel-plated.

Prices—4½ by 6 cm. .. **10/6** 3¼ by 2¼ in. .. **12/-**
¼-plate .. **12/6** Post Card .. **16/-**

Tank Developers

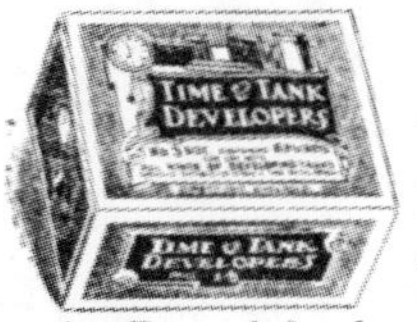

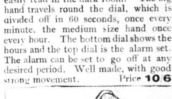

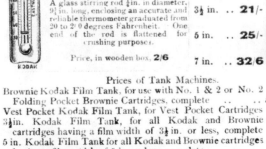

These Developers are accurately prepared with the object of obtaining the best possible results. For tank development they give fully developed results in from ten minutes, or for the time method, the duration of development depending upon strength of solution.

No. 1 size, 6 pkts., each making 1 pint		**6**d.
No. 2 size, 6 ,, ,, ,, 2 pints		**1/-**
No. 3 size, 6 ,, ,, ,, 3 pints		**1/6**

"**Klimax**" **Tank Solution**, sufficient to make 130oz. developer **1/-**

Developing Thermometer.

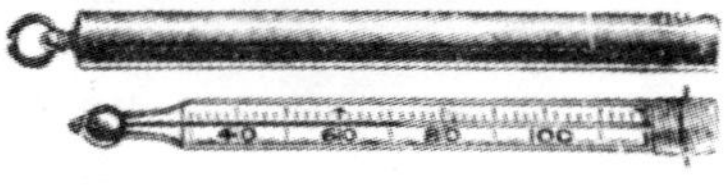

For testing the temperature of solutions—an indispensable accessory. Has a very wide and clear scale marked with a red line at 60°, the normal temperature for the developing solution.

Complete in nickel plated travelling case. price **1**/- each.

Dark Room Clock.

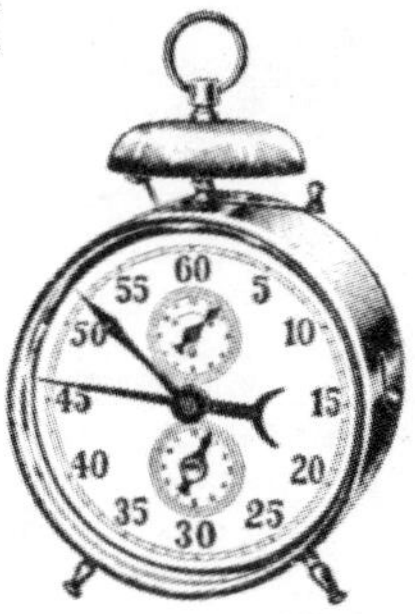

Can be stopped or started instantly. Bold clear dial and large hands, can be easily read in the dark room. The big hand travels round the dial, which is divided off in 60 seconds, once every minute, the medium size hand once every hour. The bottom dial shows the hours and the top dial is the alarm set. The alarm can be set to go off at any desired period. Well made, with good strong movement. Price **10/6**

Brownie Developing Box.

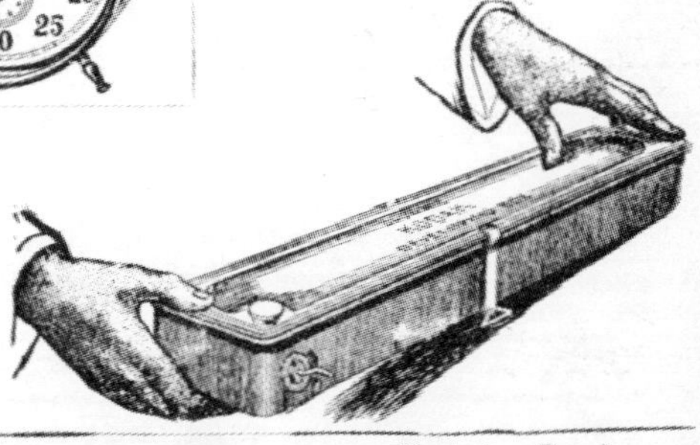

Offering the same assurance of perfectly developed film as the Kodak Film Tank, the "Brownie" Developing Box is a modified form of of the Kodak Film Tank, so simple as to be readily understood and successfully operated by any boy or girl. It is a metal box, 15 in. long, will accommodate a roll of No. 1, 2 or No. 2 Folding Brownie film in one loop. **5/-**

Brownie Developing Powders **6**d. per 6 packets.

Eastman Thermometer.

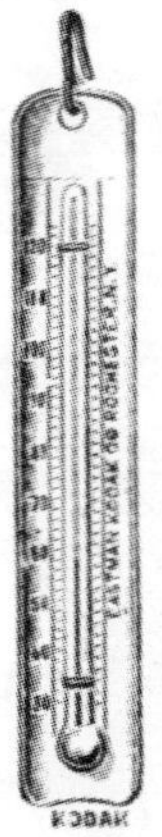

For use with Kodak Developing Tanks, etc. In cardboard box, **2/-**

☛ The glass tube is protected by a curved nickelled metal back, which is neatly and accurately marked from 40 to 140 Fahrenheit.

Kodak Thermometer Stirring Rod. (Registered)

A glass stirring rod ¼in. in diameter, 9¼ in. long, enclosing an accurate and reliable thermometer graduated from 20 to 200 degrees Fahrenheit. One end of the rod is flattened for crushing purposes.

Price, in wooden box, **2/6**

The Kodak Tank Developing Machine.

No Dark Room required. The acme of simplicity and perfection for beginner and expert alike.

Prices complete—

Brownie" **10/-**

3½ in. .. **21/-**

5 in. .. **25/-**

7 in. .. **32/6**

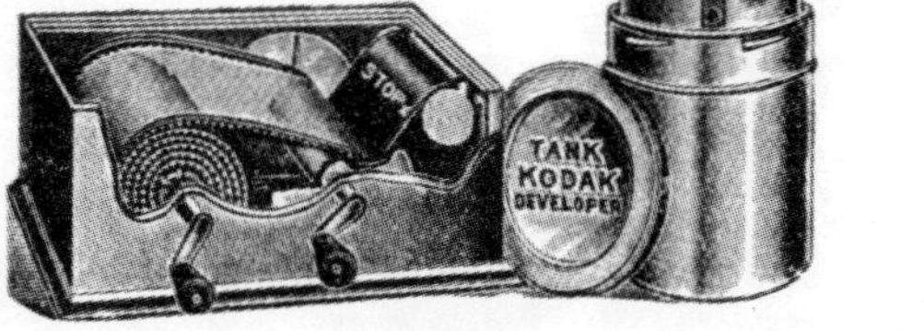

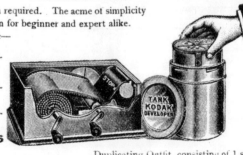

The exposed film is wound within a red celluloid band or apron in the box figured above, and then immersed as shown in the cylindrical metal tank containing the developing solution. There is no longer any turning of the handle during development—the film slowly develops itself with practically no attention. Snapshots or time exposures are all the same to the machine; it develops them perfectly, and gives equal printing quality right through the band of film. No stains, no finger markings, no scratches, and no unevenness.

Prices of Tank Machines.

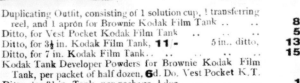

	£	s.	d.
Brownie Kodak Film Tank, for use with No. 1 & 2 or No. 2 Folding Pocket Brownie Cartridges, complete		**10**	**0**
Vest Pocket Kodak Film Tank, for Vest Pocket Cartridges		**10**	**0**
3½in. Kodak Film Tank, for all Kodak and Brownie cartridges having a film width of 3½ in. or less, complete	**1**	**1**	**0**
5 in. Kodak Film Tank for all Kodak and Brownie cartridges having a film width of 5 in. or less, complete	**1**	**6**	**0**
7 in. Kodak Film Tank, for No. 5 Cartridge Kodak or shorter film cartridges, complete	**1**	**12**	**6**

	s.	d.
Duplicating Outfit, consisting of 1 solution cup, 1 transferring reel, and 1 apron for Brownie Kodak Film Tank	**8**	**0**
Ditto, for Vest Pocket Kodak Film Tank	**5**	**0**
Ditto, for 3½ in. Kodak Film Tank, **11**/- 5 in., ditto,	**13**	**6**
Ditto, for 7 in. Kodak Film Tank	**15**	**6**
Kodak Tank Developer Powders for Brownie Kodak Film Tank, per packet of half dozen, **6**d. Do. Vest Pocket K.T.		**6**
Ditto, for 3½ in. Tank, per package, ½ doz.	**1**	**0**
Ditto, for 5 in. Tank, per package, ½ doz.	**1**	**6**
Ditto, for 7 in. Tank, per package, ½ doz.	**1**	**9**

CINEMATOGRAPHS FOR WINTER EVENINGS.

The "SILENT" Home and Educational Cinematograph

New Model. With Standard Lamp House.

An absolutely perfect, safe and cheap projector, designed especially for use in the Home, the School, or the small Hall.

For use with Standard Size Films.

This Cinematograph is a thoroughly practical instrument for showing both living pictures and lantern slides.

With this projector a perfect moving picture exhibition can be given by anyone — previous knowledge & experience being quite unnecessary. Any size picture can be obtained according to the power of the illuminant used and the distance available from the screen. The picture on the screen is as steady as a lantern slide and as flickerless. The machine is so perfectly made and works so smoothly that it is practically silent when running.

Prices : complete as illustration **£10 19 6**
Adjustable iron legs for fiting to baseboard, making a strong serviceable stand that can be adjusted for height or tilted in any direction, **£1 9 6** Extra spools, 8 in. **2/6** Spool boxes for 8 in. spools, per pair **£1 9 6** Extra Spools, 12 in. **2/6**

HOME Cinematograph

Prices :
With two Lenses and strong Wooden Case,
£5 13 6

Mechanism only without Lenses,
£2 7 6

Ditto. with Cinematograph Lens,
£2 17 0

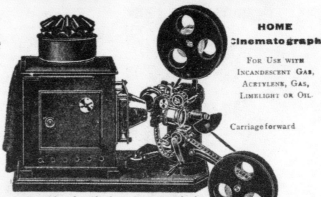

For Use with Incandescent Gas, Acetylene, Gas, Limelight or Oil.

Carriage forward

A first-rate living picture machine for side shows, home use, schools bazaars, &c. This is an excellent cinematograph and will project a steady, clear picture, with the standard size films. It is provided with feed and take-up sprockets. The re winding gear is perfectly efficient and works on the steel band system, the same as the No. 1 Machine. It takes the standard Edison gauge films, but is, of course, much smaller in all its parts, with the exception of the sprockets, gate and hanging mechanism.
Cheap continuous films are made for this Machine either in real photographic subjects or in lithographic.

Combination Cinematograph and Magic Lantern.

Nos. P. 790/1 & P. 791.

Superior make, most substantial and fitted with a best quality lamp, also six long coloured films for producing the living pictures, and adapted for using ordinary magic lantern slides 2in. wide.

Complete in box with full instructions, including 1 dozen long coloured slides **32 6**

Do. smaller size, **25/-** Carriage forward.

"PALLADOSCOPE."

The New Home Picture Machine.

Simple and .
Self-contained.

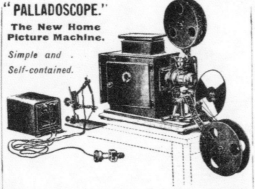

Fills a long-felt want. A Serviceable and Reliable Projector at a Popular Price, and PERFECTLY SAFE

Specially large, clear white pictures. Simple and strong, easy to manipulate Strong, silent mechanism. Large lamp house. Special Arc Lamp giving 800 C.P., taking about 6 Amperes. New ingenious Resistance which renders the Machine suitable for currents of 110, 150, or 220 volts without the necessity of spending another penny beyond the original price. Projector, Mechanism, Lamp House, Arc Lamp and Resistance, all complete in strong Wood Cabinet .. **£5 5 0**

Superior Cinematograph

Packed in strong Wood box.

Complete **£2 10 0**

Lantern body of sheet iron mounted on cast iron base, takes all films with standard "Edison Perforation," also suitable as magic lantern for the projection of glass slides 2¼ in. wide, or wood-framed slides, 2¼ in. wide. Dogaction mechanism, top sprocket, almost n iseless film movement, lower and upper film spool fitted for re-winding. Oblong coloured films, 3 superior photo-process films, 12 glass slides, lantern body sheet iron dull black finish, base, cast iron. Superior quality set of lenses, brass objective with rack and pinion, ocussing movement, double condenser (2¼ in.) and 12 in. duplex oil lamp.

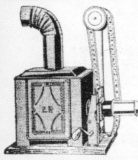

Miniature Combination Cinematograph and Magic Lantern.

No. 783/1.

Strongly made metal body, fitted with lens, condenser and paraffin lamp. Complete with 3 films producing living pictures and 6 slides, 1¹⁄₁₆ in.

Price complete, .. **4 6**

Postage 6d. extra.

Miniature Combination Cinematograph and Lantern.

No. 785. Strongly made iron body, mounted on metal base, fitted with lens, condenser, and paraffin lamp. 3 coloured films are supplied for producing the living pictures. Provision is made for using ordinary lantern slides, 1¹⁶⁄₁₆ in. wide, 6 are supplied with lantern.

Price complete in box with instructions

7/11.

Postage 9d.

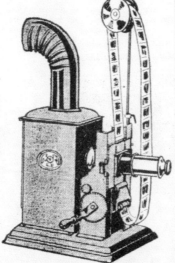

Miniature Combination Cinematograph and Magic Lantern.

No. 786. Strongly made, iron body, mounted on metal base, fitted with lens, condenser, and paraffin lamp. 3 long coloured films are supplied for producing the living pictures. Provision is made for using ordinary magic lantern slides, 1⅝ in. wide. Price, complete in box with full instructions, including 6 slides, **12/6**

Postage 9d.

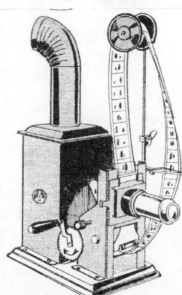

Get a Copy of our Cinematograph Book 6d. Post free.
Complete Cinematograph and Lantern Catalogue Post Free.

Electric Bells and Batteries.

Note the prices.

No. Ir. 44. Continuous Action Electric Bell. Bell will keep ringing until cord is pulled.

3 in. bell, **6/6**   4 in. bell, **9/-**
Postage 4d.
Special line 3 in. only **4/9**

No. Ir. 25.

Electric Bell, in black japanned metal case with gold lines.

Good quality.

2¾ in. plated bell.
Price **1/6**
Ditto, miniature size.
Case measures 4½ by 2½ in.
Bell 1¾ in.   Price **1/-**
Postage 3d.

No. Ir. 45.
Sheep Gong Electric Bell

With nickel plated cast gong.

Diam. of bell.   Price.
2¾ in... **2/3**
3 ,, .. **3/-**
3½ ,, .. **3/6**
Postage 3d.

No. Ir. 27.
Electric Bell.
Good quality, in walnut case.
2¾ in. bell .. Price **2/9**
3 ,, .. ,, **3/-**
3½ ,, .. ,, **3/6**
Postage 3d.

No. Ir. 1.
Electric Bell Set.
Complete with bell, push, Leclanche battery and 12 yds. wire. Price **5/6** set.
With Dry Battery, **4/9**
Post 6d.

Superior Grade
Standard Pattern Instrument.

Ir. 50772.

STANDARD PATTERN BATTERY RINGING STATION.

With induction coil, automatic switch, ringing key and bell, fitted with loud speaking Hunning's Granular Carbon Transmitter, and D.P. Watch Receiver Ir. 53763.

Mounted in Highly Polished Walnut Case.

All metal parts nickel-plated.
Price .. **30/-** each.

Ir. 50771. Ditto, with D.P. Bell Receiver Ir. 51316.
30/- each.

Ir. 51412. Instrument 50772 mounted on Backboard, with 3-cell Battery Box, highly polished Walnut.
49/6 each.

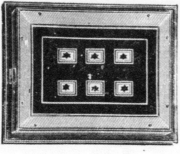

Electric Bell Indicators

Self-replacing Pendulum.

Polished Dove-tailed Case with Moulded Teak Front and Painted Glass Front.

3 Hole	..	..	Price **4/6**
4 do.	..	..	Price **5/-**
5 do.	..	..	Price **6/-**

Larger sizes up to 12 Holes, Price **1/3** per hole.
Carriage forward.

No. Ir. 41.   Electric Bell. Cast bell metal nickel plated flat gong in solid walnut case.

Diameter of Bell, 3 in.   Price **3/9**
Postage 4d.

No. Ir. 42. SPECIAL LINE. Electric Bell.
Good quality.

Diameter of bell.   Price.
2½ in. **1/1**
2¾ ,, ... **1/3**
Postage 3d.

No. Ir. 26. Electric Bell, in solid walnut case.
Best quality.
Nickel plated bell metal gong.
2¾ in., **3/6** .. 3 in., **4/-**
Postage 3d.

Write for Electrical Catalogue, Post Free on Application.

No. Ir. 50278.

SMALL Hand or Pocket Push.

Price .. 4½d.

Postage 1d.

SPECIAL LINE. Real Boxwood or Cocus Wood Bell Pushes. Cannot be repeated when sold out. 3 in. diameter, Price .. 4½d. Postage 1d.

Outdoor Electric Bell Push bright brass, with ebonite back. 1½ in. **1/6** 2 „ **2/-** 2½ „ **2/6** Post 1d. Brass Bell Push, for outdoor use, 3 by 1½ **1/3** Post 1d

Electric Bell Push. Best finish, in real Oak, Walnut or Ebonized.
2 in. Diameter .. **4½d.**
2½ „ „ .. **6d.**
3 „ „ .. **7d.**
Postage 1d.

No. 48. Wood Bell Push, hand carved, real walnut, best finish. 2 in., Price **10d.** each. Postage 1d.

Electric Bell Push, cast brass, polished and lacquered with ebonite backs for indoor use.

1½ in. **1/-** 2 in. **1/1** 2½ in. **1/3** 3 in. **1/5** Postage 1d.

Electric Bell Push, bright brass, good quality. 2½ in. diam., **1/3** 3 in., **1/4** 3½ „ **1/9** Postage 1d.

The Acorn Electric Bell Suspension Push

Art Metal Oxidised, Copper Finish. Price **1/9** each. Ditto, Oxidised, Silver Finish. Price **2/-** each. Post 2d.

Electric Bell Push, for outdoor use, with water-tight barrels, cast brass, bronzed. 4½ in. **4/9** Postage 3d. Lettered "Servants," same price.

Electric Bell Push, short barrel, for outdoor use, bright brass. 2½ in. diam., **1/3** 3 in., **1/5** 3½ „ **2/-** 4 „ **2/6** Postage 2d.

English all China Bell Push, yellow and red floral designs on cream ground. Best quality .. Price **2/-** Postage 3d.

No. 92. **Table Push.** In polished walnut or ebony, with loaded base. Diam. 2½ in. Price .. **1/3** Post 3d.

English All China Bell Push, best quality. White, Cream or Black. 2½ in. diameter .. **10½d.** 3 „ **1/-** Postage 2d.

"Floral Acorn" Electric Bell Suspension Push.

Art Metal, Oxydized Copper Finish. Price **2/6** Ditto, Oxydized Silver Finish. Price **3/-** Post 2d.

Extension Bell Push. Complete with 2 pin plugs, 3 yds. flexible cord and table push .. **3/9** Postage 3d.

Pear Shape Bell Push. Imitation Walnut or Mahogany .. **9d.** Ditto, small size **6d.** Postage 1d.

Carved wood Pear Push. With German silver spring pointed contacts and ivorine mounts. Real walnut .. **1/-** Ceiling Rosette to match. Price **9d.** Post 2d.

Ceiling Rosette. Imitation walnut or mahogany. 2 inches. Price .. **4½d.** Postage 1d.

Miniature Bell Push **9d.** Post 1d.

Suspension Set. No. 1. Comprising pear shape push, imitation walnut or mahogony, 2 in. rosette, fitted with 2 yds. 2-strand silk flexible cord, **1/6** complete. No. 3. Best quality, in real Cocus ebony or rosewood .. **2/6** Postage 2d.

Ir 50256. **Clip-on Push.** To clip on Desks, Tables &c. Nickel-plated with Ebonite interior. **2/11** each.

Flush Electric Bell Pushes.

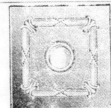

	2 way.
3 by 3	6 by 3 in.
3	4 way.
9 by 3	6 by 6 in.

With Barrel Bell Pushes.

Ir. 67159a. Polished Brass.

	1	2	3	4 way.
	3by3	6yy3	9by3	6by6in.
	2/3	4/9	7/3	9/6
Ir. 67160a.	Antique Brass.
	2/11	5/3	7/6	10/6
Ir. 67161a.	Oxidized Copper.
	3/6	5/3	7/9	10/6
Ir. 67162a.	Oxidized Silver.
	3/-	6/-	9/-	12/-

| | 1 | 2 | 3 | 4 way. |
| | 3 by 3 | 6 by 3 | 9 by 3 | 4 way. |
| With Barrel Bell Pushes. |
| Ir. 66178a. Polished Brass. |
| 2/9 | 5/6 | 8/3 | 10/6 |
| Ir. 66179a. Oxidized Copper. |
| 3/- | 6/- | 9/- | 12/- ea. |
| Ir. 66180a. Oxidized Silver. |
| 3/11 | 6/9 | 10/6 | 13/6 ea. |

| | 1 | 2 | 3 | 4way. |
| | 3by3 | 6by3 | 9 by3 | 6 by 6 |
| Ir. 67163a. Dead Gold. 5/6 10/9 16/6 21/- |
| Ir. 67165a. Ox. Copper. 5/9 11/6 17/9 22/6 |
| Ir. 67166a. Ox. Silver. 6/3 12/6 18/6 24/- |

Table Push. Walnut Push Board, Two-way only. With Bone Mounts. 5½ by 3½ in. **3/9** each.

TELEPHONES.

No. Ir. 002.

Small Pattern Battery Wall Telephone.

Comprising Revolving Granular Carbon Transmitter Induction Coil, Double-pole "Watch" Receiver, Call Bell, Automatic Switch-hook and Ringing Key. Metal parts Nickel plated. Woodwork solid walnut.

Price .. .. .. **17/9** each.

No. Ir. 013.

Table Telephone.

Comprising Transmitter, Receiver, Induction Coil, Call Buzzer, Flexible Cord, and Wall Rosette, &c. Metal parts nickel plated. Woodwork solid walnut.

Price .. .. .. **£1 6 0** each.

No. Ir. 502.

Large Pattern Battery Wall Telephone.

Specification as No. Ir. 002.

Price .. .. . **19/3** each.

Magneto Wall Telephone.

No. Ir. 023.

Comprising "Hunningscone" Revolving Granular Carbon Transmitter, Induction Coil, Double-pole "Watch" Receiver, Double-magnet Generator, 300 Ohm Polarised Call Bell, Automatic Switch-hook, Lightning Arrester and Terminals for Extension Bell.

Metal parts nickel plated. Woodwork solid walnut.

Price .. .. **£2 6 0** each.

No. Ir. 052.

Superior Quality Battery Wall Telephone.

Comprising "Hunningscone" Revolving Granular Carbon Transmitter, Induction Coil, best quality Double-pole "Watch" Receiver, "Caledonian" Call Bell, Automatic Switch-hook and Ringing Key. Metal parts nickel plated. Woodwork solid walnut

Price .. **£1 10 0** each.

No. Ir. 2412.

Portable Drum.

Containing approximately 550 yards of Insulated Line Wire, and all accessories, fitted in leather case with carrying strap.

Price .. .. **70/-** each.

SPARE DRUM with approximately 550 yards.

Price **35/-**

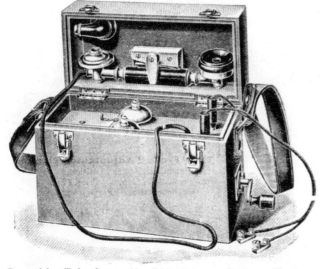

Portable Telephone (for Rifle Ranges, Railway Tracks or Testing Purposes).

No. Ir. 045. Portable Telephone (heavy type), comprising Standard Pattern Hand-combination, Induction Coil, Triple-magnet Generator, Polarised Call Bell, Dry Battery, Flexible Cord with Plugs and Terminals. In solid teak containing case, with metal-bound corners and sling carrying strap.

Price .. .. **£5 16 0** each. Weight 16 lbs.

No. Ir. 523. **Magneto Wall Telephone.**

Same as above No. Ir. 023, but mounted on polished walnut backboard, with Battery Box to accommodate one No. Ir. 2 Leclanchè Battery or Dry Cell.

Price .. .. .. **£2 16 0** each.

Write for complete Electrical List.

Telephones and Rests.

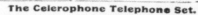

The Bothway Telephone Set.

Set of "Bothway" Wall Stations in Metal Cases, complete with Bells, 36 yards 3-strand India Rubber covered No. 20 gauge. Telephone Wire, Staples, two "Dry Cells, and instructions for fixing. Price **18/6** set. Set of 2 Instruments only, **14/-** Postage 6d.

The Gamage Complete Telephone Set.

BEST QUALITY.

Complete with batteries, bells, 30 yards wire, and two first class Instruments.

32/6 Carriage Free.

A useful and Practical Set

Cheaper Pattern

Price .. **29/6** complete.

KEEP your Telephone under your own control by using our Patent Lock Clip.

PRICE **2/6**   PRICE **2/6**

Made to suit all Instruments — G.P.O., National, etc.

Absolute Check on Calls.

Kindly state Style of your Telephone Instrument when ordering

Price .. **2/6**

The Celerophone Telephone Set.

The complete set consists of 1 portable calling station with 2 pin push ; 1 receiving station with connecting rosette ; 3 yards each of three colours connecting wire, staples, etc., and diagram, with instructions for fitting up. Price .. **10/6** set. Postage 6d. Additional Calling Instruments for rooms. Price **6/-** each.

Spare Two Pins Wall Push, with Hook.

By fitting these in place of the existing Bell Pushes, 1 Celero-phone may be used in all rooms so fitted.

Price .. **1/-** each.

Postage 1d.

Special line Telephone.

Guaranteed quality. Best finish.

Price .. **15/-** each.

Postage 6d.

No. Ir. 51398.

'Domophone' Kitchen or Receiving Station.

WITHOUT RINGING KEY.

With Automatic Switch and Bell Terminal, Granular Carbon Transmitter and D.P. Watch Receiver No. Ir. 51412. Mounted in Polished Walnut Case. All Metal parts Nickel-plated. Price .. **13/6** each. No. Ir. 51409. Ditto, with Mouthpiece to Transmitter. Price ... **14/9**

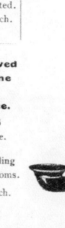

The Improved Celerophone with Mouthpiece.

Price **12/6**

Set complete.

Additional Calling Stations for rooms.

Price **6/9** each.

Postage 4d.

B 6. Table Telephone, for use with ordinary battery, with automatic switch . ringing key, bell and double pole watch receiver. Mounted on polished walnut, metal part nickel plated. Price .. **25/-** each.

Complete with cord and rosette.

The 'Domophone' Hand Combination

A HIGH-CLASS Direct-working Telephone for con-vertting an existing Bell Installation into

An Efficient Telephone Service.

No. Ir. 51441. **Portable "Domophone" Calling Station.** Highly finished ebonized handle, fitted with Ringing and Speaking Keys. Hard Rubber Mouthpiece and Receiver. All Metal parts Nickel-plated. Complete with Two Pin-plug Connection and round Walnut Push, **15/3** each. No. Ir. 51441A. Ditto, with Pear Push, **15/3** each.

Complete "Domophone" Sets.

No. Ir. 51430. Consisting of One No. Ir. 51441 and One No. Ir. 51398 ... **30/-** per set.

The Echophone House Telephone for converting ordinary electric bell circuits.

Guaranteed quality.

No. 1. To be connected to kitchen end. Price .. **7/3** each.

No. 2. Ditto, with push to enable to ring to kitchen.

Price .. **8/3** each, or **14/9** pair. Postage 4d.

The "Frollo" Adjustable Telephone

Arm adjustable to any position. Strongly made. 23 in.   Price **17/6** Telephone extra.   Postage 6d.

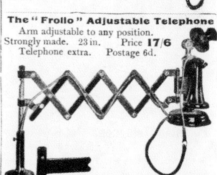

Please state if required for screwing on flat desk or side of roll top when ordering. Also in other lengths as under.

27 in. **20/-**   32 in. **22/6**   36 in. **25/-** Oxidized Copper **1/6** extra.

Electrical Catalogue post free on application.

GAMAGE'S RE-BUILT TYPEWRITERS.

We are offering **Genuine Re-built Typewriters** of every Make, with **12 Month's Full Guarantee,** at less than Half Makers' Prices. These Machines are thoroughly re-built, and not simply re-enamelled and re-nickelled. Wearing parts, such as Type, Key Tops, Platen Roller, Ribbon Attachment, Release Springs, etc., are replaced by entirely new parts, and all other parts thoroughly overhauled. Thus giving a Machine the appearance and wear of a New Machine from the Factory. **Note our Guarantee.**

Oliver N. 3. Complete with Metal Cover.

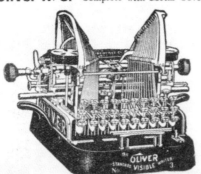

£10 10 net. **No. 5 Oliver £13 10** net

The Royal Typewriter. NEW MODEL.

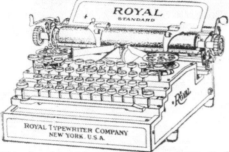

List price, £15 15 0 Gamage's price, **£15 0 0**
Complete with Metal Case.
You may pay more, but you cannot buy more !
Perfect Visible Writing.
Perfect Carbon Copying.

TYPEWRITER ACCESSORIES.
Carbons. Special Value.
Box of 100 Carbons. F'cap size. Purple.
Medium weight. **2/3** per box. Worth 5/6 Post free.
Typewriter Ribbons.
GAMAGE'S Special Quality for any Machine.
Record or Copy, Purple, Blue or Black.
Price .. **1/9 & 2/3** Worth 3/6
Ditto. Two-colour Ribbons .. **2/6**
Typewriter Oil. 6d. and 10½d. Bottle.
Typewriter Brushes.
Special Quality. Wire Centre. **1/-** Post 1d.

The Stencilette Painting Outfit.

An instructive pastime for Children.

Box complete with Stencil, Sheets, Colours and Brushes.

Splendid Pictures may be painted by the little artist.
Price complete

2/-

Post 3d.

The Remington.
No. N. 7. Price .. **£10 10 0** net.
Two-colour Ribbon Attachment **8/6** extra.

Metal Case .. .. .. **12/6** extra.

The "Bijou" Typewriter.
NEW MODEL.

Weight only 12 lbs. Complete in case. Perfect visible writing, universal keyboard, every modern improvement, single or 2-colour ribbons can be used. Specially suitable for Travellers, Ministers, Secretaries, &c. Price, complete in solid leatherette Case .. **£12 0 0** net

The Improved Simplex Typewriter.
N. 1. This is a very complete Machine, having key for each letter roller fed, automatic inking and spacing sight writing. Will take a small letter head, and can be easily and rapidly operated. Has 36 characters and stops. With full instructions. Price .. **4/6** Post 4d.

The Simplex. No. N. 2.
GREATLY ENLARGED AND IMPROVED.
Similar to N. 1 but has 2 sets of alphabets, capital and small, numerals and punctuation stops.
Fitted on wood base. Price ... **8/6** Post 5d

The Smith Premier. No. N. 4.

Price .. .. **£10 10 0** net.			
Metal Covers **12/6** extra.			
Monarch, No. N. 2 ..	from	£15	0 0
Bar-Lock, No. N. 10-11	,,	11	0 0
Royal Standard ..	..	11	0 0
Underwood, No. N. 5	..	14	5 0
L. C. Smith, No. N. 2	..	15	15 0
Yost's No. N. 10, Elite Type		12	10 0

The Home Model Blickensderfer Typewriter.

Price .. .. **£6 6 0** net.
Interchangeable Type Wheel. Perfect Sight Writing.

Dear Sir;
See! This is the best present I ever got.

The Simplex Typewriter. No. N. 3.
Similiar in style to No. N. 2, has 2 sets Alphabets, Numerals, etc. Will take paper up to Foolscap size. Will print very clearly and has perfect alignment, **12/6** Post 4d. Larger size, **21/-**

PLIERS and PINCERS.

Scotch Gas Pliers.
Best English Make.
Guaranteed quality, black finish with polished nose.

Length	6	7	8	9 in.
Price	**1 3**	**1 9**	**2/-**	**2 3**

Postage 3d.

Long Nose Pendulum Pliers.
Best quality.   Black finish.
Length 5½ inches.

Price .. **1/3**   Postage 1d.

Flat or Round Nose Pliers.
Good quality.   Bright Finish.
Length 5 inch. Price .. **6**d.
,, 5½ ,, ,, .. **7½**d.
,, 6 ,, ,, .. **9**d.
Postage 1d.

Combination Cutting Pliers.
Half Round Nose for Electricians, etc.

Best quality guaranteed.

Length 5½ in.   Price **2 3**   Post 2d.

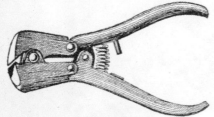

Wire Cutters.
Compound Lever. Good quality. Stamped Steel.
Black Finish.
5 in. **1 6**   6 in. **1 9**   7 in. **2/-**   Postage 2d.

New Line   **Electricians' Pliers.**
With insulated handles.   Guaranteed quality.
Length 6½ inch   Price **2 -**   7 in. .. **2 3**
Postage 3d.

Electricians' Combination Tool Pliers.
Guaranteed quality.   Combining Cutting Nipper,
Gas Tong, Wire Cutter, Rimer and Turnscrew,
besides the Nipper Jaws have 3 special size holes
for cutting and scraping off the insulation on wire.
Length 8 in.   Black finish.   Price **3/9**   Post 3d

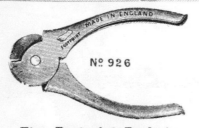

The Footprint Pocket Wire Cutter.
Guaranteed quality.
Will cut up to 12 gauge iron wire.

Length 4 in.   Black finish.   Price .. **8**d.
,,   ,,   Plated ,, ,, .. **1/3**
The "Domino." Cheaper quality.
Ditto, 3½ in. long.   Black finish.   Price .. **6**d.
Postage 1d.

Electricians' Pliers.
With Insulated Handles.   Guaranteed Quality.
Length 7 in. Price **2 3** Length 8 in.   Price **2 6**
Postage 3d.

Tower Pincers.
Guaranteed quality.   Black finish.
6 in. **8**d.   6½ in. **10½**d.   7 in. **1/-**
Postage 2d.

Wire Cutter.
Best Forged.   Steel Jaws.
5 in. **9½**d.   6 in. **1/-**   7 in. **1/3**
Postage 3d.

Footprint.
Fit all pliers. All
steel. Double box
joint, hollow
rounded handles,
3 different adjust-
ments by means of
thumbscrew,
length 7 in. Black
finish with bright
jaws .. **1/6**
Postage 2d.

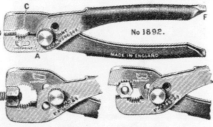

No 1892.
MADE IN ENGLAND

Pincers.
Guaranteed Quality.   Polished Steel Jaws.
5 in. **7½**d.   6 in. **9**d.   7 in. **10½**d.   8 in. **1/3**   Postage 3d.

Turners Encore Combination Pliers.
Every pair tested and fully guaranteed best
Sheffield make.
Especially useful for Motor Car and Electric Work.
A—Flat Nose Pliers.   **B**—Square Hole, acting as Spanner for
small nuts (will take up to ¼-in. nut).   **C**—Cutting Edge, with
Circular Grip on under side for Electrical Nuts.   **D**—Wire
Cutter.   **E**—Grip for Gas Burner.   **F**—Claw.   **G**—Turnscrew.
7 in. long   Black finish   Price **3 6**   Postage 3d.
7 ,,   Nickel Plated ,, **4 6**   ,,

Top Cutting Nippers.
Best make.   Guaranteed quality.
4 in. .. **1/9**   5 in. .. **2 5**   6 in. .. **2/6**
Special Line—Second quality, but fully guaranteed.
4 in. .. **1/1**   5 in. .. **1/3**   6 in. .. **1 5**   Post 2d.

Combination Pliers.
Guaranteed quality, best English make, black finish.
Length	5	5½	6	7 in.
Price	**1 4**	**1 6**	**1 9**	**2/-**

Ditto without burner hole
Length	5	5½	6	7 in.
Price	**1/2**	**1 4**	**1 6**	**1 9**

Postage 2d.

Write for Complete Tool Catalogue.

Flat Nose Pliers
Best Lancashire make.   Every pair guaranteed.
5 in. **1/-**   5½ in. **1/2**   6 in. **1/3**   6½ in. **1 6**
Postage 1d.

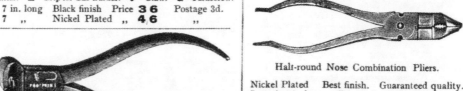

Half-round Nose Combination Pliers.
Nickel Plated   Best finish.   Guaranteed quality.
Length 6 inches.   Price .. **1 9** Postage 3d.
With half round nose.   Nickel Plated.
Length 7 in.   Price **2/9**   Postage 2d.

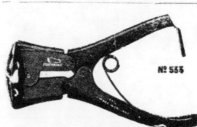

No 555

The Footprint Toggle-jointed Wire Cutting Nippers.
Guaranteed quality.

6½ in. long.   Black finish.   Price **2 3**   Post 3d.
Leather cases to take above with loop at back for
slinging on belt or saddle.   Price **2/-**   Post

BRACES AND DRILLS

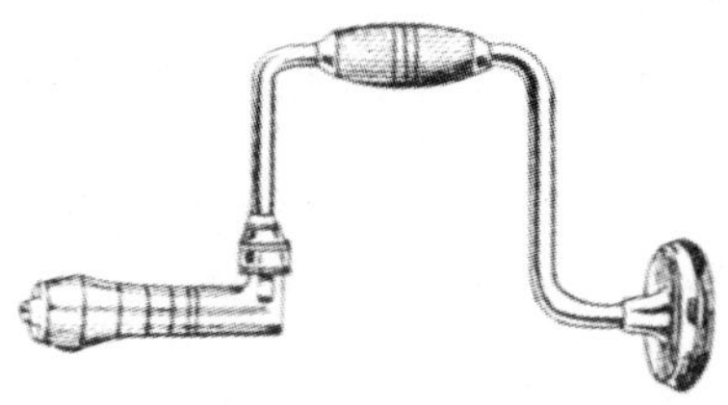

No. 941. **RATCHET BRACE.**
Best Quality, Bright Finish, with polished head and grip, octagon chuck with spring jaws and ball head. Size 1, 8 in. sweep, **4/3** Size 2, 10 in. sweep, **4/6**
Ditto, nickel plated, best finish, 8 in. sweep, **5/-** 10 in. sweep, **5/3** Post 4d.

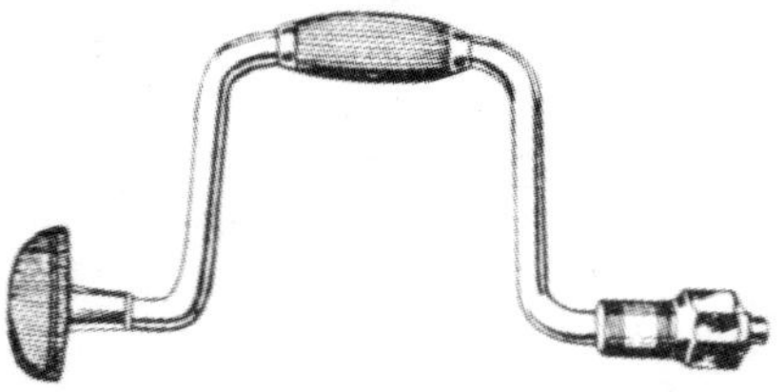

No. 931. **PLAIN BRACE.**
English make. Best Bright Finish, with polished head and grip, octagon chuck and spring jaws and ball bearing head. Guaranteed Quality.
Size 1, with 6 in. sweep, **1/8** Size 2, 8 in. sweep, **2/-** Size 3, 10 in. sweep, **2/3** Postage 4d.

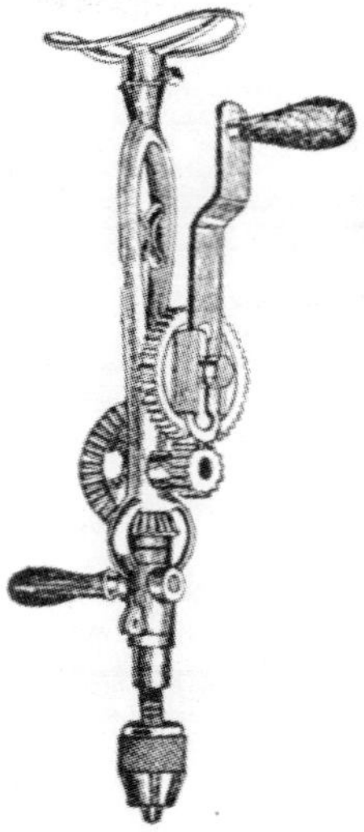

The Record High Speed Breast Drill.

Far superior to any other Breast Drills, geared to make it possible to get 1000 revolutionsper minute will do any class of work and save its cost over other Breast Drills in Drills Bits alone.

Spindle runs in double ball bearings.

Very easy running.

Total length of Drill about 19 in.

Chuck takes up to ½ in.

Weight about 6½ lb.

Price **18/-**

Carriage forward.

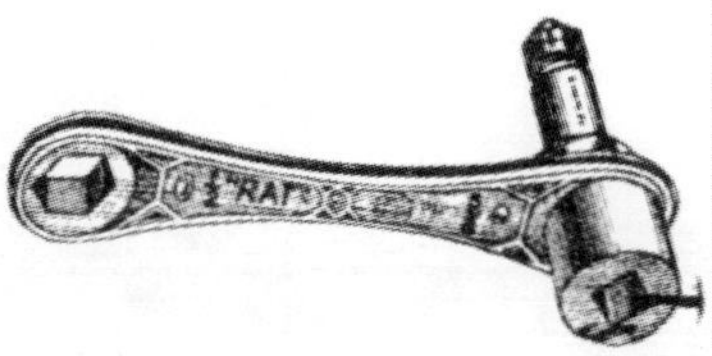

The Simplex Detachable Engineer's Ratchet Brace.

The Ratchet Spanner is fitted to drill chuck and held in place by lock nut.

A great improvement over ordinary brace, as when not required for drilling.

Spanner can be used for other purposes.

No.	With Ratchet Spanner. Whitworth Standard	Length of Drill Stock	Length of Spanner	Net W'ght of Combination.	Each
1.	⅜ in. by 7/16 in.	3 in.	8 in.	1 lb.	7 6
2.	½ ,, by ½ ,,	4 ,,	10 ,,	2 lb.	9 6
3.	¾ ,, by ⅝ ,,	5 ,,	12 ,,	3 lb.	12 6
4.	⅞ ,, by 1 ,,	6 ,,	14 ,,	4½ lb.	15/-

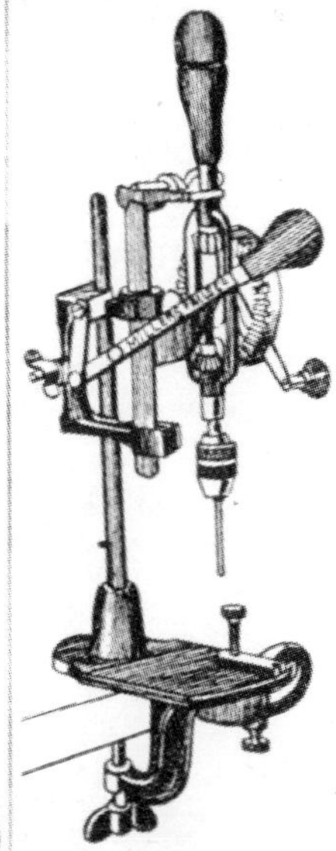

No. 22. **Millers Falls Bench Drill Press.**

For use with Nos. 1 and 5 Hand Drills.

Feed supplied by compound lever, sensitive and effective.

Steel frame and iron japanned.

Distance between chuck and table when No. 1 or 5 hand drill is used at highest point is 7½ in.

Weight 7½ lbs.

Height over all from table, 15½ in.

Price of Frame only, **7/-**

Carriage extra.

Special Line.

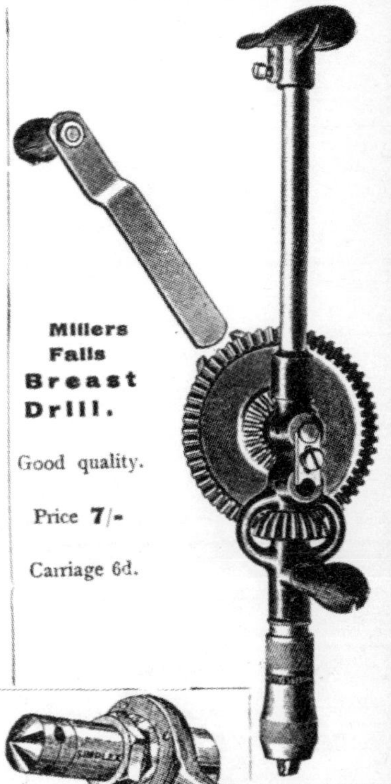

Millers Falls Breast Drill.

Good quality.

Price **7/-**

Carriage 6d.

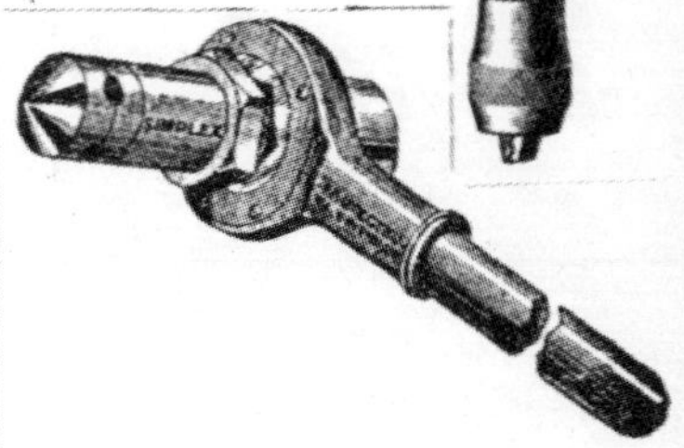

The Simplex Brace.

Larger size for heavy work fitted with single ended Ratchet Spanner.

The head is made of malleable steel, and handle of weldless steel tube.

No.	With Ratchet Spanner. Whitworth Standard	Length of Drill Stock.	Length of Spanner	Net W'ght of Combination.	Each
5.	¾ in.	7 in.	16 in.	4½ lb.	17/-
6.	¾ ,,	7½ ,,	20 ,,	5 lb.	20/

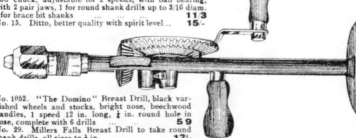

BREAST DRILL. Guaranteed quality.
No. 635. Black Japanned Frame with nickelled crank and chuck, adjustable for 2 speeds, with ball bearing, with 2 pair jaws, 1 for round shank drills up to 3/16 diam. for brace bit shanks **11/3**
No. 15. Ditto, better quality with spirit level ... **15/-**

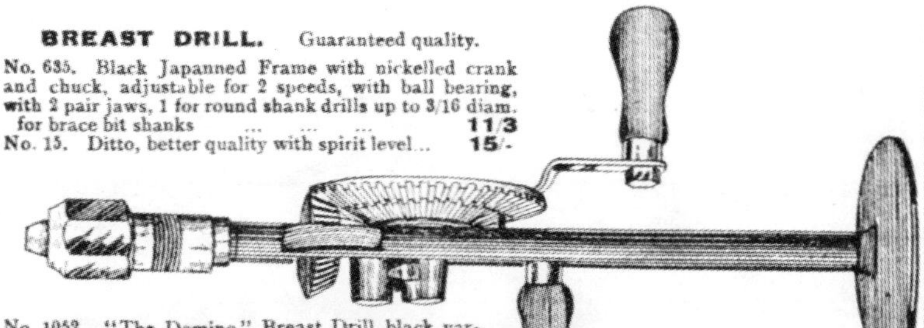

No. 1052. "The Domino" Breast Drill, black varnished wheels and stocks, bright nose, beechwood handles, 1 speed 12 in. long, ½ in. round hole in nose, complete with 6 drills **5 9**
No. 29. Millers Falls Breast Drill to take round shank drills, all sizes to ½ in. **12/-**
Postage 6d.

All Tools Guaranteed Quality.

Hand Drill.

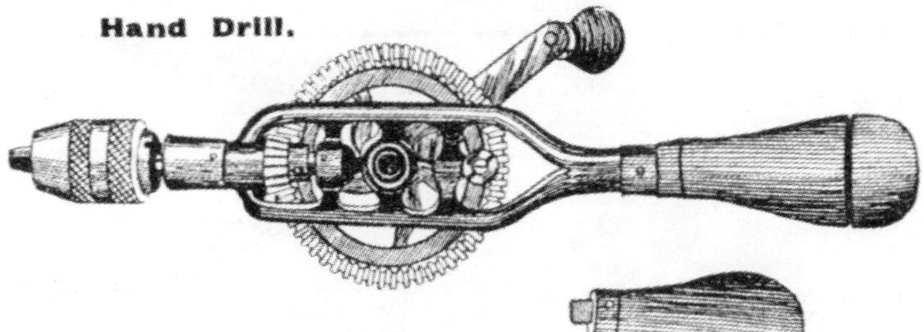

No 5. Best Quality Double Geared, and is provided with a wide rim gear so that the operator may, when using very small drills, revolve it by the rim of the wheel instead of the crank handle, this giving a steady and uniform motion, reducing the liability to break the drill points. Complete with 8 Fluted Drill Points. Price .. 5/11 Postage 4d.

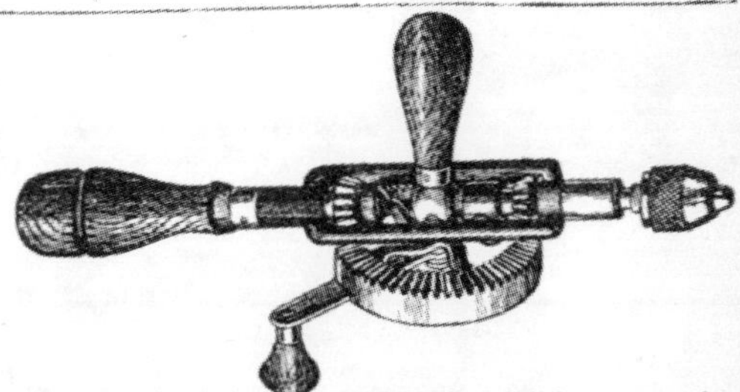

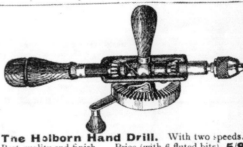

The Holborn Hand Drill. With two speeds. Best quality and finish. Price (with 6 fluted bits), **5/9** Postage 4d. Every Drill fully Guaranteed.

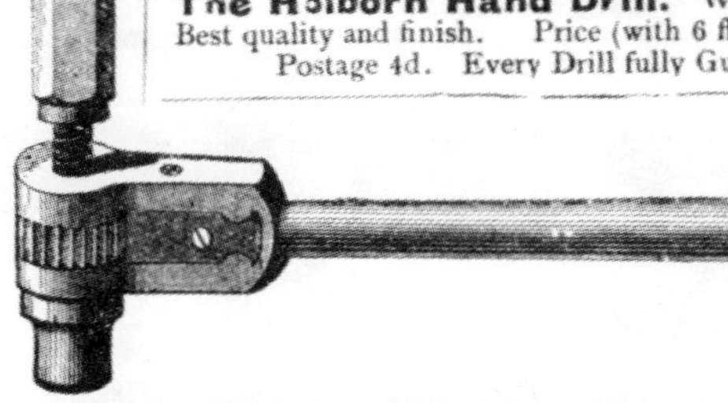

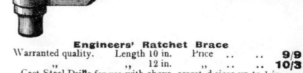

Engineers' Ratchet Brace
Warranted quality. Length 10 in. Price **9/9**
,, ,, 12 in. ,, ... **10/3**
Cast Steel Drills for use with above, assorted sizes up to 1 in.
Price .. **10½d.** each. **10 3** doz.
Ditto, 1¼ to 1½ in. Price .. **1/2** each. **12/6** doz.

No. 1 **American Single Geared Hand Drill.** Will take drills from 0 to 5/16 in. Complete with 8 Fluted Drills, good quality . **4 6** Postage 4d.

Write for Complete Tool Catalogue.

DRILLING MACHINES, &c.

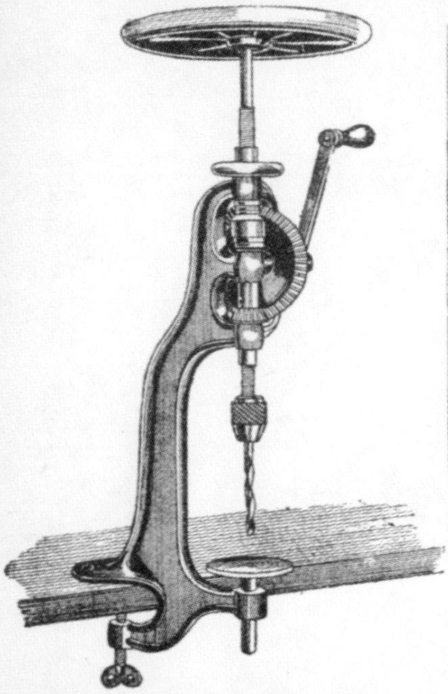

The Record Bench Drilling Machine.

Latest Pattern. Best make and finish.
With automatic and adjustable feed, the special **feature** of the drill is that the speed can be regulated for any class of work.
Well balanced fly wheel and cast steel ball bearings. Easy running.

No.	Weight.	Distance between Table and Chuck.	Distance between Frame and Spindle.	Total Height.	Ch'ck takes up to.	Price.
0	9¼ lb.	4 in.	1½ in.	19 in.	5/32 in.	18/3
1	16½ ,,	4½ ,,	2½ ,,	23 ,,	¼ ,,	24/-
2	25¼ ,,	7½ ,,	3 ,,	28 ,,	11/32 ,,	33/6
3	31 ,,	8¼ ,,	3½ ,,	32 ,,	½ ,,	46/9

Carriage forward.

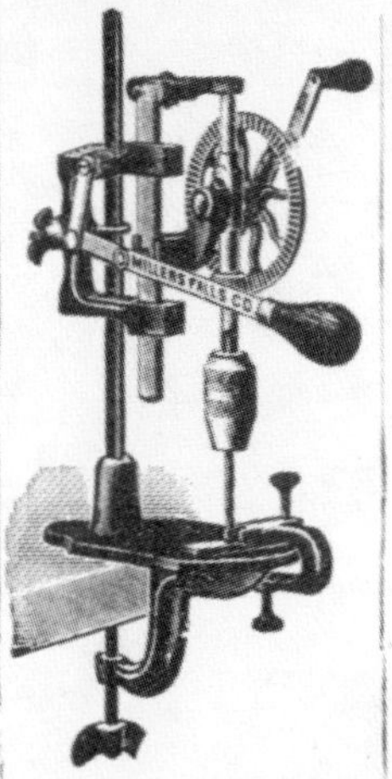

This Press is like No. 22 in construction, except that it has a permanent operating attachmen with **geared** spindle and **drill chuck** hold-rom 0 to ⅜ of an inch.
The distance from chuck to table, with sliding frame at highest point is 6¼ in.
Finished in japan and bright nickel, weight 6¾ lbs **14/-** each. Carriage forward.

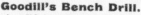

Goodill's Bench Drill.

A solid iron frame, cut gears, steel feed screws, adjustable table, and 3 jaw chucks to take 0 to ¼ in. drills
Height from table to feed wheel 13 inches.
Complete with 8 fluted drills.
Price .. **15/-**
Ditto, large size, with 3 jaw chucks, to take 0 to ⅜ in.
Height from table to feed wheel 18 inches.
Price **23/6**
Special Vice to suit above, and opening 2 inches.
Price .. **6/-** Carriage forward.

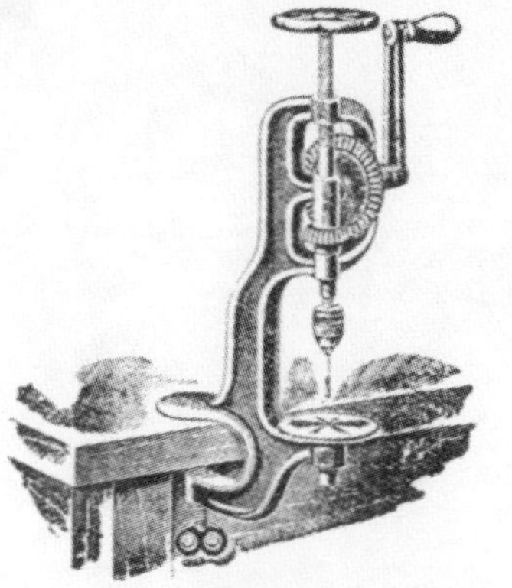

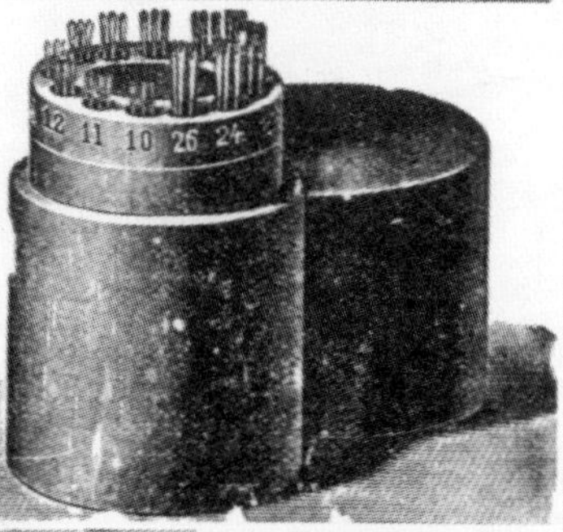

Drills.

Polished Wood Box.
Containing 3 dozen good quality bright finish Drills. Round Shanks. Quarter dozen each size.
Price **1/6** per box.
Postage 3d.

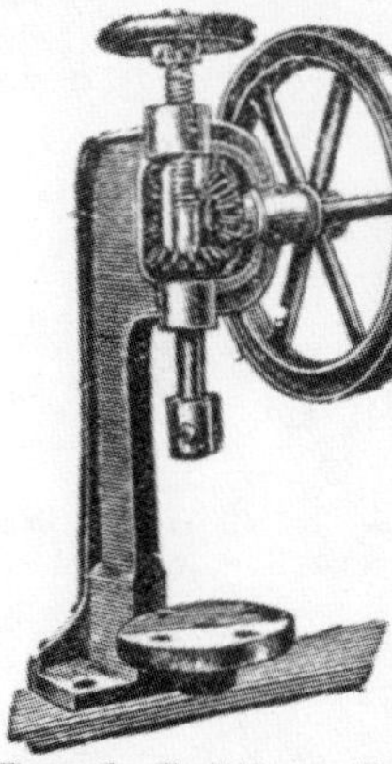

Bench Drilling Machine.

English Make.
A really good reliable Machine. Weight, 30 lbs. Has ⅜ in. hole in spindle. Drills hole up to ⅜ in. Price .. **29 6**
Ditto, with 3-Jaw Clutch. Takes drills from 0 to ½ in. Price .. **39/6**
Carriage forward.

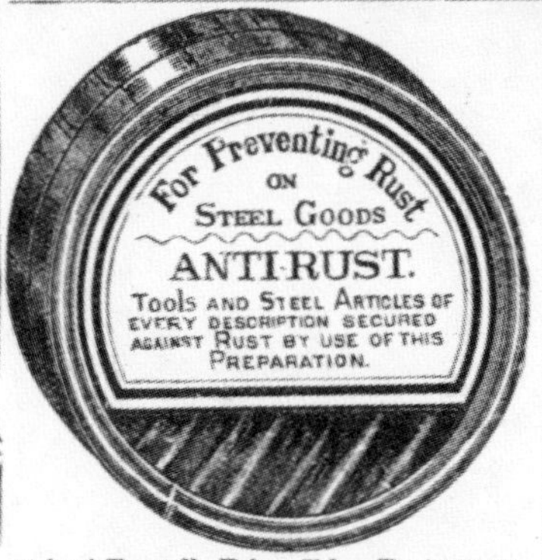

"Anti-Rust." Price **5d** Postage ex.

Archimedian Drill

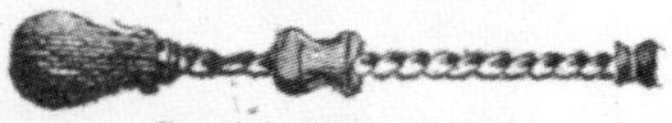

Special Cheap Line!
With 6 Drills. Price **4½**d. Post 1d.

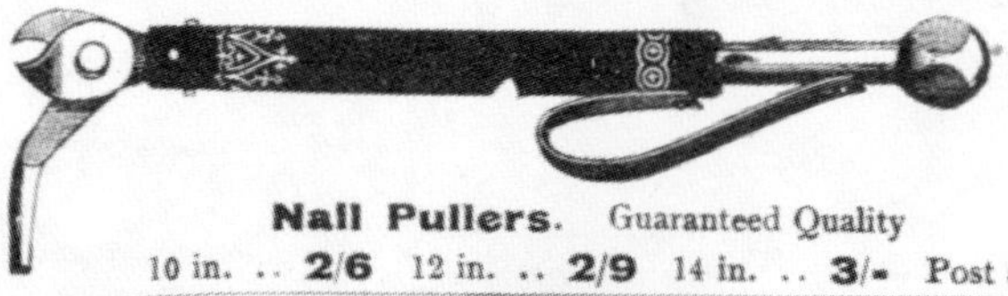

Nail Pullers. Guaranteed Quality
10 in. .. **2/6** 12 in. .. **2/9** 14 in. .. **3/-** Post 5d.

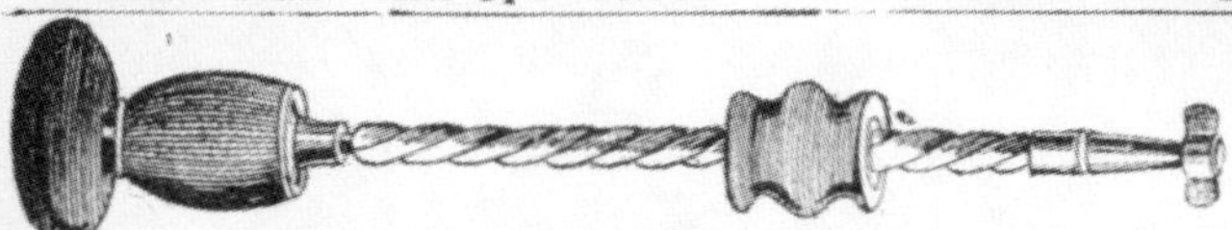

Archimedian Drill.
Warranted Quality, with Screw Chuck and Six Bits.
Size .. 6 in., **1/3½** 7 in., **1/6** 8 in., **1/7** 9 in. **1/8½** Post 2d.

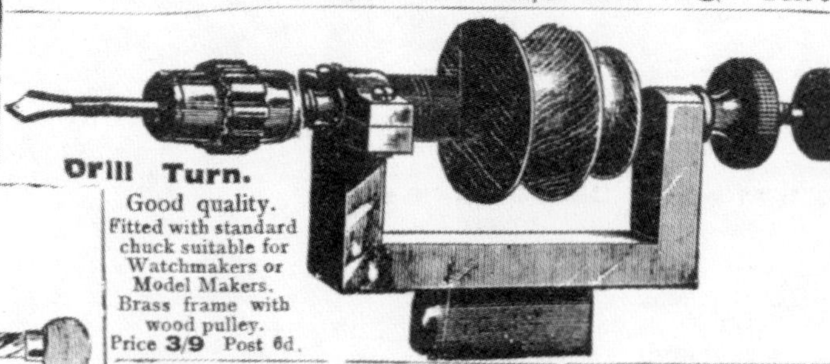

Drill Turn.
Good quality.
Fitted with standard chuck suitable for Watchmakers or Model Makers.
Brass frame with wood pulley.
Price **3/9** Post 6d.

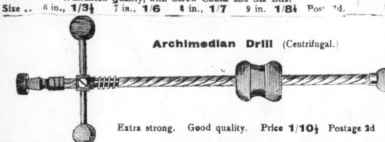

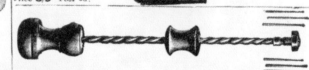

Archimedian Drill (Centrifugal.)

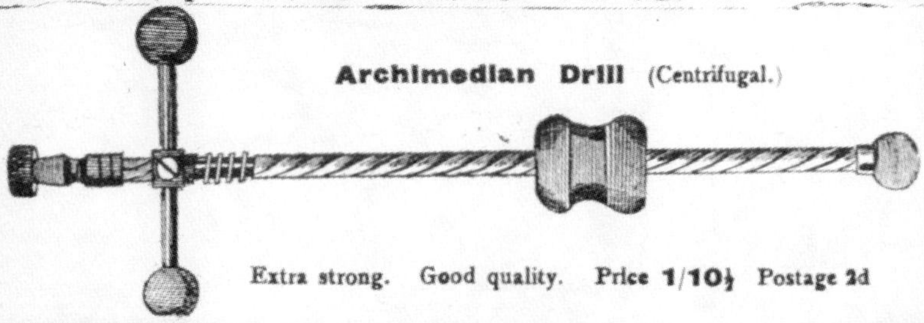

Extra strong. Good quality. Price **1/10½** Postage 2d

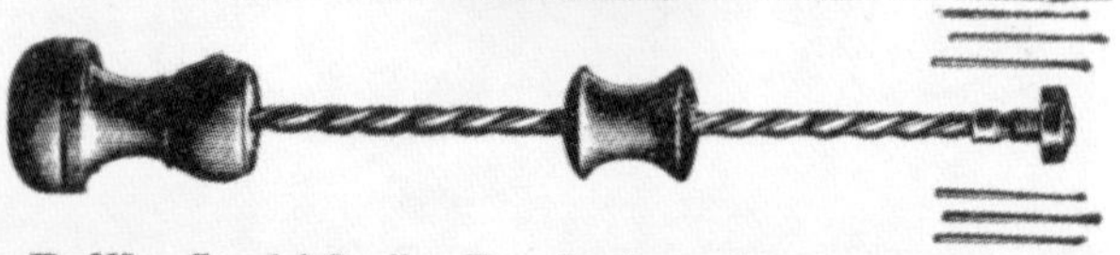

Archimedian Drill. Special Quality, Easy Motion. Complete with 6 Drills.
7 in., **6½**d. 9 in., **1/3** Postage 2d.

No. 54. **Gas Pipe Tongs**
Chain Pipe Tongs.

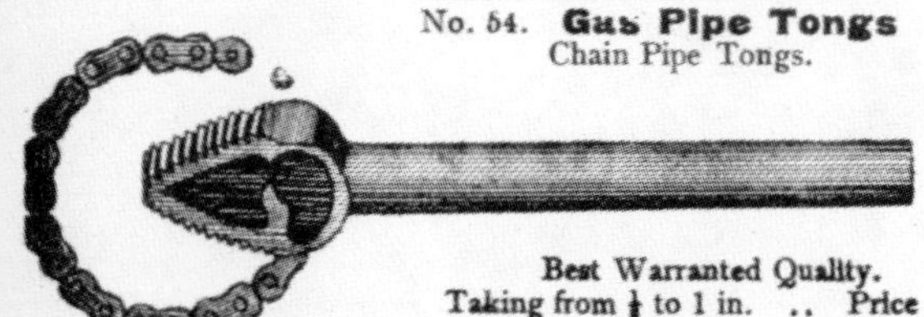

Best Warranted Quality.
Taking from ½ to 1 in. .. Price **4/-**
,, ,, ½ to 2 in. .. ,, **6/6**
Postage 6d

Gas Pipe Tongs

Best Bright Finish
Interchangeable to Various Sizes.
Postage 6d.

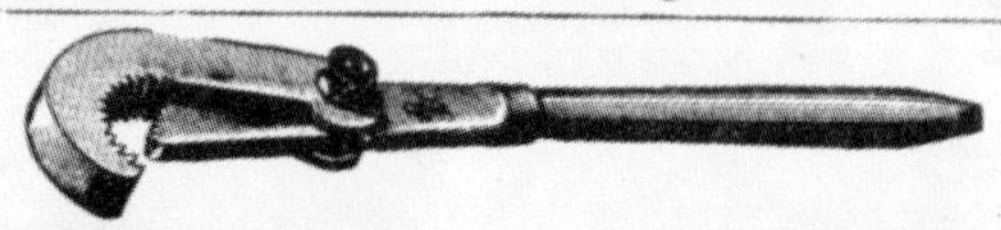

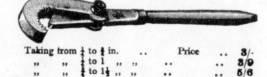

Taking from	¼ to ¾ in.	..		Price	..	**3/-**
,, ,,	¼ to 1	,, ,,	..		..	**3/9**
,, ,,	¼ to 1½	,, ,,	..		..	**5/6**

Write for Complete Tool Catalogue.

PLIERS, CALIPERS, etc.

No. 106. Bernard Parallel Jaw Pliers, pointed nose, nickel plated. 4½ in. long, **1/6** 5 in. long, **1/9** Postage 2d.

No. 109. Bernard Gas Pliers, parallel jaws, open throat, Guaranteed quality, nickel plated. 7 in. long, **2/8** Postage 3d.

No. 40. Starrett Screw Pitch Gauge, for Whitworth Standard Thread. Can be used inside a nut or on the outside of a screw or bolt. 22 pitches, viz., 9, to 40. Guaranteed quality. Price **3/3** Post 1d.

No. 101. Bernard Parallel Plyers, round nose, nickel plated, heavy pattern. 4½ in. long, **1/4**, 5½ in., **1/9** 6½ in., **2/2** 7½ in., **3/-**
No. 104. Ditto, light pattern, suitable for jewellers, etc. 4 in. leng, **1/2** 4½ in., **1/4** 5 in., **1/6** Postage 3d.

No. 102. Bernard Cutting Pliers, parallel jaws, guaranteed quality, nickel plated. 4½ in. long, **2/6** 5½ in., **3/2** 6½ in., **3/10** 7½ in., **5/2**
No. 105. Ditto, light pattern, suitable for jewellers, etc. 5 in. long only, **2/8** Postage 3d.

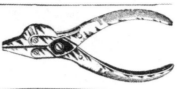

Wyke's Improved Universal Screw Cutting, Centre, Depth, Angle and Twist Drill Gauge. Best quality. No. 1. 2½ in. long, 1½ wide, 2 in. scale, **4/6** No. 2. 4 in. long, 1½ in. wide, 3 in scale, **7/6** Postage 1d.

Starrett's Centre Gauge, graduated 1 corner. Each in 32nds, 24ths, 20ths and 14ths.

Price **9**d.

Postage 1d.

No. 100. Bernard Flat Nose Pliers, parallel jaws, nickel plated, heavy pattern. 4½ in. long, **1/4** 5½ in., **1/9** 6½ in., **2/2** 7½ in., **3/-**
No. 103. Ditto, light pattern, suitable for jewellers, etc. 3½ in. long, **1/1** 4 in., **1/2** 4½ in., **1/4** 5 in., **1/6** Postage 2d.

No. 110. Bernard Gas and Cutting Pliers, with parallel jaws. Guaranteed quality, 5½ in. long, nickel plated, **2/2** Postage 2d.

No. 1. Screw Pitch Gauge. British Association Standard Thread. Sizes 0 to 10 .. **7/6** Postage 1d.

Starrett's Spring Divider. Guaranteed quality. With spring nut.

3	4	5	6 in.
3/3	**3/11**	**4/-**	**4/11**

Postage 1d.

Starrett's Lock Joint Outside Calipers, instantly adjusted and quickly locked. With sensitive adjustment, best quality and finish.

4	6	8	10	12in.
2/6	**2/8**	**3/9**	**4/6**	**5/3**

Postage 2d.

Starrat's Lock Joint Inside Caliper. Instantly adjusted and quickly locked. Best quality and finish.

4 in. long	...	**2/6**
6 "	...	**2/8**
8 "	...	**3/9**
10 "	...	**4/6**
12 "	...	**5/3**

Postage 2d.

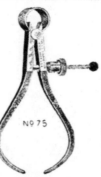

Starrett's Outside Calipers, guaranteed quality, best finish, with spring nut.

3	4	5	6 in.
3/3	**3/6**	**3/6**	**4/2**

Postage 2d.

Starrett's Inside Calipers, improved firm joint, best quality and finish.

3 in. long	**1/3**
4 "	**1/6**
5 "	**1/9**
6 "	**2/-**
8 "	**2/6**
10 "	**3/-**
12 "	**3/3**

Postage 2d.

Starrett's Outside Calipers, improved firm joint, best finish and quality.

3	4	5	6	8
1/3	**1/6**	**1/9**	**2/-**	**2/6**
10	12 in. long,
3/-	**3/3**

Postage 2d.

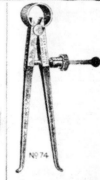

Starrett's Inside Calipers, guaranteed quality, best finish, with spring nut. In. long.

3	4	5	6
3/3	**3/6**	**3/6**	**4/2**

Postage 2d.

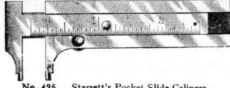

No. 425. Starrett's Pocket Slide Calipers. Graduated in 32nds and 64ths. With improved clamping device. 3 in. long. Price **6/6** Postage 1d.

Starrett's Surface Gauge.

3 in. base with 9 in. spindle. Price **9/6**

3 in. base with 9 and 12 in. spindle. Price ... **11/3**

Heavy base, grooved through the bottom and end, adapting it for use on or against circular work as well as flat surface.

The spindle may be set upright or at any position, or turned to work under base.

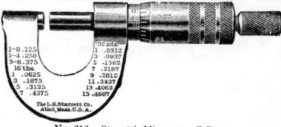

No. 216. Starrett's Micrometer Caliper. For measurements up to ½ in. by thousandths of an in., without lock nut, but with ratchet stop. Price **15/9**

Ditto, with lock nut. Price **16/9**

No. 216M. Ditto for millimetres up to 13 m/m by hundredths of a m/m. Price **18/-**

Ditto, with lock nut. Price **20/-**

Leather Cases to fit above Price **1/8** each.

Postag 2d.

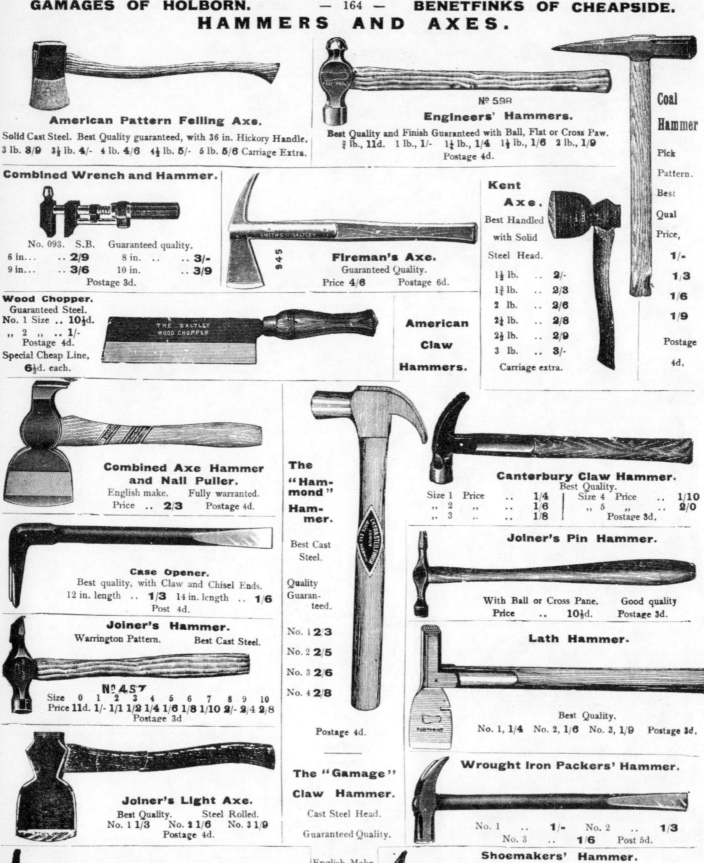

American Pattern Felling Axe.
Solid Cast Steel. Best Quality guaranteed, with 36 in. Hickory Handle.
3 lb. **3/9** 3½ lb. **4/-** 4 lb. **4/6** 4½ lb. **5/-** 5 lb. **5/6** Carriage Extra.

Nº 598
Engineers' Hammers.
Best Quality and Finish Guaranteed with Ball, Flat or Cross Paw.
¾ lb., **11d.** 1 lb., **1/-** 1¼ lb., **1/4** 1½ lb., **1/6** 2 lb., **1/9**
Postage 4d.

Coal Hammer
Pick Pattern.
Best Qual
Price,
1/-
1/3
1/6
1/9
Postage 4d.

Combined Wrench and Hammer.
No. 093. S.B. Guaranteed quality.
6 in... .. **2/9**   8 in. **3/-**
9 in... .. **3/6**   10 in. .. **3/9**
Postage 3d.

945
Fireman's Axe.
Guaranteed Quality.
Price **4/6**   Postage 6d.

Kent Axe.
Best Handled with Solid Steel Head.
1½ lb. .. **2/-**
1¾ lb. .. **2/3**
2 lb. .. **2/6**
2¼ lb. .. **2/8**
2½ lb. .. **2/9**
3 lb. .. **3/-**
Carriage extra.

Wood Chopper.
Guaranteed Steel.
No. 1 Size .. **10½d.**
„ 2 „ .. **1/-**
Postage 4d.
Special Cheap Line,
6½d. each.

THE SALTLEY WOOD CHOPPER

American Claw Hammers.

Combined Axe Hammer and Nail Puller.
English make. Fully warranted.
Price .. **2/3**   Postage 4d.

Case Opener.
Best quality, with Claw and Chisel Ends.
12 in. length .. **1/3** 14 in. length .. **1/6**
Post 4d.

Joiner's Hammer.
Warrington Pattern. Best Cast Steel.
Nº 457

Size	0	1	2	3	4	5	6	7	8	9	10
Price	11d.	1/-	1/1	1/2	1/4	1/6	1/8	1/10	2/-	2/4	2/8

Postage 3d

Joiner's Light Axe.
Best Quality. Steel Rolled.
No. 1 **1/3** No. 2 **1/6** No. 3 **1/9**
Postage 4d.

London Pattern Hammer.
Best Cast Steel.

Size	0	1	2	3	4	5	6	7	8	9	10
Price	8d.	9d.	10d.	1/-	1/2	1/4	1/6	1/8	1/10	2/-	2/3

Post 3d.

The **"Hammond" Hammer.**
Best Cast Steel.
Quality Guaranteed.
No. 1 **2/3**
No. 2 **2/5**
No. 3 **2/6**
No. 4 **2/8**
Postage 4d.

The **"Gamage" Claw Hammer.**
Cast Steel Head.
Guaranteed Quality.
English Make
No. 1 **11d.**
No. 2 **1/-**
Postage 3d.

Canterbury Claw Hammer.
Best Quality.
Size 1 Price .. **1/4**   Size 4 Price .. **1/10**
„ 2 „ .. **1/6**   „ 5 „ .. **2/0**
„ 3 „ .. **1/8**   Postage 3d.

Joiner's Pin Hammer.
With Ball or Cross Pane. Good quality.
Price .. **10½d.** Postage 3d.

Lath Hammer.
Best Quality.
No. 1, **1/4** No. 2, **1/6** No. 3, **1/9** Postage 3d.

Wrought Iron Packers' Hammer.
No. 1 .. **1/-** No. 2 .. **1/3**
No. 3 .. **1/6** Post 5d.

Shoemakers' Hammer.
Good Quality.
Price .. **6d.** each.
Post 3d.

Write for Complete Tool Catalogue.

Iron Planes, etc.

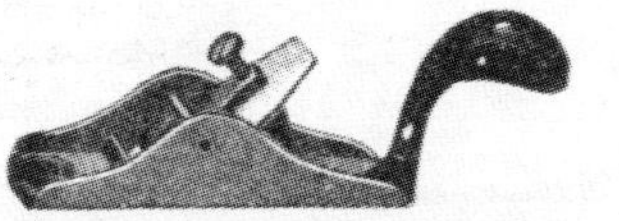

Stanley Iron Plane.

No. 100. Length 3½ in.. cutter 1 in.
Price .. **9**d. Postage 3d.
Extra cutters, 2½d. each.

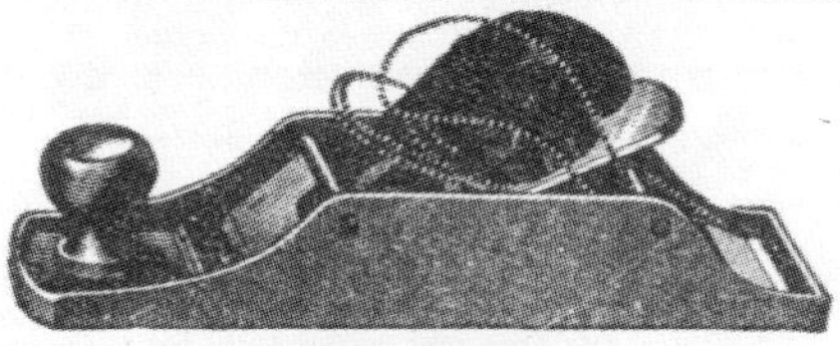

Stanley's Plane.

No. 130. Block plane (double-ender), 8 in., 1¾ in. cutter. This plane has two slots and two cutter seats. By reversing the position of the cutter and the clamping wedge, it can be used close up into corners, or other difficult places.
Price .. **2/3** Postage 4d.
Extra cutters, 6d. each.

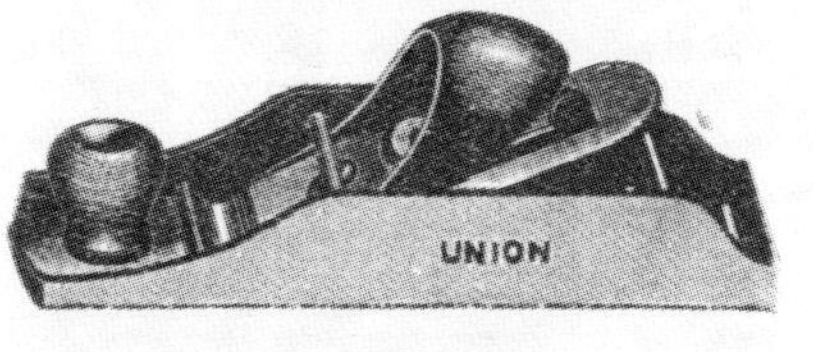

Iron Plane.

No. 137. Block plane, with double ends. By changing blade from one end to the other, it is possible to plane close to corner.
Price **2/-** Postage 3d.

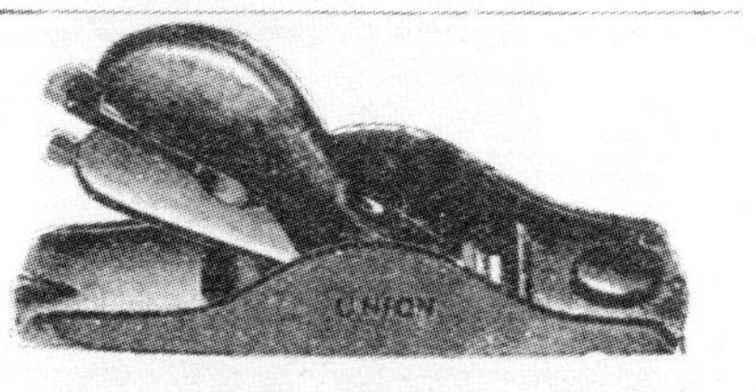

Iron Plane.

No. 102. Block plane, 5½ in. long, 1¼ in. cutter.
Price .. **1/-** Postage 3d.

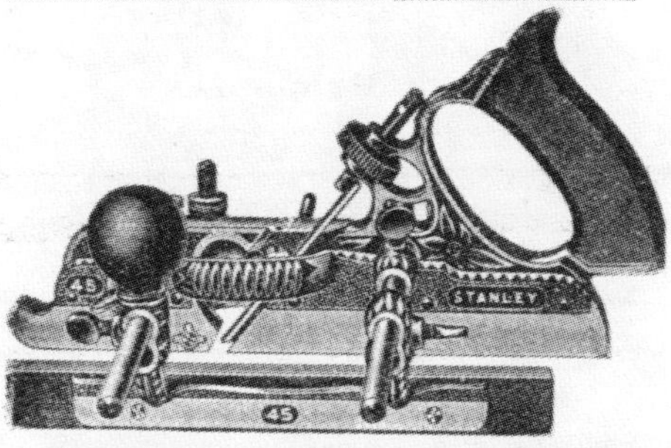

Stanley's Adjustable Beading Rabbet and Matching Plane

No. 45. This Plane combines a main stock and a sliding section so arranged that cutters of differen twidths can be used. Each plane is fitted with an adjustable fence or guide and a depth gauge, and also with spurs for use in working across the grain. This Plane can be used right or left hand. An adjustable stop, to be used in beading the edges of matched boards is inserted on the left hand side of sliding section. A patent adjustable cam rest is now furnished with each No. 45 Plane for use when fence and main stock are used some distance apart.
his Plane embraces (1) Beading and Centre Beading Plane; (2) Rabbet and Filletster; (3) Dado; (4) Plow; (5) Matching Plane; (6) Sash Plane; and (7) a superior Slitting Plane. Each Plane has seven Beading Tools—(⅛, 3-16, ¼, 5-16, ⅜, 7-16, and ½ inch), ten Plow and Dado Bits (⅛, 3-16, ¼, 5-16, ⅜, 7-15, ½, ⅝, ¾ and ⅞ inch), a Slitting Blade, a Tonguing Tool and a Sash Tool.
Nickel plated with 20 Tool Bits. Price, **27/6**

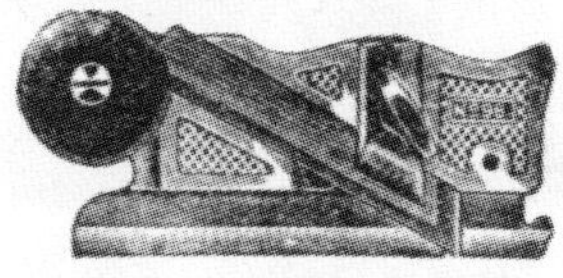

Stanley's side Rabbet.

No. 98. A convenient tool for side-rabbetting and trimming dados, moulding and grooves of all sorts. A reversible nose-piece will give the tool a form by which it will work close up into corners when required.
Right or left hand. Price .. **3/3**
Please state which hand required.
Postage 3d.

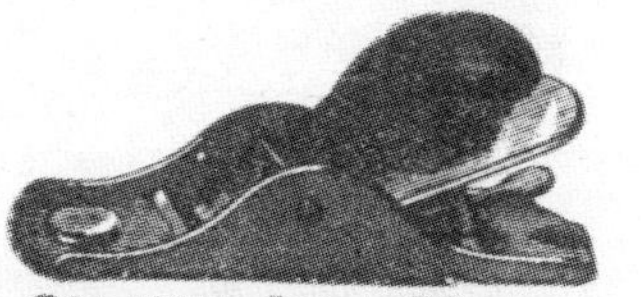

Stanley Iron Plane.

No. 103. With adjustable iron, length 3½ in., cutter 1¼ in.
Price .. **1/8** Postage 3d.
Extra cutters, 4d. each.

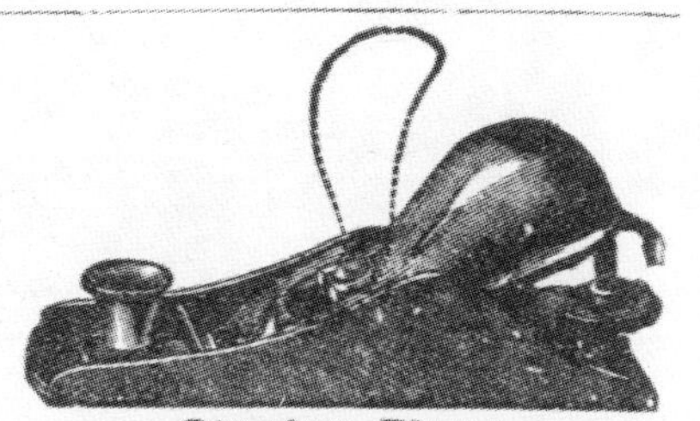

Stanley Plane.

No. 18. With adjustable throat, Bailey adjustment and Lateral adjustment, the knuckle joint makes it a lever too, and placing the cap in position clamps the cutter in its seat.
Length 6 in. Price .. **4/2** each.
No. 19. ,, 7 ,, ,, .. **4/6** ,,
Postage 4d.
Extra cutters, 5d. each.

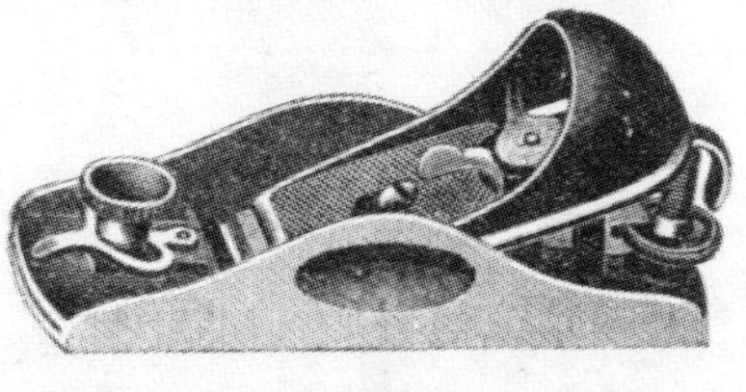

Stanley Iron Plane.

No. 9½. With improved throat adjustment.
Length 6 in., cutter 1¾ in. Price .. **3/6**
No. 15, 7 ,, ,, 1¾ ,, ,, .. **3/9**
Postage 4d.
Extra cutters, 6d. each.

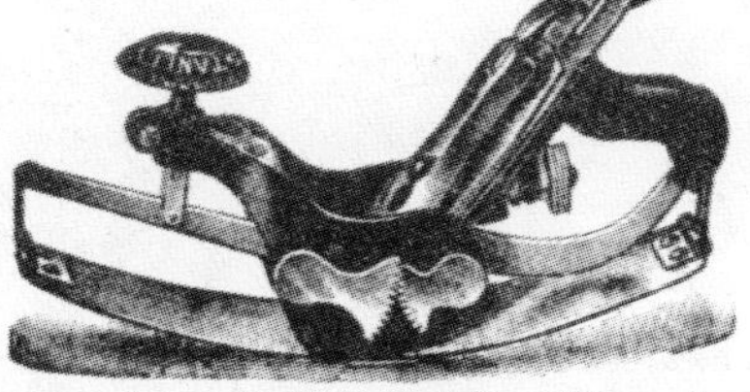

Stanley Adjustable Circular Plane

No. 113. With 1¾ in. cutter. Price .. **10/3**
Postage 4d.

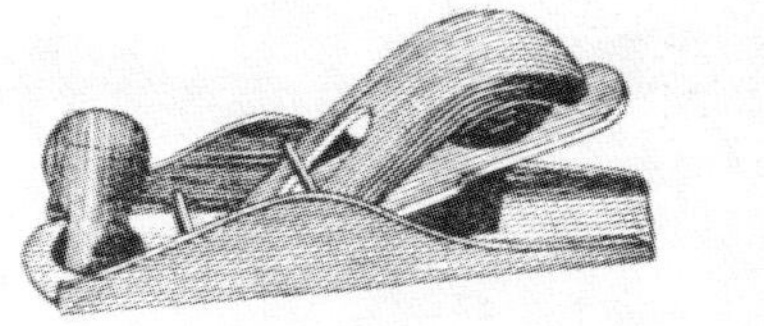

Iron Plane.

No. 110. Block plane, 7 in. long, with 1¾ in. cutter.
Price .. **1/6** Postage 3d.

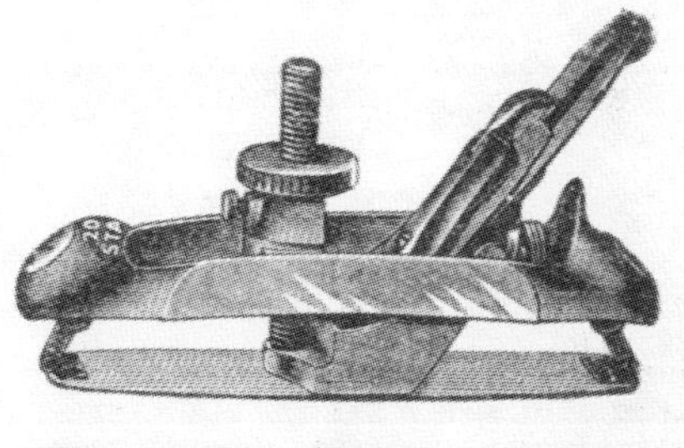

The Victor Circular Plane.

No. 20. The flexible steel face on this plane can be made convex or concave, by simply turning screw. Nickel plated with 1¾ in. cutter.
Price .. **12/9** Postage 4d.

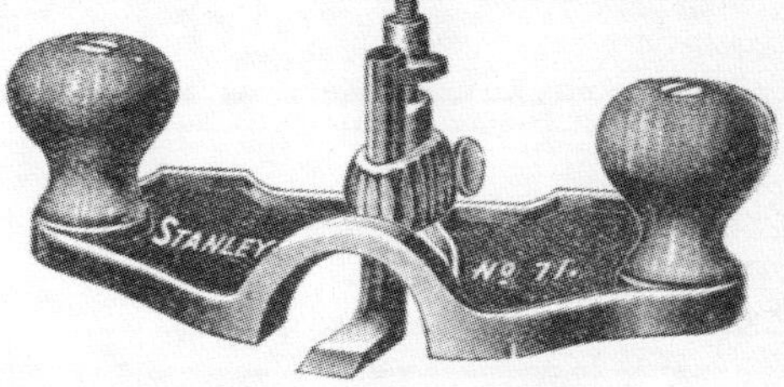

Stanley's Router Plane.

Good Quality.
This Tool is perfectly adapted to smooth the bottom of grooves, panels, and all depressions below the general surface. With 2 cutters, ¼ and ½ in. Price, **6/6** Postage 4d.

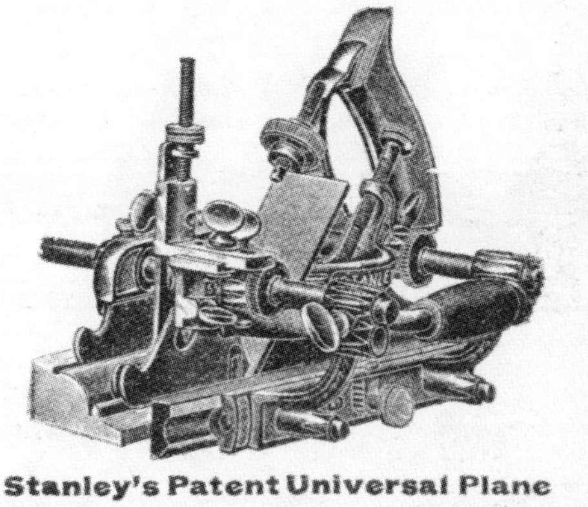

Stanley's Patent Universal Plane

No. 55. A most useful tool. Combines the following Planes—Matching, Sash, Beading, Reeling, Fluting, Hollow, Round, Plow, Rabbet, Filletster, Dado, and Slitting in fact will do almost any Plane work that is required, in an up-to-date carpenter's shop, and all being combined saves great trouble, in keeping so many different varieties of planes (the illustration shows the plane fitted up for moulding).
Nickel plated, complete with 52 Tool Bits and the Cutters arranged in 4 separate cases. The complete set all being in one wood box.
Price .. **57/6**

Write for Complete Tool Catalogue.

Planes and Spokeshaves.

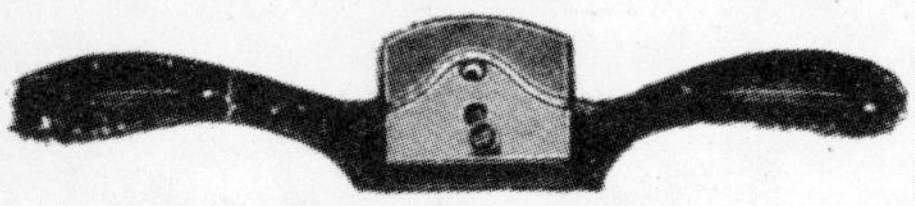

Iron Spoke Shave.

Good quality. Double Iron.

With 1¾ in. Cutter .. .. Price **9d.** each.

With adjustable mouth, 2⅛ Cutter „ **1/2** „

Postage 2d

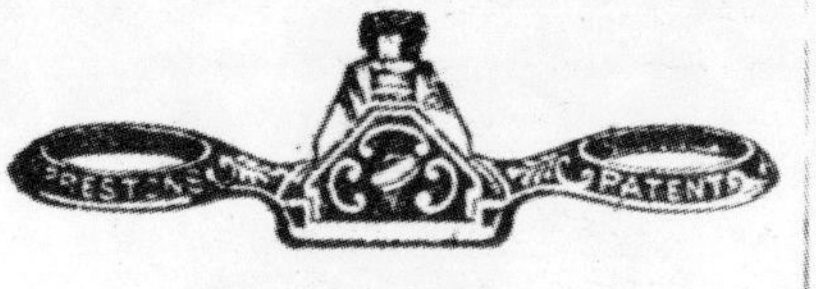

Spoke Shave.

10 in. Hollow-Raised Handles, Nickel Plated Flat Face, 2 in. Cutter.

Price .. **2/9** Postage 3d.

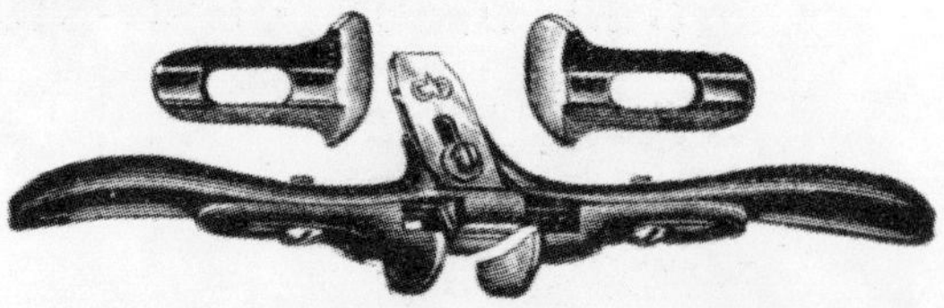

Improved Circular Rabbeting & Fillister Routes

with one Cutting Iron and two pairs of adjustable Fences which enable it to he used either as a Rabbeting or moving Fillister Router. The Fences are adjustable from ⅛ to ⅞ in.

Price .. **2/9** Postage 3d.

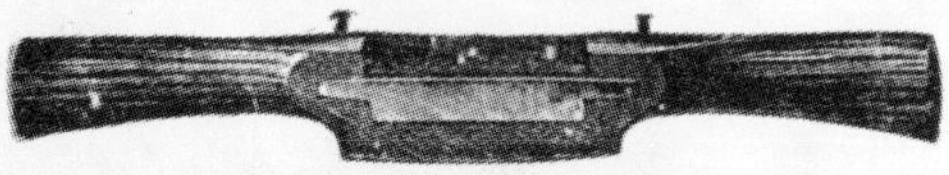

SPOKE SHAVE.

Beechwood handle, best Sheffield Make.

Size.	Price.	Size.	Price.	Size.	Price.
1½ in.,	**9d.** each.	2 in.,	**9d.** each.	2½ in.,	**9d.** each.
1¾ in.,	**9d.** „	2¼ in.,	**9d.** „	3 in.,	**11d.** „
		Best Boxwood.			
1½ in.,	**11½d.** each.	2 in.,	**1/-** each.	2½ in.,	**1/1** each.
1¾ in.,	**1/-** „	2¼ in.,	**1/-** „	3 in.,	**1/3** „

Postage 3d.

Stanley's Universal Spoke Shave

Has two detachable bottoms, adapting it equally well to circular work or straight and, by means of a moveable width gauge, the tool can be used in rabbeting. Both Handles are detachable, and either of them can be screwed into a socket on top of the stock, thus enabling the owner to work into corners or panels.

Price .. **5/6** Postage 3d.

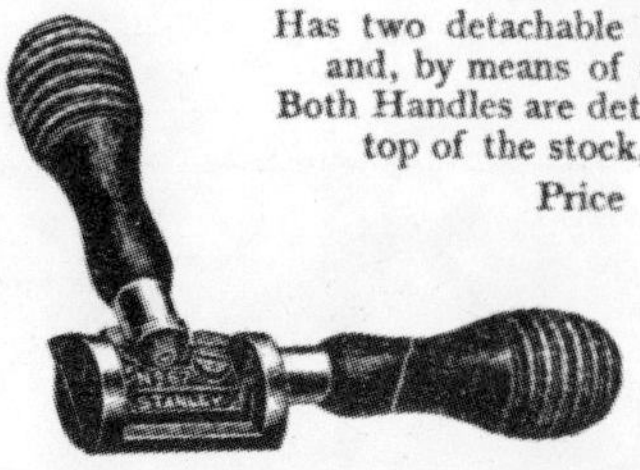

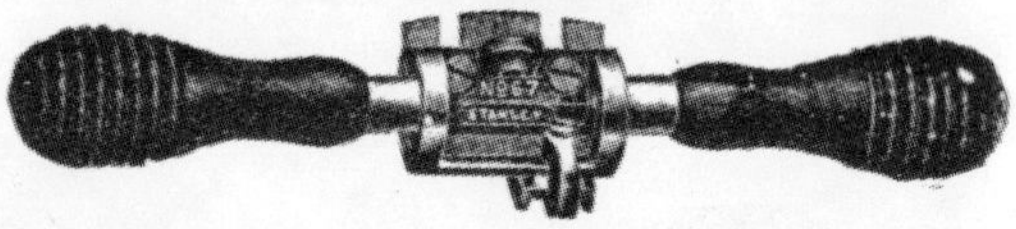

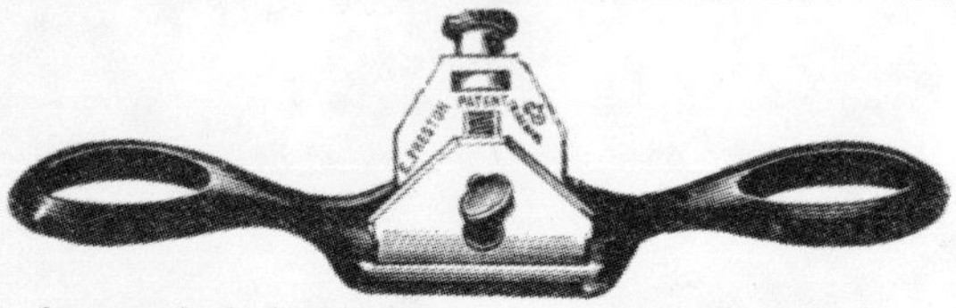

Improved Adjustable Iron Spoke Shave.

Good Quality. With 2⅛ in. Cutting Iron.

Price **2/3**

Adjustable Bull Nose Rabbet Plane.

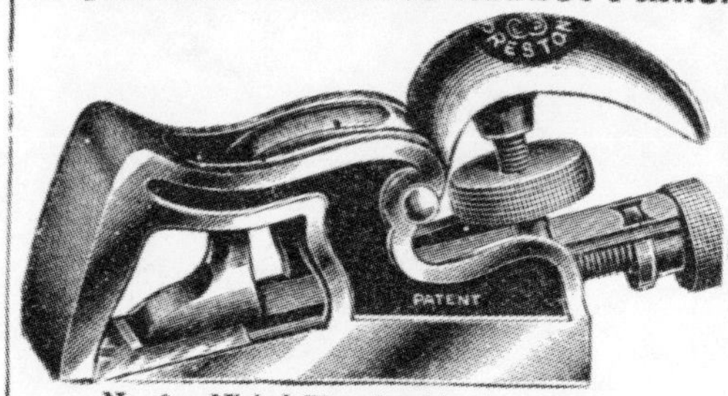

No 9 Nickel Plated, with 1⅛ in. Cutter

Price .. .. **5/6** Postage .. 3d.

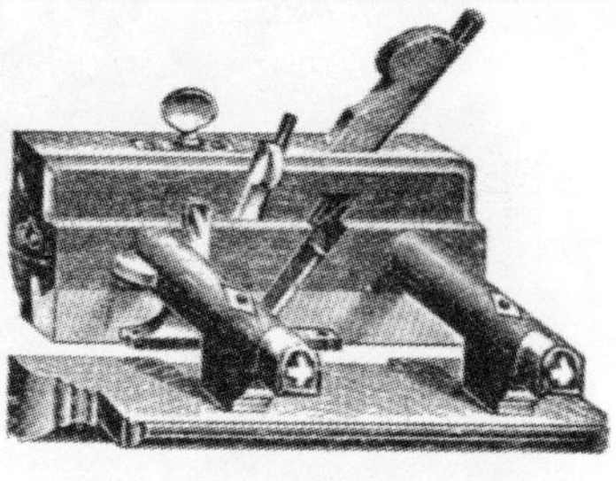

Sash Fillister Plane.

Best Quality. Double Plate with Bright Irons. Improved Stop and extra work on Fence.

Price .. **21/-** Carriage Paid.

Smoothing Plane.

Best Seasoned Beech. With Warranted Quality Double Irons

No. 1 With 1¾ Iron Price **3/6**
„ 2 „ 2 „ „ **3/7**
„ 3 „ 2⅛ „ „ **4/-**
„ 4 „ 2¼ „ „ **4/3**

Postage 4d.

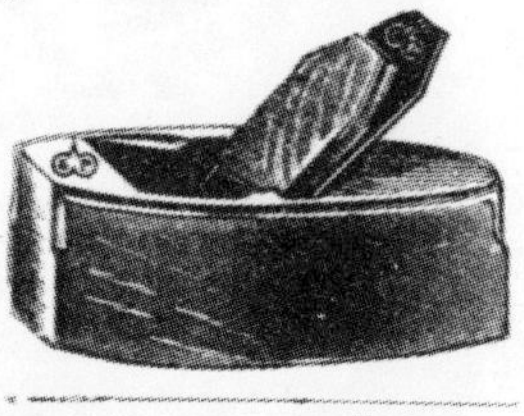

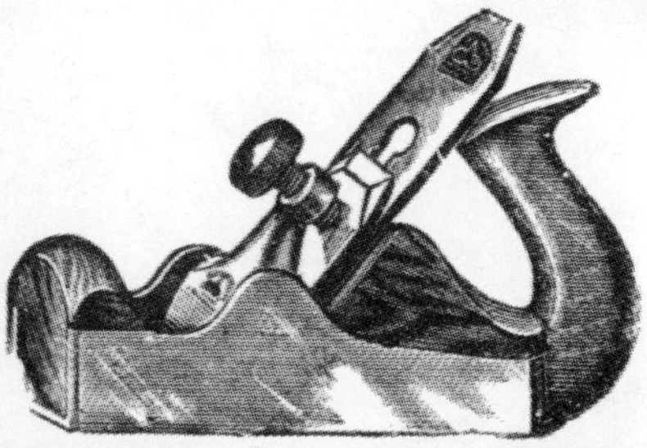

Steel Smoothing Plane.

With Rosewood handled, dovetailed, parallel sides. Best bright cast steel Iron.

2⅛ in., **21/-**
2¼ in., **21/6**
Carriage 6d.

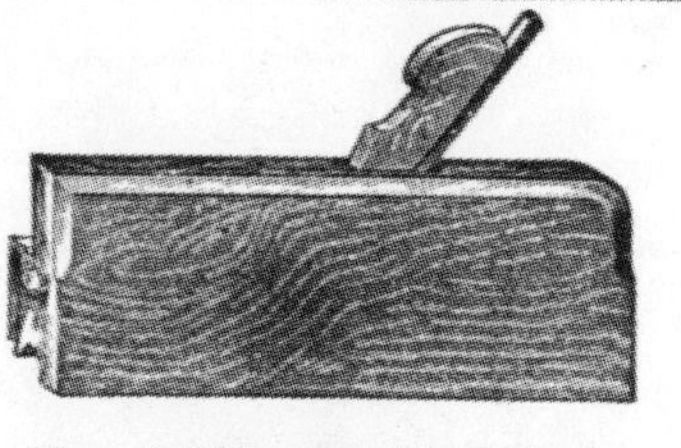

Bead Plane. Single Boxed.
Best quality Cast Steel Iron.
Best selected Beech.

Sizes—⅛ 3/16 ¼ 5/16 ⅜ 7/16 ½ ⅝ in.
Price **2/3** each.

sizes—¾ in., **2/9** ⅞, **3/-** 1 in. **3/3** each
Ditto Slipped, sizes ⅛ to ⅝ in. **3/-** each·
¾ in. **3/3** ⅞ in. **3/6** 1 in. **3/9** each,

Double Boxed Bead Planes.

Size—⅛ in. to ⅝ in., **3/-** ¾ in., **3/3**
⅞ in., **3/6** 1 in., **3/9** each. Post 3d

Bull Nose Rabbet Plane.

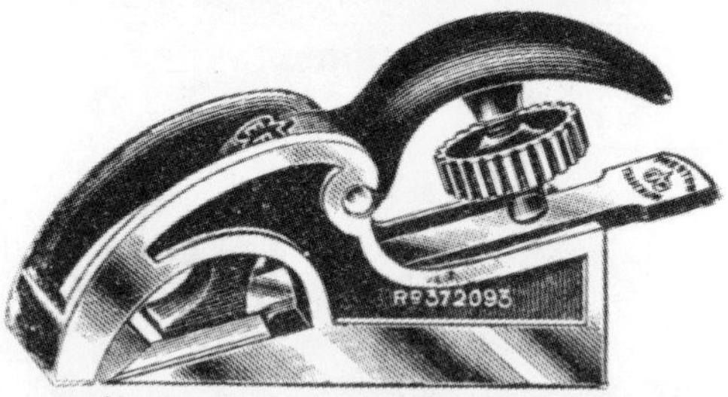

No 8. Japanned, with Bright Parts.

Price .. .. **3/4** Postage 3d.

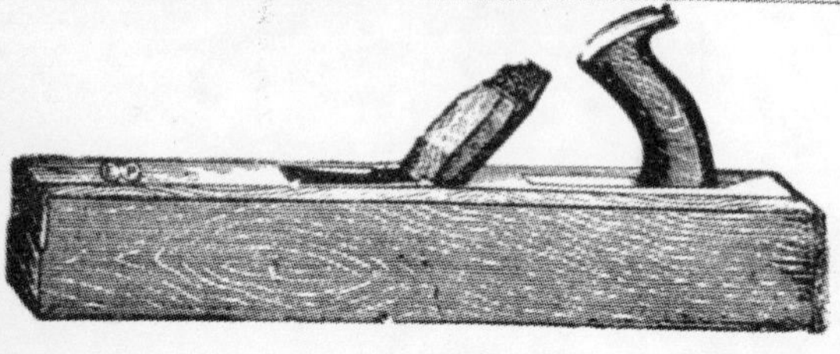

Jack Plane.

Best Seasoned Beech. With Warranted Quality Double Irons

Size 14 by 2 Price **4/6** Size 17 by 2¼ Price **5/-**

Ditto, Technical Pattern, with Sunk Handle and Boxwood Striking Knob. Size, 14 by 2 in.

Price .. **5/6** Postage 6d.

Trying Plane.

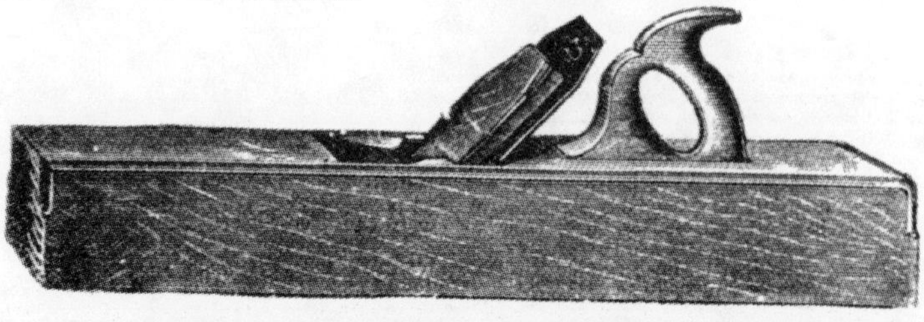

Best Seasoned Beech. With Warranted Quality Double Iron.

Size .. .. 22 in. by 2½ in. Price **6/6**

Postage 6d.

Write for Complete Tool Catalogue.

High Grade Sheffield Steel Combination and Sports Knives.

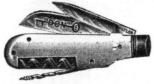

The "DON." Useful inexpensive Combination Knife. Two blades, corkscrew and gimlet. Length 2½ in. White Buffalo or Stag handle, **2/-**

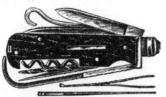

F. 2104 The 'All-round" Combination Knife FOR SPORTSMEN. Length 3½ in. Stag horn handle, **5/6** Genuine Ivory handle, **6/9**

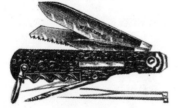

No. F. 1686. The "Sports" Combination Knife. Two blades, saw, gimlet, piercer, corkscrew, etc. Length 4 in. Stag handle, **7/6** Ivory handle, **9/6**

No. F. A227. The "GENERAL" 3½ in. **9/9**

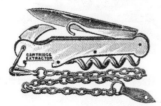

No. F. A214. New "CARTRIDGE" KNIFE **5/3**

No. F. B 364.
6 in., **10/-** 7 in., **11/6** 8 in., **13/-**

Gamage's Popular Combination Sports Knife.
Stag handle, with shackle and chain complete **2/6**

No. F. 757. Nickel-handle Champagne Knife. Length 3½ in , **2/6** Length 4 in., **3/6**

No. F. A216. Useful Knife. Nickel scales. Two blades, button hook and corkscrew, **3/11**

No. F. 2210. **Handsome Knife.** Contains 2 Blades, Saw, Button Hook, Nail File, Piercer, Corkscrew, Gimlet, Screw-driver, Horse Hook, Tweezer, Toothpick, &c., &c. Stag Handle, **16/6** Ivory Handle, **19/6**

No. F. B359. BOWIE KNIFE. Stag handle. Complete with Sheath. 5 in. 6 in. 7 in. **2/6 3/- 3/9**

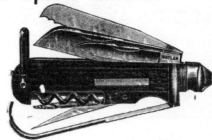

No. F. 2204. Strong Combination Knife. FOR TOURISTS, CYCLISTS, &c. Stag handle, **3/11** Ivory handle, **4/9**

No. F. B400. The "GEM." Combination Sports Knife with chain complete. Ivory handle, **5/6**

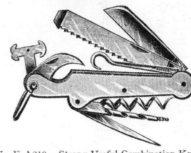

No. F. A219. Strong Useful Combination Knife. Fitted with strong blade, saw, gimlet and corkscrew. Length 4 in. Nickel handle, **10/6**

No. F. A223. The "Colonial" Camp Knife. Fitted with two strong blades, turnscrew, tin-opener, corkscrew, button-hook, etc. Length 5 in. Nickel handle, **18/9**

No. F. 185½. Strong Lock-back stag handle. Length closed— 4 5 6 7 in. **3/- 4/- 5/- 6/9**

S 1

Facsimile of the Model and Wireless Catalogue Cover.

THE HOME SCIENTIST

A.W.GAMAGE LTD.
HOLBORN   LONDON. E.C.

Wireless ..
Telegraphy

although in its infancy, has already been of inestimable value, and there is little doubt that when perfected, it will prove to be the greatest science of all time.

"Experimenters, that sane body of voluntary workers who take up the art as a hobby, study, or spare time vocation, and who are generally misnamed 'amateurs.'"—

PHILIP E. EDELMAN.

There is a big field open

to the Experimenter in Radio Telegraphy, and we commend this Catalogue to his notice, and would add that the Apparatus described therein has **been designed by Experts and made by first-class Mechanics,** enabling anyone of average intellect to instal a Wireless Station and receive signals transmitted hundreds of miles distant.

To the Prospective Purchaser.

A. W. GAMAGE LTD., specialised in the design and manufacture of Apparatus for Radio Telegraphy years before the General Public took any interest in what is now admitted to be the greatest invention of all time. During the last twelve months quite a number of "Firms" have come into existence who claim to be pioneers and specialists in the manufacture of Wireless Instruments. Having regard to the tactics of some of these "Firms" it behoves us to warn intending purchasers that

☞ **Instruments manufactured by us are not obtainable elsewhere.**

MODEL RAILWAYS, YACHTS, AEROPLANES, KITES, DYNAMOS AND MOTORS

WE SUBMIT this Catalogue to our Customers and the General Public in the belief that they will find it to be the most comprehensive and up-to-date List dealing exclusively with Mechanical and Scientific Toys, Models and Accessories.

THE PRICES need no comment, these being essentially competitive and framed on the usual Gamage basis of small profits.

☞ **Either of these Catalogues will be sent Post Free to any address.**

BILLIARD DEPARTMENT.

Our Speciality.

6 by 3 ft. mahogany frame Billiard Table, covered with good quality cloth. Set of Ivory Balls, 2 Cues, Rest, Marker, Chalk, Level, etc. For standing on dining table.

£4 4 0

SPECIAL STANDS FOR MINIATURE TABLES.

Hardwood, Stained and Polished and specially well finished.

4 ft.	..	27/6
5 ft.	..	33/6
6 ft.	..	45/-
7 ft.	..	50/-

Carriage extra.

Miniature Slate Bed Billiard Tables.
For Standing on Dining Table.
Fitted with adjustable Screw Legs for levelling. Rubber Cushions, Ivory Balls, 2 Cues, Marking Board, Chalk, Spirit Level, Rules, etc.

Outside Measure.	Size of Balls.	Price.				Outside Measure.	Size of Balls.	Price.		
4 ft. 4 in. by 2 ft. 4 in.	.. 1½ in. ..	£3	6	6		6 ft. 4 in. by 3 ft. 4 in. .. 1¾ in. ..		£7	15 0	C quality
5 „ 4 „ 2 „ 10 „	.. 1⅝ „ ..	4	6	6		7 „ 4 „ 3 „ 10 „ .. 1⅜ „ ..		7	10 0	A „
6 „ 4 „ 3 „ 4 „	.. 1¾ „ ..	4	15	0 A quality		7 „ 4 „ 3 „ 10 „ .. 1¾ „ ..		9	10 0	C „
6 „ 4 „ 3 „ 4 „	.. 1¾ „ ..	6	0	0 B „						

Carriage extra.   10/- charged for cases which is refunded on their return carriage paid.
Rests supplied with Tables, 6 ft. and upwards.

COMBINED BILLIARD AND DINING TABLES.
THE REVERSIBLE.

Showing manner of Reversing.

These Tables are of simple construction and of the finest quality material, they are fitted with screw toes, whereby a perfect level can be obtained, covered with superior West of England Cloth. Best rubber cushions, ivory balls, cues, etc.

Billiard Table.	Dining Table		Price.		
6 by 3 ft. ..	7 by 4 ft. ..	Stained and Polished ..	£12	12	0
7 „ 3 ft. 6 in.	8 „ 4 ft. 6 in.	„ „ ..	16	10	0
8 „ 4 ft. ..	9 „ 5 ft. ..	„ „ ..	22	7	6
6 „ 3 ft. ..	7 „ 4 ft. ..	Mahogany ..	18	10	0
7 „ 3 ft. 6 in.	8 „ 4 ft. 6 in.	„ ..	22	12	6
8 „ 4 ft. ..	9 „ 5 ft. ..	„ ..	28	0	0

These Tables to order only, sample on show in Showroom. Carriage extra.

THE "IDEAL" TABLE.
In solid Mahogany, Walnut or Oak.   To order only.

6 by 3 ft. ..	Suitable for a Room 14 by 11 ft. ..		£19	0	0
7 „ 3 ft. 6 in.	„ „ „ 15 „ 11 ft. 6 in. ..		25	5	0
8 „ 4 ft. ..	„ „ „ 16 „ 12 ft. ..		30	0	0
9 „ 4 ft. 6 in.	„ „ „ 17 „ 12 ft. 6 in. ..		35	0	0

THE "IDEAL."

The distinguishing feature of the "Ideal" is the extreme ease with which the change from billiard to dining table—or vice versa—is effected. By merely working handle (see illustration above) the adjustment to correct height can be quickly made by one person, and, even in the largest size, no exertion is required. The mechanism employed is of the simplest and not liable to get out of order. Recommended where an inexpensive but reliable and accurate table is required.

SPECIFICATION.—Made in stained hardwood (polished any colour) with slate bed, low and fast rubber cushions, good West of England cloth, improved invisible pocket plates, and stout cord nets, turned legs with adjusting toes, Metal raising rollers. Tables with wood raising slides can be supplied to order at cheaper rates. Complete with accessories as follow: 3 ivory or Crystalate balls, 2 ash cues, marking board, rest, spirit level, chalks, Rules, Extra cue tips and waters.

5 by 2 ft. 6 in., £12 2 6 6 by 3 ft., £13 17 6 7 by 3 ft. 6 in., 8 by 4 ft., £22 15 0 9 by 4 ft. 6 in., £27 17 6

All prices include delivery in London or packing for country and abroad. Any of the above tables can be polished to match existing furniture, colour pattern should be sent with order. The billiard table can be made without pockets for playing the cannon game.

All Tables Delivered and Fixed Free in London.   **Cases and Carriage Extra.**

BILLIARD TABLE DEPT.—*continued.*

A Quality.

Polished Mahogany Folding Bagatelle Board, lined green cloth, complete with cue, mace, bridge, nine ivory balls, rules and pegs.

Sizes.	Price.
5 ft. by 15 in., 1 in. balls ..	31/-
5 ft. 6 in. by 16 in., 1 in. balls	35/-
6 ft. by 18 in., 1⅛ in. balls ..	40/-
7 ft. by 21 in., 1¼ in. balls ..	54/6

B Quality.

Polished Mahogany Folding Bagatelle Board, lined with super. green cloth, fitted with india rubber cushions, well finished, complete with cue, mace, bridge, nine ivory balls, rules and pegs.

Sizes.	Price.
6ft. by 20 in., 1⅛ in. balls	.. 50/-
7 ft. by 22 in., 1⅜ in. balls	.. 66/6
8 ft. by 25 in., 1½ in. balls	.. 86/-

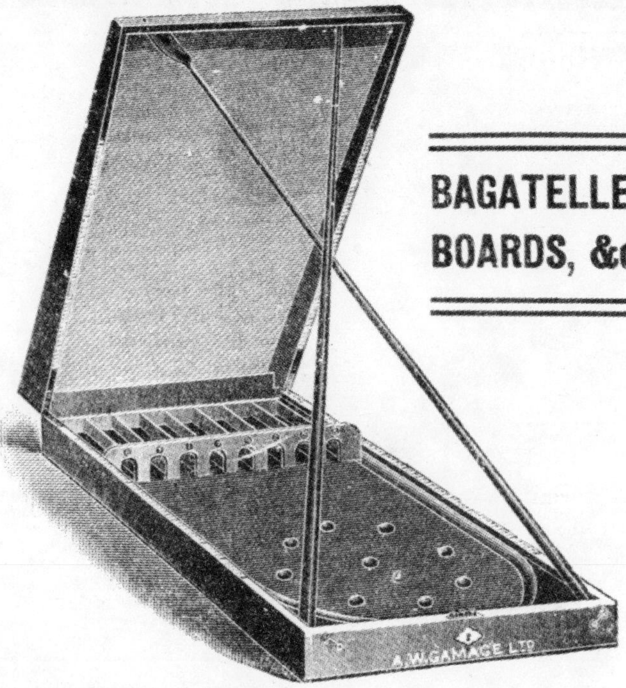

BAGATELLE BOARDS, &c.

C Quality.

Best Polished Solid Mahogany Folding Bagatelle Board, lined best green cloth, best india rubber cushions, complete with nine best ivory balls, cue, mace, bridge, pegs and rules.

Sizes.	Price.
6 ft. by 20 in., 1⅛ in. balls ..	63/-
7 ft. by 22 in., 1⅜ in. balls ..	77/6
8 ft. by 25 in., 1⅝ in. balls ..	95/-

Special Quality.

Size 9 ft. by 30 in., 1⅝ in. balls.
Price .. £6 19 6

Panel Top Boards.

Sizes.	Price.
7 ft. by 24 in., 1½ in. balls ..	84/-
8 ft. by 27 in., 1¾ in. balls ..	126/-

Carriage and packing extra on all Bagatelle Boards. 7/6 charged for cases, which is refunded on their return carriage paid.

TABLE BILLIARDS.

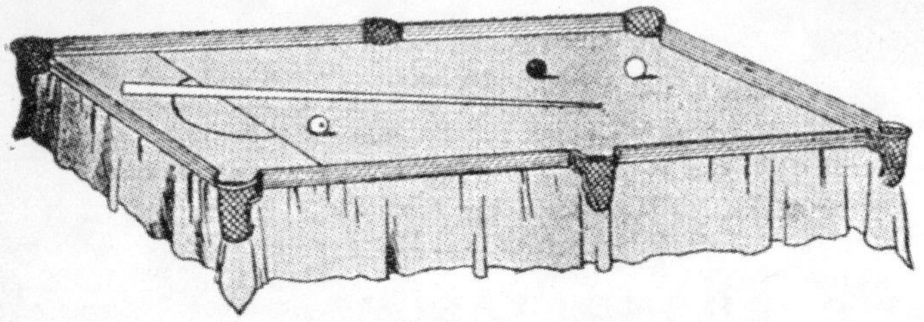

For adaptation to an ordinary dining table, the ordinary table cover forming billiard cloth. Can be fitted in a few minutes to any table.

No. G0. Containing 6 pockets to screw on to table, set of stout linen bands to form cushions, 2 cues, rest, boxwood balls, each .. 10/6

No. G1. Complete in box, containing a set of billiard pockets with india-rubber fittings, a set of boxwood billiard balls, 2 polished ash cues 38 in. long, cue rest, a set of stout linen bands with buckles, markers, marking board and French chalk 15/9
Suit a table not exceeding 8 ft. by 4 ft. 6 in.

No. G1x. Ditto with composition balls 21/-
Suit a table not exceeding 12 ft. by 6 ft.

No. G1a. Ditto, in polished box, extra quality ivorine balls, 4 ft. cues, etc. 33/-
Suit a table not exceeding 12 ft. by 6 ft.
Carriage extra.

Special Small Size Billiard Tables.

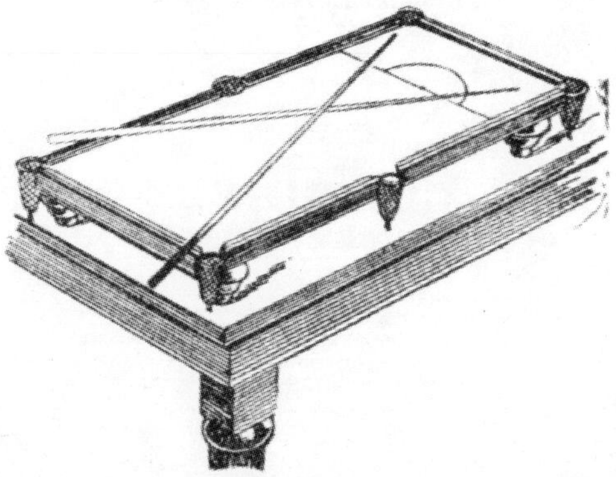

3 ft. 4 in. by 1 ft. 9 in. solid mahogany frame, slate bed, covered with billiard cloth, on short adjusting legs, complete with marking board, 3 ivory balls, 2 cues, indiarubber cushions, spirit level, rules, chalk, &c.

Price .. 50/- Cases 5/- returnable. Carriage extra.

OPEN SLATE BED BAGATELLE BOARDS.

Suitable for Clubs, Missions, etc.

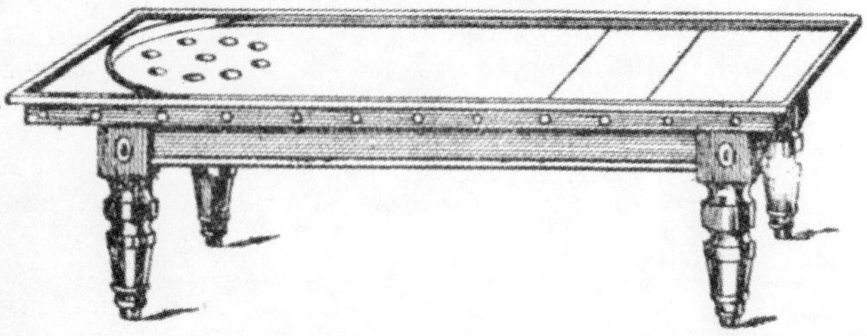

The Tables are made of thoroughly seasoned wood, best Bangor slates, fitted with best rubber cushions and cloths, including 4 cues, 9 balls, marking board, rules, etc. Complete with Stand as illustrated.

8 ft. by 2 ft. 9 in., 1⅞ in balls ..	..	£8	15	0
9 ft. by 3 ft. 3 in., 1⅞ in. balls ..	..	10	0	0
10 ft. by 3 ft. 4 in., 1⅞ in. balls ..	..	11	2	6

2 Pockets, 12/6 extra Carriage extra.

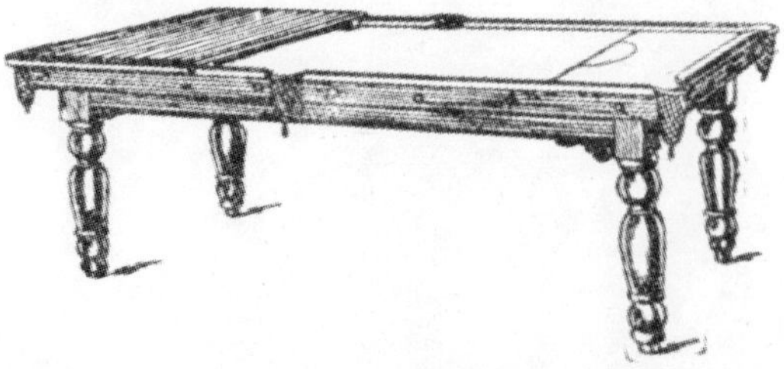

The Holborn Combination Billiard and Dining Table.

Instantaneous Action.

Perfectly rigid when in use, is quite portable, and can be quickly stored away if necessary, no expert knowledge being required to fix it. Made in hardwood, stained and polished any colour, with mahogany cushion rails, slate bed, best frost-proof cushions, West of England cloth. Complete with two cues, ivory balls, rules, spirit level, marking board, &c. To order only. Carriage extra.
6 by 3 ft., £9 17 6 7 by 3 ft. 6 in., £12 17 6 8 by 4 ft., £16 12 0

Misfitz and other Card Games.

9d. each. Post 2d.

The Misfitz Series consist of 72 beautifully illustrated Cards, Making up 24 Complete Pictures.

9d. each. Post 2d.

The Misfitz Series consist of 72 beautifully illustrated Cards, making up 24 complete Pictures.

These Series are well known for the Fun and Amusement they cause at Children's Parties, etc.

A New Round Game for several players.

Price .. **9**d. Post 2d.

Advance Australia.
An Instructive Geographical Game on Ludo lines.

Price .. **9**d. Post 3d.

Cape to Zambesi ditto. Price .. **9**d. Post 3d.

Nations and Flags.
An amusing and educational game for children. Printed in correct colours. Very artistic.

Price .. **9**d. and **2/3** Post 3d. and 4d.

Bobs or Bridge Bagatelle.
An Ideal Parlour Game. Complete with bridge, cue and balls.

Prices. 9d., **1/9** Post 3d. **2/6, 3/6** Post 4d.

Fox Hunting.

A Game of Real Fun and Excitement, bringing in all the exciting elements of the chase.

BILLIARDETTE.

The New Table Game.

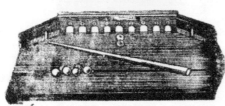

A game of skill for those who cannot afford the space for Billiards.
Some of the strokes are similar to those used in billiards, some similar to bagatelles Simple enough for youngsters—interesting enough for adults. Any number can play. It is played on an ordinary table. The fittings comprise : Cloth ready marked up, balls, cue, billiardette frame, marking board, etc.

Price, complete **8/6**
Carriage extra.

Price **3/3** **5/11** **7/6**
Post .. .. .. 4d. 5d. 6d.

E 1 ...

Pictorial Card Games.

ALICE IN WONDERLAND.

10d. each.
Post 2d.

"Shilling" Pictorial CARD GAMES.

Painted on fine Cardboard. Enamelled on both sides and printed with Ornamental Design at back. Each pack, with Rules, neatly boxed. The Cards composing the Games are printed in colours from new and original designs of a most taking character, and the Games will be found highly amusing both to young and old.

10d. each.
Post 2d

A Round Game with Cards.
Price 9d. Post 2d.

Price .. 1/4½
Postage 2d.
The one and only original card game

Snap, original edition .. 9d. Post 2d.
Happy Families .. .. 9d. Post 2d.
Kingdoms of Europe, 3 series .. 9d. ,, 2d.
Counties of England, 2 ,, .. 9d. ,, 2d.

THE LATEST CRAZE PIT THE GREAT GAME

Quit.
A good game for four players.
Price .. 1/4

The NEW GAME QUIT

Latest Card Games.
Birds,
Music,
Our Fleet,
Flowers,
Derby Day.
Price 9d.
Post 2d.

American Blue Jay,

Cavalry.
A New Round Card Game for 4, 6 or 8 players. Beautifully illustrated.
Price .. 1 9

Cavalry.
41 Cards. Illustrated with the numbers and names of the British Cavalry Regiments.
Price .. 1/9

UNITED STATES OF AMERICA.

Latest Card Games.
Language of Flowers
Flags,
Domestic Animals,
Wild Animals,
Authors.
Price .. 9d.
Postage 2d.

SNAP

h Edition de Luxe
Happy Family Card Game.
Price .. 4½d. & 9d. Post 2d.

Sherlock Holmes.
An exciting Card Game,
Price .. 1/4
Post 2d.

PETER PAN.

Peter Pan.
A Card Game founded on the well-known play, all the principal figures introduced.
If you have seen the play you must have the game.
Published with the authority of J. M. BARRIE.
The Drawings are by CHAS. A. BUCHEL.
Price .. 1/9 Post 2.

JUNGLE JINKS

Jungle Jinks.
The latest and one of the most Amusing Card Games ever published.
Consisting of 48 Pictorial cards illustrating the adventures and games of Dr. Lion and his School.
Price .. 1/9
Post free.

Happy Families

The Old Familiar Game of **Snap.**
Price 4½d. and 9d. Postage 2d.

The New Card Game "Precedence."
Dedicated (by permission) to the Speaker of the House of Commons (Rt. Hon. James W. Lowther, M.P.)
By Royal Letters Patent. Copyright Gt. Brit. & U.S.A. 1896. Price ... 1/4½ set. Post 2d.
The great feature of the game is that it permits of playing with any number of persons from two to six being able to take part. Although the Rules are easily mastered, there is great scope for judgment and skill.

Card Games.
Pit .. .. .. 1/4½ Post 2d.
Quit .. .. .. 1/4½ ,, 2d.
Rook 1/4½

Card Games.
Counties of England .. 1/2 Post 2d.
Kingdoms of Europe .. 9d. ,, 2d.

SPECIALITIES IN CRICKET BATS AND BALLS.

THE
Boitel-Gill.

THE
Australian.

**|The BOITEL-GILL
Patent Rubber-protected Splice,
Cricket Bats**

are the outcome of many years' experience in Cricket.

The manner in which the handle is spliced to the blade, absolutely prevents any jarring, and greatly adds to the driving power of the Bat. The finest Cane and Willow it is possible to procure is used in the manufacture.

One price only .. .. **25/=** each.

THE REFEREE

Made from Selected Material by First-class Workmen only.

CRICKET BALL

Hand-made throughout. Perfect shapes.

4/6 each,
51/- doz.

The AUSTRALIAN.

A perfect Match Bat with an Ideal Rubber and Leather Handle, which is so made that it is impossible for the hand to slip, the rubber being inter-bound with the leather forming a perfect grip. Blades are from the very best selected willow and well seasoned.

Price .. .. **21/-** .. .. Post free.

The Australian

The ball is as near perfection as is possible to obtain in the making of a Cricket Ball.

Cricket Ball.

It is hand-made from start to finish, only the very best materials being used. Every ball is guaranteed.
5/- each.
57/- doz.

PATENT.
Selected blades only.

25/- each.

A BAT WITH A REPUTATION.

21/-

CRICKET BATS. By Noted Makers.

CLAPSHAW AND CLEAVE'S
Express Driver.
Largely used by MEMBERS of the AUSTRALIAN CRICKET TEAMS
Price
21/-

GUNN and MOORE'S
THE **"Autograph"**
Finest selected blades and spring handles.
Price .. **20/-**
The Harrow size, **17/6**
No. 6 .. **12/6**

THE "Force" Cricket Bat.

The Mysterious Bat with a Mighty Handle.
PRICE—
18/6 26/- 30/-
As used by Hobbs and other leading Professionals.
Harrow size .. **21/-**
No. G. 6 .. **15/-**
No. 5.. .. **12/6**
These Bats were used by J. B Hobbs and others during the past seasons and throughout the
M.C.C. CRICKET TOURS AND COUNTY MATCHES
during which many records were made.

BOBBY ABEL'S "Guvnor" CRICKET BATS.
Selected Blades and Patent Handles.
Price **20/-**

CLAPSHAW AND CLEAVE'S
Patent Spring Handle.
Price **18/6**

GRADIDGE'S Imperial Driver MEN'S.
Price **20/-**
Selected Quality.

ODD'S Improved
Spring Handle.
Price **13/6**
Selec ed.
A Good Club Bat.

QUAIFE BRO.'S Lilley Driver.
A splendid Bat for hard wear.
Price **18/6**

DARK'S Cork Cased
Spring Handle.
SELECTED.
Price **20/-**

GARDINER'S BEST SELECTED.
First Pick.
———
As used by many Leading Amateur and Professional Players.
———
Price **25/-** each.

COBBETT'S Special
Spring Handle
MEN'S; Club Bats.
Price **12/6**

PATENT Jubilee Driver
MATCH BATS.
Price **20/-**

Postage 6d. on all Bats under 10/-
Our specially prepared Cricket Bat Oil, 4½d. tin. Post 3d. Specially prepared Bat Plaster, 6 yd. Roll, 1/- Post 4d.
Bats Re-bladed, 4/6, 6/-, 7/6, 8/6 Re-handled, 3/- to 7/- Pegged or Bound in two or three days. Bat Twine, 1/3 per Ball. Post 2d.

GAMAGE'S THREE LEADING LINES IN GOLF BALLS.

These Balls represent the utmost value it is possible to give, consistent with the price at which they are sold, and will be found to be far in front of many of the higher priced Proprietary Brands.

A SAMPLE BALL WILL CONVINCE YOU.

The "Referee" Golf Ball.

The "Ilixum" Golf Ball.
Bramble or recessed marking.

The "Ariel."
Dimple marking. Floating and heavy.

The Cores of these Balls are made from the very finest Elastic, which is wound by special machinery at a very high tension, giving it that elasticity which is not obtainable in many balls. The covers are made of the finest Para rubber, and are tape wound, making it almost impossible to hack, crack, or split them. Every ball is guaranteed for 18 holes. These balls are noted for their length of drive and also their steadiness on the green.

Price **14/6** doz. Sample balls **1/3**, post paid

This Ball has been introduced by us to meet the pressing demand for a Good Ball at a low price; no expense has been spared to produce the desired effect, and we are positive that no better article can be supplied at this price. We can thoroughly recommend them, and suggest that they should be compared with other makes of balls at higher prices.

Price **11/6** doz. Sample ball **1/,** post paid.

The Core of the "ARIEL" Ball is made throughout of the very best rubber thread procurable. The inner core is hand wound with the finest Para rubber tape to a diameter of $\frac{7}{8}$ in., after which it is placed in an automatic winding machine and wound to the standard size—1$\frac{1}{2}$ in.— with best quality rubber thread. The covering material used is so tough and resilient as to render the ball practically indestructible. The "ARIEL" Ball is guaranteed not to crack, and the paint is also guaranteed not to chip off in play.

Price **18/6** doz., post free.

PROPRIETARY GOLF BALLS AT GAMAGE PRICES.

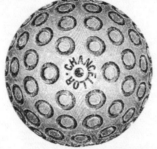

	Per Doz.	List Price.
Spalding's Bramble Midget	19/-	24/-
" No. 1 Black & White	19/-	24/-
" Corker	24/-	30/-
" No 4. Red and Black	24/-	30/-
" Midget Dimple	24/-	30/-
" Glory	24/-	30/-
" Domino	24/-	30/-

	Per Doz.	List Price.
The Chancellor. Recessed	19/-	24/-
" Bramble	19/-	24/-
The Chemico Bob	11/6	—
" White Flyers	27/-	30/-
Miller & Taylor's Superior	27/-	30/-
Adam's A 1	17/-	18/-

COLONELS.	Per Doz.	List Price.
The Patent Colonel	19/-	24/-
" White Colonel	24/-	30/-
" (Floating or Heavy).		
" Arch Colonel	24/-	30/-
" (Floating or Heavy).		
" Heavy Colonel	19/-	24/-
" Water Core Colonel	19/-	24/-

	Per Doz.	List Price.
The Dunlop Floater	18/6	24/-
" Junior. Heavy	18/6	24/-
" V. Recessed	24/-	30/-
" V, Heavy	24/-	30/-
" V, Bramble	24/-	30/-

Postage extra on all Golf Balls sold at Cut Prices.

The attention of our customers is particularly drawn to the large assortment of Golf Balls of all leading makers at GAMAGE'S SPECIAL PRICES, and are GUARANTEED NEW BALLS as sold elsewhere at full prices.

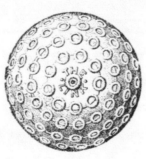

		Our Price.	List Price.
The Challenger.	Bramble	19/-	24/-
"	Star Marking	19/-	24/-
"	26½	19/-	24/-
"	King Bramble	24/-	30/-
"	Recessed	24/-	

		Per Doz.	List Price.
The Link		19/-	24/-
" Pal			24/- Post free
" Why Not.	Purple Dot	30/-	"
" "	Golden Dot	30/-	"
" Silver King	Mesh Marking	30/-	"
" "	Bramble	30/-	"

RE-COVERED GOLF BALLS.		
Ordinary Qualities	per doz.	10/6
Best Named "	"	12/6
Re-made Gutty Balls	"	5/6
Re-paints. Ordinary Quality	"	10/6
Best Selected Balls	"	14/6
Re-covered Colonels	"	16/6

MARTIN'S ZODIAC BALLS.	Per Doz.	List Price.
The 1914 Zodiac	19/-	24/-
" Zodiac Zone	19/-	24/-
" S.S.	19/-	24/-
" Floating	19/-	24/-
" Bramble Zodiac	19/-	24/-

Old Balls exchanged in part payment of New.

CUSTOMERS' OWN GOLF BALLS RE-COVERED EQUAL TO NEW, 7/6 AND 8/9 PER DOZEN   Guaranteed 18 Holes.

GOLF LAWN GAMES AND SUNDRIES.

The Boomerang Golf Ball
which returns to the Striker. Price **2/11** Post 3d. Superior Quality Ball, **4/3** Post 3d.

(Patent No. 10349/1906).

The "Ion" Golf Ball Trainer.
A capital device for indoor use or any limited space when the favourite game can be practised without fear of lost ball or any damage being done. Price **3/3** each. Post 4d.

Golfstacie.
The New Putting Game (Patent). The Game is played with Golf Balls and Putters. The Balls are four to the set, and are coloured like Croquet Balls. The obstacles to be played through include Hoops, Rings, a Tunnel a Bridge and a Tray, which has to be entered up an incline. Price per set, **28/-** With Excelite Balls, **30/-** Carriage paid.

Gripolin.
Gives a cool firm grip. Prevents blisters. Clean and Antiseptic. Does not stain the hands. Price **6d.** per tube. Post free.

Lauder's Antiseptic Grip Wax .. **4½d.**
Irish, ditto.. .. .. .. **4½d**
Post 1d.

Rubber Adhesive Plaster.
For repairing Shafts. Price **5½d.** Post 1d.

Z.O. or Heft Band.
For binding on fingers to prevent blisters. Price **5d.** roll. Post 1d.

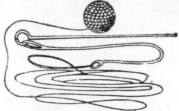

Captive Golf Ball.
Outfit consists of an Iron Stake to be securely fastened in ground, and attached to which is a piece of rubber and about 75 feet of cord, to the end of which is securely fastened a good quality Golf Ball. This outfit will enable the player to practise the different strokes in an ordinary field, and is specially recommended to beginners. No G 1. Captive Golf Outfit complete. **3/3** Post 3d.

The Champion Captive Ball.
With Cord and Pin, **1/3** each. Post 1d.

The "Varsity" Patent Home Golfer.

Best "Varsity" Patent Home Golfer. No. 1 .. **30/-**
No. G. 2, as illustration .. **42/-**
The "Varsity" Home Golfer is a boon to players on board ship, etc. It accurately registers the length of drive and elevation of the ball, and enables one to keep in good practice without going to the Links.

This is a Game which is equally amusing and instructive to the expert and the novice, and can be played by any number of players. It embraces the most important elements of Golf, and affords much amusement either as an indoor or outdoor game. Each set contains 2 Gunmetal Clubs, 5 Holes, 2 Balls, Numbers and Markers. Price complete **12/6** Carriage paid.

India Rubber Golf Club Handle Covers.
Tapered Smooth, or Corrugated. Price **7½d.** each. Post 1d.
Fulford Grip, re-inforced Leather **1 6** ,,
Duro Grip, Leather .. .. **1/-** ,,
Rubbered Cloth Strip Grips **6½d.** ,, Post 1d.
Black Cloth Grips .. .. **4½d.** ,,
Golf Club Cleaner. Polita Metal Polish in Cakes. **4½d.** each. Does not soil the fingers. Post 1d.
Kaddizhelp, the new metal club polishers. **6d.** each Post 2d.

Golf requisites supplied at short notice.

Leather Armlets for Golf Caddies.
Strongly made with brass numbers, 1/- ea. **10 6** doz.
Over No. 12, **1 3** each.
12/- doz. Post 2d.

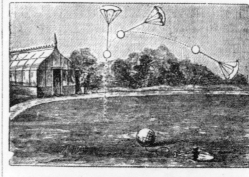

The Parachute Captive Golf Ball.
1/3 1/6 and **2/-** each. Post 3d.

LINKA.

This ingenious instrument will automatically register with accuracy the distance that would be reached when playing a free ball. It affords most excellent practice with any club. Price **21/-** Carriage paid

Home-Putt.
Home-Putt is played on any Carpet without the least risk of damage.
Price **1 6** Post 2d.

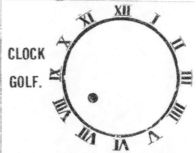

CLOCK GOLF.

Set of Metal Clock Figures painted white, Cup Pins, Flag and Chain for marking circle, with Rules, in wood box. Price **9/6** Carriage extra. Cheaper quality do., with Pin, Flag and Chain. **7/6**

The Midget Set. With 3¾ in. Figures painted white, Hole Cup Pin Flag and Chain for marking circle. Complete **3/6** Carriage 6d.

MISCELLANEOUS CONJURING TRICKS

No. E. 1. The Weird Pedestal Ball Trick.

A pedestal of polished wood, a cone-shaped cover and a marble are given for examination. The marble is placed on the top of the pedestal and covered with the cone; on removing the latter immediately, the marble is found to have vanished. Cone and pedestal are given for examination. Complete with full instructions, **4**d. Postage 1d.

The Ball of Wool Trick.

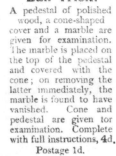

No. E. 31.

A borrowed shilling is marked by a member of the company, and is then handed to the performer. He immediately vanishes same, and a member of the company is requested to unwind ball of wool which is in the tumbler, and to the surprise of all the marked coin is discovered in the centre of the ball. We are anxious to impress upon our customers that the coin is not changed during the whole of the trick. Complete with full instructions, **5½**d. Post 1d.

The Melting Pot or Coin of Mercury.

No. E. 36.

A coin is placed in this little pot and the lid put on. When same is removed the coin is found in a molten condition, when again covered, it is at once restored to its original form.

Also very useful for changing coins. Price, complete with full instructions, **10**d. Postage 2d.

The Wonderful Rattle Box.

No. E. 41.

A borrowed and marked coin is placed in the box by a member of the company. The performer now commands the coin to leave the box. A lady is requested to hold the box without the conjurer going near it, commands coin to vanish; upon lady drawing out the lid the box is proved to be empty. Price, complete with full instructions, **1/6** Postage 3d

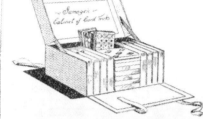

No. E. 104. The Gamage Cabinet of Card Tricks.

This handsome Cabinet contains a number of first-class card tricks, same as performed by our famous professional magicians. We wish to point out that it is absolutely impossible to obtain a more complete and surprising set of up-to-date card tricks at the price. Cabinet, complete with full instructions and apparatus, **21/-** Post 6d. Small Cabinets. **10/6** Postage 4d.

No. E. 198. Set of Conjuring Tricks.

No. E. 1. Containing 7 good tricks **1/9** Post 3d.
No. E. 2. Containing 9 good tricks **2/9** Post 4d.

No. E. 199. Gamage's Boys' Box of Conjuring Tricks.

With instructions .. **10½**d.   Post 2d.

Box B contains 12 good effective tricks, viz.: The Figure-it-out Trick. The Penetrative Coin. The Penny in the Bottle, The Enchanted Corks, The Magic Candle Case, The Magic Handkerchief, The Wizard's Changing Cards, The Ball Box, The Magic Book, The Card under Glass Trick, The Changing Card, The Enchanted Rose Trick and a Book of Modern Tricks. With full and lucid instructions to enable anyone with a little practice to perform all the foregoing marvellous illusions.   Price ... **5 6**   Post 4d.

This Cabinet **12/6** Post 9d.

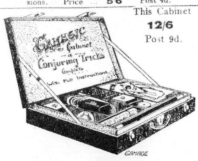

No. E. 195. Ribbon produced from the Mouth.

The magician produces yards and yards of coloured ribbon from his mouth. Suitable for both amateurs and professionals.

A laughable trick.

Price, complete with instructions, **5½**d. per doz. Postage 1d.

No. E. 189. The Mysterious Bottle Imp.

The most wonderful part of this bottle is that, unless you know the secret, it cannot be made to ti down. Complete with full instructions.
Price **2**d.   Postage 1d.

No. E. 191. The Magic Nail.

A common nail is given for examination and then passed instantly through the finger. After withdrawal, the finger is found to be perfectly uninjured, and the nail is again given for examination.
Price **3**d.   Postage 1d.

No. E. 201.

Changing Flower.

A beautiful large white flower is seen in performer's hands; by touching it with his fingers it changes to blue, and then to red. Effective and easy to perform.

Price, complete with full instructions, nicely made in silk, **9**d.   Postage 1d.

Large professional size, **1/-** Postage 1d.

- THE -

Magician Monthly.

If you are interested in Magic you must have it.
Specimen Copy, Post Free, **5**d.
Annual Subscription, **4/6**

The Latest Billiard Ball Trick.

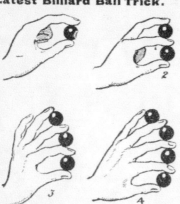

No. E. 11. Having magically produced a solid billiard ball, which is first examined, the performer seizes it by the tips of the thumb and first finger, asking everyone to watch him as closely as possible.

While they are doing so a second billiard ball mysteriously makes its appearance beside the first one. A third one then appears, and finally a fourth one, all the balls being held by the tips of the fingers only. These now vanish as mysteriously as they came. From four they become three solid balls; from three, two, until finally one ball is left, which after being tossed up vanishes also. The balls may at any time be passed for inspection to prove that they are solid Complete with full instructions, **4/6** Set Ivorine Balls, **8/6** Postage 3d.

Can be Performed Anywhere.

No. E. 217. The Birth of Flowers.

A lady places some seed in a vase of mould and covers it over; on removing the cover, a beautiful tree of flowers appears. Price, complete with full instructions, small size .. .. **2/6** Medium size .. **8/6** Postage 3d. Full professional size, **25/-** Postage 6d.

The Magic Handkerchief Case.

No. E. 205. New Method. A highly ornamental tube is shown quite empty, a borrowed lady's handkerchief is placed within, and at command of the performer, the handkerchief disappears, and the tube is found to be filled with flowers or sweets. Price, complete with full instructions, **2/6** Post 3d.

Old Method, price **1/-** Postage 1d.

No. E. 236. The Japanese Rings.

Eight large rings, with which many extraordinary manoeuvres can be performed. The rings are proved to be solid and are handed round for examination; but at the command of the performer they become linked together in chains of two, three or more, and yet continually keep becoming connected, and disconnected. Finally, when the rings appear to be in inextricable confusion, they suddenly dissentangle and fall on the floor. Price, complete with full instructions, **2/6** Post 3d. Larger size, **5/-** Postage 6d. Brass, full size, **12/6** Extra heavy, **20/6** Postage 9d.

No. 38. Multiplying Plate.

A number of coins are counted upon the plate by one of the audience and poured into an empty hat where they most mysteriously multiply This plate is the best and cheapest on the market. Complete with full instructions, **1/-** Postage 2d. Small size **6d.**

The GAMAGE Special Boxes of Conjuring Tricks.

No. E. 200

Box A contains 10 really good tricks as follows: The String Trick, The Egg Ball Illusion, The Bottle Imp, The Magic Book, The Card Book, The Magic Handkerchief, The Candle Case, The Marvellous Ball Box, The Cap and Halfpence, &c.

Extraordinarily Cheap. English Made. Thorough good workmanship. The youngsters' delight, complete with instructions for performing every trick .. .. **4/3** Post 4d.

No. E. 421.

The "Demon" Thimble Case.

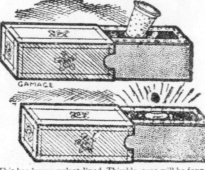

This handsome velvet-lined Thimble case will be found very useful by conjurors who manipulate thimbles. After a few sleights with the thimble, the performer places it into the case, then handing same to lady in the company requests her to pull out drawer of case. To the astonishment of all present the Thimble has vanished, and can be produced by the performer at any time he chooses. Price, complete with full instructions, **1/6** Postage 3d.

No. E. 343. Improved Egg Bag Trick.

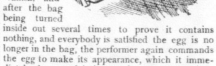

By the aid of this wonderful bag, an egg is made to mysteriously vanish, and after the bag being turned inside out several times to prove it contains nothing, and everybody is satisfied the egg is no longer in the bag, the performer again commands the egg to make its appearance, which it immediately obeys, and is seen between network at corner of bag. Price, complete with full instructions, **1/6** Another Method, **6d.** and **1/-** Postage 2d. Latest Bag, handsomely made in Velvet, **4/6**

No. E. 342. The Slate of Mystery.

A slate, shown both sides to contain no writing, and afterwards cleaned with wet sponge, is placed on the table with a piece of chalk. One or two members of the audience then place their fingers lightly on the top of slate. Names of selected cards or other questions appear in writing mysteriously.

Price complete with full instructions, **2/-** Postage 3d.

The Magic Cards.

With the aid of this pack of cards the performer can read the thoughts of members of the company Price **6d.** Postage 1d.

No. E. 120A.

The Newest Card Mystery.

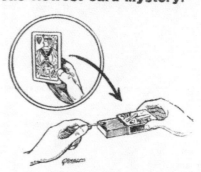

A court card after being shown is instantly made to change into a box of matches.

Box can be opened and matches taken out.

Price .. **6d.** Postage 1d.

No. E. 151.

The Merry Pastry Cook.

This is a very novel and undetectable manner of performing the laughable "Pudding in the Hat" trick. After the hat is borrowed and placed on a cane-seat chair, the performer mixes up a quantity of flower, water, eggs, &c., in a thin silvered plate, and to the discomfiture of the possessor of the hat, deliberately pours the mixture into the latter. As a true representative of his art, he repairs the damage, then produces a cake from the hat, returning the latter uninjured to its owner. The newest and best method for performing this trick. Price, complete with full instructions and large handsome plate, **4/-** Postage 3d.

Send for a Complete Handsome Conjuring Catalogue post free Anywhere.

Exclusive Magical Secrets

JUGGLING SECRETS

25/- Postage and Packing in England, 2/-
Ditto   do.   Abroad 5/-

EVERY READER IS INVITED to APPLY FOR A FREE PROSPECTUS. One will be sent POST FREE to every applicant who writes for it to :—

The 'Magical Department,'
A. W. GAMAGE, Ltd.,
Holborn, London, E.C.

THE PROSPECTUS IS A BOOK IN ITSELF and will be of permanent value to all Magicians whether or not they ultimately become subscribers to **"Exclusive Magical Secrets."**

No. E. 473.

Miscellaneous Puzzles.

By PROFESSOR HOFFMANN

This useful book is very instructive and amusing, containing a large range of Miscellaneous Puzzles.
Price .. **9d.** Post 2d.

Smoke and Rag Pictures.

How to make them in an entertaining manner.

The only Book on the subject in existence.

Fully Illustrated.

The Editor has pleasure in announcing that he has obtained from Mr. DAVID DEVANT the only explanation ever given by Mr. DEVANT of the way to make PAPER PICTURES.

If the book contained nothing else it would be well worth many times its price.
Price **1/-** Post 2d.

Bunkum Entertainments.

Being a Collection of Original Laughable Skits on JUGGLING, CONJURING, SECOND-SIGHT, etc., etc.
Price .. **2/6** Post 3d.

Just Published.

Juggling Secrets.

96 pages.

About **100** illustrations.

Price .. **1/-**
Post 2d.

Conjuring For Amateurs.

A Practical Treatise on **How to Perform Modern Tricks.**

By ELLIS STANYON, One of our best writers.

Price **1/-** Post 2d.

No. E. 794.

Conjuring Tricks

WITH **Watches, Rings, etc.**

By Prof. HOFFMANN. This book is a revised section of Prof. Hoffmann's great work— "Modern Magic."
Price **9d.** Postage 2d.

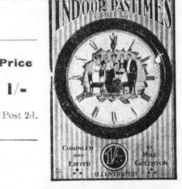

Price **1/-**
Post 2d.

Price **1/-**
Post 2d.

Indoor Pastimes.

THE BOOK OF THE SEASON. NO PARTY SHOULD BE ATTEMPTED until someone who is coming to the party has BOUGHT THIS BOOK.   Price .. **1/-** Postage 2d.

GAMAGE'S Entertainment Bureau.

Artistes of every description for every style of Entertainment.
None but First-class Talent whose performances are well known.
The Fees quoted will be found **less** than any other Agency in London.

SPECIAL ENTERTAINMENT LIST
Post Free on request.
ESTIMATES FREE.

All enquiries respecting Entertainments should be addressed to :—
ENTERTAINMENT MANAGER,
Entertainment Department,
GAMAGES, Holborn, E.C.

This interesting Book on **Card Tricks** is profusely Illustrated.
Pub. at 2/6.
Price .. **1/-**
Post 3d.

Send for Free Conjuring Catalogue Post Free anywhere.

F2..

New and Up-to-date Lawn or Parlour Games.

Bat, Trap and Ball

No. G. 0.   Bat, Trap and Ball **1/-**
        Postage 3d.
„ G. 1.   Stronger do.   **2/3**
        Postage 4d.
„ G. 2   Set **2/9**
        Postage 4d.
„ G. 4.   Set **4/6**
        Postage 6d,
„ G. 5.   SPECIAL SET, containing two willow bats with eather bound handles, polished shoe, two superior balls, with lines and pegs for marking distance and rules. Complete in a polished pine box.. **7/6**
        Postage 9d.

Rounders.

Rounder Bat, half cane handle .. **2/3** each.
        Postage 4d.

Rounder Stick .. **6½d.** each.
        Postage 2d.

Rounder Balls .. **6d.** each.
        5/6 doz.
        Post 4d. doz.

Fives Bats.

No. G. 1.   Polished, plain handle   **1/4**

No. G. 2.   Polished bound handle   **1/8**

No. G. 3.   Polished, leather bound handle   .. **1/10**
        Postage 4d.

Rugby Fives Balls. **29/6** gross.

Three Figure-head Ball Target.

39 in. high   **5/11** Carriage extra.

Indian Ball Game.

No. G. 1   .. **5/11**
„ ,, 2   .. **6/11**
„ ,, 3   .. **7/11**
„ ,, 4   .. **8/11**
„ ,, 5   .. **10/6**
        Complete.
        Carriage extra.

THE GAME of SKITTLE JACK FOR THE LAWN

A very enjoyable game that can be played on the smallest lawn. Coloured Pegs with cup ends are driven into the ground. Balls, the same colour, are placed in the cups— the game being to knock them out, either by bowling or throwing with other balls.
No. G. 1.   With 5 pegs and balls.. .. **4/3**
No. G. 2. With extra peg and ball, starting pin, mallet, etc., in polished box .. **7/9** Carriage extra.

Polished and Painted Hardwood Skittles.

In strong wood box.
8 in.   9½ in.   11 in.
6/3   **7/9**   **8/11**
        Carriage extra.
Cheaper quality, Ordinary pattern.
No. G. 1, **1/5**   No. G. 2, **1/8**
No. G. 3, **2/3**   No. G. 4, **4/-**
        Carriage extra.

Revolving Hoopla.

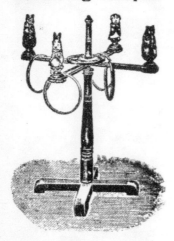

Stand with Animals and Rings, complete. Good strong Game.

Price **11/6**

The Game of Target Ball.

PROTECTED.

This is an attractive game for Playground or Schoolroom, designed by the lecturer on the games appointed by the Education Department of the London County C'cil. It is easily learned, is a splendid exercise, and any number of players can participate
    Set consisting of 2 4 ft. 6 in. Portable Goals with painted circular metal discs, 2 wooden Pat Bats, & 1 soft India-rubber Ball.

Complete with rules, **13/6** set.
Book of Rules of Target Ball 1/- each.
Carriage paid.

New Victoria Ball Game.

A harmless, interesting game of skill for any number of players. For either in or outdoor use.
Complete with all accessories, **8/11** Carriage extra.

The Three Bell Rolling Ball Game.

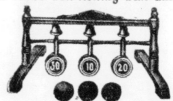

An amusing and scientific game, requiring great skill. Very superior finish. Price **7/6** Carriage extra.

BADMINTON SETS, &c.

BADMINTON SETS.

F. H. Ayres' New Regulation Straight Feather Shuttlecocks.

5/9 per doz.

1 dozen, post free.

Per 6 doz., **5/6** doz.

We carry a large Stock of Selected Shuttlecock and Rackets.

lazenger's Association Badminton Shuttlecock.

With Leather Bottoms.
Price **5/9** dozen.

F. H. Ayres', 5/9 doz.
1 dozen, post free.

Any make of Shuttlecock not catalogued can be procured at short notice.

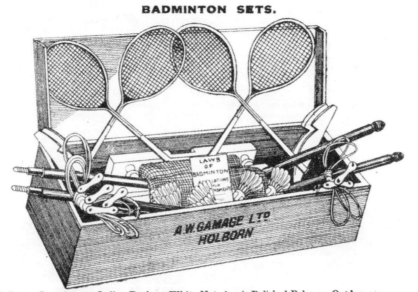

No. G. 1. Containing 4 Indian Rackets, White Net, 1 pair Polished Poles for Outdoor use,
4 Shuttlecocks, Mallet, Rules, etc., in strong Box **17/6**
" G. 2. Do., do., with Poles for In and Outdoor use **22/6**
" G. 3. Do., do., with Superior Fittings..   ..   ..   **30 -** Carriage paid.

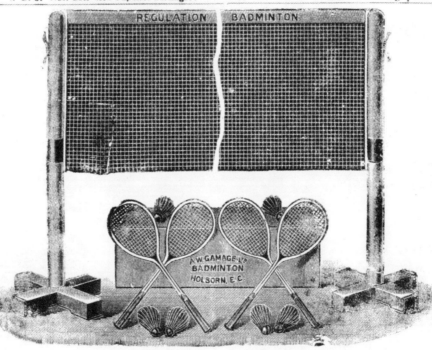

The "G.B." Special Association Set.

Containing 4 Oval face English-made Association Rackets with Cedar handles, 1 pair of Jointed Posts with weighted feet, Best Tanned Net with Linen Top Band, 6 Regulation Shuttlecocks, Rules, etc.   In Box complete   ..   **£2 5 0**   Carriage paid.

Regulation Shuttlecocks.

Straight, Regulation Shape, leather bottom Shuttlecocks (as illustration), **3/11** doz. Post 3d. doz.

Selected ditto **4/9** doz.

India Rubber Bottom Regulation. Price **4/9** dozen.

Ordinary Shape Rubber Bottom Shuttlecocks.
Not strung.

16   20 Feathers.
3/6   5/3

Postage 3d. per dozen.

Badminton Shuttlecocks.

Velvet covered bottoms, white feathers, not strung

16 feathers	..	**1/6** dos.
20	,,	.. **1/9** ,,
24	,,	.. **2/4** ,,
30	,,	.. **2/11** ,,

Postage 3d. per dozen.

Badminton Nets.

Made in conformity with the Laws of the Badminton Association Tanned Twine, ¾ in. square mesh, bound with 3 in. white band doubled over top edge of net, and suitable cord run through the band.

20 by 2½ ft., .. **3/-**   22 by 2½ ft. .. **3/3**   24 by 2½ ft. .. **3/6**
White Nets .. **2/2** each.   Postage 3d.

Association Poles.

Turned and Polished.   With Weighted Base.   Price .. **15/-** pair.
Extra Heavy Tournament Do. **29/-** Pair.
Carriage Extra.

Badminton Balls.

Worsted Balls	..	..	..	**6/6** per doz.	Postage 3d.
Rules ..	..	..	..	No charge.	,, 1d.

Badminton Poles.

No. G. 1.   2 piece hard wood, for outdoor use ..   ..   .. **4/11** pair.
In and outdoor use   ..   .. **8/3** ,,
No. G. 2.   Ditto, extra stout, in and outdoor use   .. **11/6** ,,
Carriage extra under 10/-

Carriage paid on all Badminton Sets.

Best English-make Association Badminton Rackets.

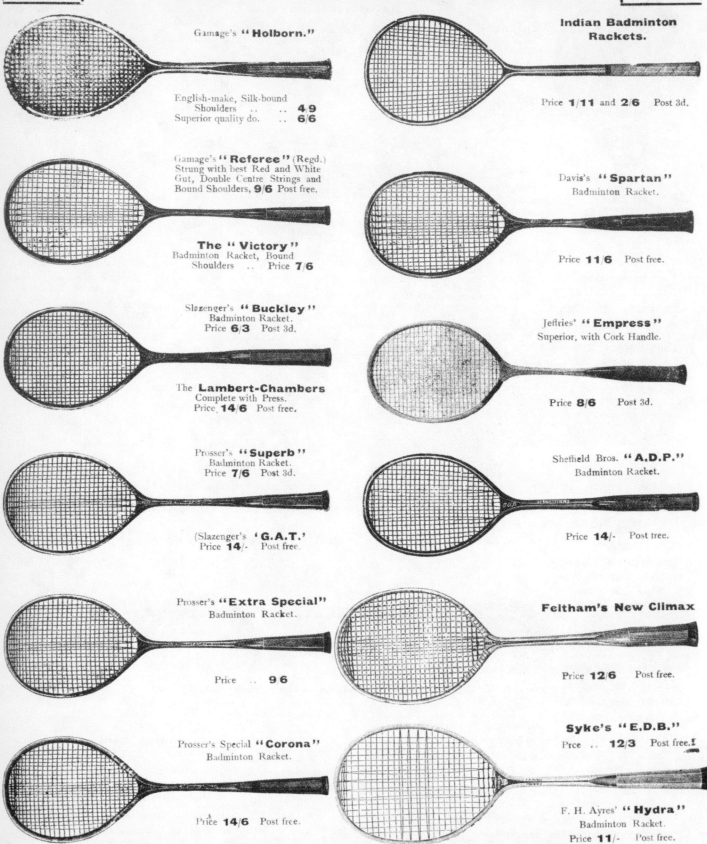

Gamage's **"Holborn."**

English-make, Silk-bound
Shoulders **4 9**
Superior quality do. .. **6/6**

**Indian Badminton
Rackets.**

Price **1/11** and **2/6**   Post 3d.

Gamage's **"Referee"** (Regd.)
Strung with best Red and White
Gut, Double Centre Strings and
Bound Shoulders, **9/6** Post free.

The **"Victory"**
Badminton Racket, Bound
Shoulders .. Price **7/6**

Davis's **"Spartan"**
Badminton Racket.

Price **11 6**   Post free.

Slazenger's **"Buckley"**
Badminton Racket.
Price **6/3**   Post 3d.

The **Lambert-Chambers**
Complete with Press.
Price **14/6** Post free.

Jeffries' **"Empress"**
Superior, with Cork Handle.

Price **8/6**   Post 3d.

Prosser's **"Superb"**
Badminton Racket.
Price **7/6** Post 3d.

(Slazenger's **'G.A.T.'**
Price **14**/- Post free.

Sheffield Bros. **"A.D.P."**
Badminton Racket.

Price **14**/-   Post free.

Prosser's **"Extra Special"**
Badminton Racket.

Price .. **9 6**

Feltham's New Climax

Price **12/6**   Post free.

Syke's "E.D.B."
Prce .. **12/3**   Post free.

Prosser's Special **"Corona"**
Badminton Racket.

Price **14/6** Post free.

F. H. Ayres' **"Hydra"**
Badminton Racket.
Price **11**/- Post free.

Regd. Presses with four screws for Badminton Rackets, 1/4½ and 2/- each.   Postage 4d.

LAWN BOWLS AND SUNDRIES.

Selected Lawn Bowls.

In pairs.
With
Ivory Mounts.

Stocked in No. 3
Bias, and 5, $5\frac{1}{16}$,
$5\frac{1}{8}$ and $5\frac{3}{16}$ in sizes.

These Bowls are made from selected wood and each pair is guaranteed Association Bias.
price **8/6** pr. Carriage extra. Super do. **10/6** pr.

For Set of 8, with two Jacks, in box complete, Super French polished selected wood.

No. 3.	8 Lignum Vitæ Bowls, $4\frac{1}{2}$ in.	**25/6**
,, 4.	8 ,, ,, ,, 5 ,,	**28/-**
,, 5.	8 ,, ,, ,, $5\frac{1}{16}$,,	**33/-**
,, 6.	2 pairs each $4\frac{3}{4}$, 5, $5\frac{1}{8}$, $5\frac{1}{8}$	**27/6**
,, 4a.	4 pairs do. do.	**33/-**
,, 7.	2 pairs ea. 5, $5\frac{1}{16}$, $5\frac{1}{8}$, $5\frac{3}{16}$,,	**30/-**
,, 8.	4 pairs ,, .. ,, $5\frac{3}{16}$,,	**35/-**

The Holborn Special Club Set.

Containing 4 pairs selected Bowls, stained and polished black, with ivory discs and engraved numbers, each pair bearing the English Bowling Association's Official Testing Stamp. The Tournament set.

Size, $5\frac{1}{16}$ in. .. .. price **45/-**
Size, $5\frac{3}{16}$ in. .. .. ,, **55/-**
Carriage paid.
Any Size and Bias to order.

The New Excelite Lawn Bowls.

Size 5, $5\frac{1}{16}$, $5\frac{1}{8}$ .. .. **30/-** pair.
Any Size or Bias to order.

THE Taylor= Rolph IMP. BRAND Lawn Bowls.

The St. John's. A real good Club Bowl, thoroughly recommended, is adopted by many Corporations and Clubs. Any size. Price **13/-** pair.

The Drake. Best Club quality .. **15/-** pair.

The Imperial. A very fine selected Bowl, full normal weight. Ivory mounted and engraved, as illustration. Price .. .. **18/-** pair

The King's Bowl. Choicest selected wood, richly ornamented and fitted with large ivory mounts. Cannot be surpassed for quality. Any size or bias.

Price .. .. .. **20/-** pair.

JACKS.

Lignum Vitæ Jacks, in any bias.
No. G. C1, **3/6** C2, **3/-** C3, **2/6** C4, **2/-**
Each.
No. G. C5. Round Lignum Vitæ Jacks **10d.**
,, C6. Round Boxwood, polished or painted white .. .. **8d.**
,, C7. Round White Porcelain .. **6d.**

F. H. AYRES' Association Lawn
Bowls. Standard Size, bearing the Official Stamp of the Bowling Association.
Price **12/6 15/- 18/6** pair. Carriage paid.

Engraving on Lawn Bowls.

Initials only, **1/-**; Full Name, **1/6**; Monograms, **2/-**; Monograms and Number, **3/-**; Initials and Number, **1/6**; Inscriptions, from **4/6** pair extra.

Superior Set of Taylor's Scotch Lawn Bowls.

Comprising two pairs each $5\frac{1}{16}$ and $5\frac{1}{8}$ in. Taylor's first quality bowls and two china jacks, in strong box.
Price .. .. .. **£3 10 0** complete.

Bowls for . . Crown Greens .

The following sets are fitted with ivory mounts, the bias side being concave unless otherwise ordered.

No. G. A20. **The "Challenge" Set.**
A pair of Bowls in No. G. A2 quality, in any Crown Green size or bias, with best quality Jack to match. Guaranteed accurate .. .. .. Per set **22/-**

No. G. A22. **The "Tournament" Set.**
A pair of Bowls in No. G. A4 quality, with Jack to match .. .. Per set **19/-**

No. G. A24. **The "Match" Set.**
A pair of Bowls in No. G. A5 quality, with Jack to match .. .. Per set **16/6**

No. G. A26. **The "Club" Set.**
A pair of Bowls in No G. A7 quality, with Jack to match .. .. Per set **12/-**

Thos. Taylor's Scotch Bowls. .
As used by the Bowling Association.

3rd quality, Ivory Mounts .. .. .. pair **10/-**
2nd ,, ,, ... ,, **12/-**
1st ,, Club quality .. .. .. ,, **15/-**
Stocked in No. 3 Bias, but any Bias can be procured to order in a few days. The following sizes we can generally supply from stock—$5\frac{1}{16}$, $5\frac{1}{8}$ and $6\frac{1}{16}$ in.

Presentation Bowls.
With large Ivory Mounts .. .. .. pair **19/-**
Silver Mounts . .. **21/- 28/- 36/-** to order only.
Carriage extra.

UP-TO-DATE PUZZLES

No. E. 525.

The Wonderful Pyscho Box Puzzle.

A small wooden box to hold matches or other small subjects. Nobody but the person in the secret can open it.

Price, complete with full instructions (Wood) **6½**d. Metal plated, **1/6**   Postage 1d.

The Balls in The Hole Puzzle.

Interesting

and

Entertaining.

Price .. **3**d.

Postage 1d.

No. E. 542.

The Unique Surprise Corkscrew.

You cannot extract cork from bottle unless in the secret.

Great fun at the dinner table.

Price, complete with full instructions, **1/**-   Post 1d.

Cheaper Quality .. **6**d.   Postage 1d.

No. E. 565.

Lighthouse Puzzle.

The lantern of which turns round. There is a ring round the body of lighthouse, which is very difficult to get off unless in the secret

Price, complete with full instructions .. **6**d.

Postage 1d.

Assorted Wire Puzzles. Without Instructions, **1**d. ea. Post 1d. 13 for **1/**- Post 3d. Great fun when you don't know how to do them.

The Castle Money Box.

A puzzle of great ingenuity.

You may put money in and safely promise it to the person who can get it out. Very puzzling and at the same time highly amusing.

Price, complete with full instructions, **6½**d.

Postage 1d.

The Gamagic Box of Puzzles and Novelties.

Seven selected.   Price **1/6**   Postage 3d.

No. E. 561.   **Dumbell Puzzle.**

A wooden dumbell with a ring on it; the puzzle is to get the ring off.

Price, complete with full illustrated instructions, **1/**-   Postage 2d.

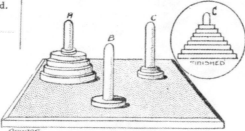

The "Bramah" Puzzle

The original of this interesting and ingenious puzzle is said to date back to the legendary history of the creation. This puzzle has 8 discs, and **can be solved in four minutes, 15 seconds.** If there were 64 discs, it would take 5,849,424,173 centuries to accomplish.

5½d.   Post 1d.

Two Eyes and a Mouth.

A good puzzle for anyone. In the Nigger's Head are 3 bullets, two to represent the eyes and one for the mouth. The puzzle is to pick them out with the fingers.

It looks easy enough, but—

Price .. **9**d.

Postage 2d.

No. E. 556.

Diplomacy Puzzle.

You have to get a coin out of the lid; although it is under a piece of glass and can be seen, you cannot get it unless you know how.

Price, complete with full illustrated instructions, **9**d.   Postage 2d.

No. E. 564.   **The Invisible Gift.**

A piece of money is concealed somewhere in the box. If anyone can discover it within a certain time, you tell them they can have it, but they never succeed.

Price, complete with full instructions, **6½**d.

Postage 1d.

No. E. 555.

Egyptian Match Box.

A box without an opening of any kind. Beautifully made in brass with a real halfpenny pivoted on top. Anyone can turn box over and over, and turn halfpenny on top round for hours without being able to get at the matches which they can hear inside, yet you can get them out yourself with ease.

Price, complete with full directions, **1/6**   Post 2d.

No. E. 557.   **Boxes of Puzzles.**

Price, complete with full illustrated instructions,

6d. **2/6** **5/-** **10/6** **21/-** **42/-**

Postage 2d., 3d. and 6d.

Send for complete List, Puzzles, Jokes, Novelties, etc., etc., post free anywhere.

NOVELTIES & JOKES

The Sebackroscope.

With the aid of this instrument the possessor can see behind him. You will find lots of fun in owning a Sebackroscope Made of hard rubber and finished in an excellent manner.

6d. Post 1d.

No need to wish for eyes in the back of your head, as with this article you can observe all that occurs in that direction without even turning the head. How often you are anxious to see faces at back of you or to observe who is following without attracting attention by turning around. This instrument does this for you.

The Latest Snake Camera.

Just as you are about to snap your friends, a huge snake jumps out of the Camera.

YOU MUST HAVE ONE!

Small size 1/- 1/6 1/11½
Full size 2/6
Postage 3d. and 4d.

The Go-Bang Cigarette Box.

When this pretty Cigarette Box is opened, a loud report is heard. Great joke for parties, etc.

Price .. .. **6**d.
Post 1d.

The Improved "Holborn" Box of Puzzles.
2/- worth of Puzzles for 6d.
Postage 2d.

A Great Novelty.

By turning a knob at the side of holder the victim receives a spray of water in the face, although he expected to see a pretty picture.

The Kinematograph is handsomely made in metal, nickel plated.

Price **6½**d. Post 1d.

The Scent Bottle Joke.

When your friend removes the cork to smell the perfume, the contents of bottle empties down his sleeve.

Price .. **3**d. Postage 1d.

The Bank Note Maker.

This machine will turn sheets of plain paper into bank notes. 2/-
Postage 3d.

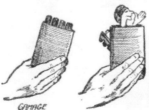

The Comic Cigar Case.

Just when your friend is about to take a cigar a dummy jumps up, as illustrated.

Price **8½**d. Postage 2d.

Send for complete List of Jokes, Novelties, Puzzles, etc., Post Free anywhere.

The Mutoscope Joke.

The victim when turning the handle and keenly looking through the glass to see the change, to his horror a monster snake jumps out, giving him a slight shock to the delight of the onlookers.

Price .. 1/9
Postage 4d.

The Distorting Mirror.
"DO I LOOK LIKE THAT"?
Price .. **3**d. and **6**d. Post 1d. and 2d.

The Ladies' Cigarette Box.

This dainty box has a small ball fitted in the cover.

When your lady friend presses the ball to obtain a cigarette, she receives a spray of water on the nose.

Price 1/-
Post 1d.

Always something NEW in PUZZLES and JOKES at GAMAGES.

The Beer Jug Joke.

The contents of the Jug make a speedy exit in the wrong direction.

Price **2/9**

Postage 4d.

Crash Bang Joke.

A number of pieces of tuned metal when thrown on the ground give the sound of glass smashing, Great fun for the home .. .. **5½**d. Post 2d.

The Kaliscope Joke.

You hand the Kaliscope to your friend requesting him to look through the glass and see the Ballet dancer.

When he remarks there is nothing to be seen, then ask him to press the spring at the side, which he does, and receives a shock. **8½**d. Post 1d.

A Matchless Joke.

A Match Stand, as illustrated, is seen on the smoker's table. Immediately a match is struck on the box, the whole of the contents are shot out of the box.

A Startling Novelty.

Price .. **1/6**

Post 3d.

A. W. GAMAGE, Ltd.,

Carry the Largest Stock of

Jokes and Puzzles
IN THE WORLD.

Squinting Eyeglasses.

Make everyone laugh. Mechanical movements.

Price **4½**d. Postage 1d.

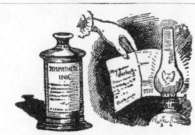

The Sympathetic Ink.

If you wish your letter kept secret, use this ink. The writing is invisible until heated.

Price **6**d. Postage 1d.

The Stocking Purse.

The owner of one of these Stocking Purses creates great laughter every time he pays.

Price .. **1/6**

Post 1d.

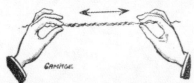

The Endless Wire. A Puzzle and Trick combined

Price .. **3**d. Postage 1d.

--- THE ---

Shooting Cigar Case.

Next time you meet the "Got-a-Cigar Gentleman," TRY THIS JOKE!

Price .. **8½**d. Post 1d.

The Scissors Joke.

This pair of Scissors and Cigar Cutter cannot be opened. Get one if you are fond of joking.

Plain, **4½**d. Superior plated, **1/-** Postage 1d.

The Magic Aquarium.

The heat of a person's hand makes the fish in the bulb bustle.

Price .. **9**d.

Post 3d.

The Musical Chair.

This ingenious device will be the means of making your party a high success.

Price **3**d. Improved Method, **6**d. Post 1d.

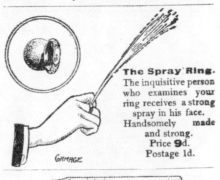

The Spray Ring.

The inquisitive person who examines your ring receives a strong spray in his face. Handsomely made and strong.

Price **9**d.

Postage 1d.

The Hinged Pencil.

Nothing like it for laughter. Price **2**d. Post 1d.

Beards, Wigs, Make-ups, Make-up Boxes.

No. 3A.
Special Swell's Wig.
Price .. **2/9**
Post 3d.

No. 1A.
Scratch Straight Hair Wig,
suitable for beggar or tramp.
Price **2/6** Post 3d.

Moustaches.

VARIOUS SHAPES. Real Hair, **1/4½**
Crêpe Hair, mounted on gauze .. **10½d.**
Ditto, on Net .. **4½d.** Post 1d.

Beards.

Assorted Colours.
Manufactured Hair,

1/- and **1/4½**

Postage 3d.

REAL HAIR, **5/6**

No. 787.
Pocket Grease Paint Case.

A flat black enamelled box which may be carried in the pocket, will pack flat in a bag, and contains 12 sticks of grease paint and liners, and has separate divisions for each stick.
Price—Filled, **3/4½** Unfilled, **1/4½** Post 3d.

A Varied Assortment of Make-up Boxes kept.

No. 489.
Chinese,
Price **9½.**
Post 3d.
Superior
qualities,
1/3 3/6
7/6 10/6
and 21/-

No. 491.
Old Man, bald.
Price 6d. Postage 3d

A Large Assortment of Wigs and Beards in Stock.

No. 154.
Specially
made Crepe
Hair.
For making
false mousa-
tache, etc.,
in all colours
4½d. yard.
Post 1d.

No. 512. Comic Bald Wig, black,
grey, carroty, etc. Price **2/9** Post 3d

No. 30A. Dame Wig, with Side Curls,
Parting and Bun. **4/6** Post 3d.

No. 494. Nigger Wigs. **1/-** each.
10/6 doz.
No. 495. Corner Man, with Tuft.
1/6 each. **16/-** doz,
No. 496. Nigger Wig, with moving
Tuft, **3/6** each.
No. 497. Bald Nigger Wig, black,
white or grey, **2/9** each. Post 3d.
No. 498. Astrachan Nigger Wig,
5/6 each.

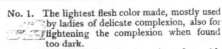

No. 1. The lightest flesh color made, mostly used by ladies of delicate complexion, also for lightening the complexion when found too dark.
No. 1½. Slightly darker, the favourite colour with ladies, very useful for chambermaid parts.
No. 2. The lightest flesh color used by gentlemen and is also used by ladies.
No. 2½. The most popular colors for all youthful make-ups.
No. 3. The most popular color with gentlemen.
No. 3½. Slightly darker, suitable for men 30-35.
No. 4. Very dark, suitable for countryman, soldier, sailor, etc.
No. 5. A light yellow, for very sallow old man.
No. 5½. For Chinaman, improved if used with No. 7.
No. 6. A yellow flesh tint for old man, darker than No. 5.
No. 7. Brown shade, copper color.
No. 8. Japanese.   No. 11. Othello.
No. 9. Red Indian.   No. 12. Negro black.
No. 10. Opera, " Aida." No. 13. Mulatto.
No. 14. Moor, North African.
No. 15. Indian.
No. 16. Bohemian (gipsy).
No. 17. Deep yellow.
No. 18. Yellow.
No. 19. Carmen, Spain.
No. 20. White, for statuary and clowns faces and heightening the effect of flesh tints.
Light, dark and middle blue, for unshaven chins, or making up old men.
Grey, light and dark, for hollows in old age, also useful for death scenes.
Carmine, vermilion, carmine 1 and 2 for clown's faces, the lips, cheek and burlesque characters. Carmines for dark cheeks. Rose for ladies' cheeks.
Gamage's Grease Paint, **3d.** per stick. Post 1d.
2/9 per dozen. Postage 3d.

Grease Paint.
About actual size.

No. 153.
Specially prepared Spirit Gum,

FOR THEATRICAL PURPOSES.

The best Spirit Gum, specially Manufactured. Will adhere strongly in the hotest weather.

Price .. **4½d.** bottle.

Postage 1d.

In metal screw-stoppered bottle,
Price **10½d.** Postage 2d.

No. 152.
Gamage's Cocoa Butter.
Special Manufacture.

An article which is universally used for effectually and quickly removing grease paint, spirit gum, and all make-up and colour from the face. A cooling and health application.
Price **4½d.** or **4/-** doz.

Large size, **9d.** per stick.
8/- per doz. Post extra.

Powders.
In White,
Cream and
Pink.
3d.. **4½d.**
8½d.
Post extra.

Gamage's Liners,

In the following Shades :—

BLACK, LAKE, LIGHT AND DARK BROWN,
LIGHT, MEDIUM AND DARK BLUE, CARMINE,
AND GREY. Short, **2d.** Long, **3d.** each. Post 1d.

LEICHNER'S GREASE PAINTS
3½d. per large stick. (Usually sold at 4½d.) Postage 1d.

No. 102.
Eyebrow Pencils.
In metal Case.
Black or Brown.
Price **4½d.**
Postage 1d.

Send for Theatrical List. Post free on application.

Roulette, Watches, Boards and Accessories.

New Watch Roulette.
Nickel-plated. With Spring.
Price .. **5½d.**
Post 3d.

Superior ditto in Oxydised Steel Case, Spring movement.
Price .. **3/6**
Post 3d.

No more Cheating at Dice!

Watch Race Game.
With fly-back movement, horses painted on dial.
Price **3/11**
Post 2d.

The Dice Watch prevents it.
Price
5½d. & 2/3
Postage 2d.

Crown and Anchor, ditto, **2/3**
Postage 2d.

Roulette Watch

This Roulette Watch works on the same system and principle as the large Roulette Games with a small spinning ball.

Price .. **2/6**

Postage 2d.

Roulette Boards.
Superior quality, best French pattern.

8½	10	12	13½
10 6	**13 6**	**17 6**	**23 6**

Carriage paid over 10/-

Roulette Cloths, painted on green American cloth.
Single, 24 by 18 in., **1/-** .. 30 by 22 in. **1/9**
Double, 56 by 22 ,, **2/6** .. 72 ,, 26 ,, **4 6**
Postage 3d.

Best French Green Melton Cloths with printed figures. 72 by 19½, **8 6** 77 by 20, **10 6**
93 by 27, **12/6** each.
Single ditto. Small, **3 9** Large, **6 3**
Roulette Rules, 3d. Postage 1d.
Roulette Balls, 4d. **6d.** and **8d.** Postage 1d.
Croupier Rakes, Plain, polished black .. **1/6**
Inlaid ivory **2/6**
Superior quality French make **3/6** & **5/-** Post 4d.

The fairest, cleverest, simplest and most fascinating game of chance ever invented.
Played with pack of cards and Twirlette. **5/6** Post free.

Baccaratte Accessories.

Sabots or Slippers, best French make with ball-bearing block, **45/-**
Cloths, &c., to Order only.

Bone Checks.

1d.	2d.	3d.	4d.	6d.	1/-

18/- per gross.

Roulette Boards.
Polished wood. Fancy coloured disc.
No. G. 1 **6½d.** No. G. 2 **1/-** Post 3d.
As illust. Ordinary quality, best black finish
7 in., **3/-** 8 in., **3/9** 9½ in., **5 3**
Nickel mountings and zinc bottom—

10½	12	13½	17½	19 in.
10/6	**15/6**	**21/-**	**37/6**	**45/-**

Carriage paid over 10/-

Crown and Anchor Game.
Cloths .. 18 by 18, **2/6** 18 by 27, **3 6**
27 by 27, **4/6** Post 3d.
Dice .. .. .. **6d.** and **9d.** each.
Dice Cups .. **1/-** and **1/6** each. Post 2d.

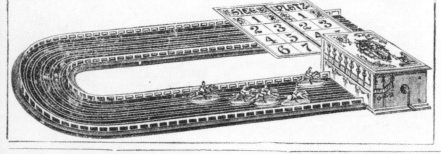

"Derbygo."

The only realistic mechanical Horse Racing Game existing. Instructions for use.
The racing cloth is spread on a table at least 6 ft. 6 in. in length, after which the apparatus is placed to the right end of it, the crank handle in front. Open the box and give the crank handle two or three turns to the left, then place the horses in position at the other end of the cloth.
The box may now be closed again.
The racing game is worked by turning the handle to the right.
The race is over as soon as the base of the first horse touches the box.
5 Horses with cloth, **25/6** 7 do., **32/6** 10 do., **45/-**
Straight Wood Track. 5 Horses, **42/-**
Circular Track as illustrated **50/-** Carriage paid

GAMAGE'S
TABLE TENNIS

Interest in this old famous Game is being revived.

TABLE TENNIS.

No. G. 1. Containing 2 wood bats, 1 pair strong clamps, net and 3 balls in box. **2/3**
No. G. 2. Superior bats and fittings 6 balls .. **3/3**
No. G. 3. With projecting iron clamps and 6 balls **4/6**
Superior qualities at **6/11 7/6 10/6** and **14/6**
Carriage extra under 10/-
Table Tennis Nets. 6d. and 9d. each. Post 2d.
Wood Table Tennis Bats.
Plain Wood, **4½d.** and **6½** each. Superior do. **10½d.** each.
Cork Faced, single side, **1/3** ,, Cork Faced, on both sides, **1 6** ,,
Rubber Faced, **2 6** each.
Table Tennis Balls. Best quality **10d.** and **1/-** per doz.
9 by 5 ft. Table Tops.
Painted and Lined, **25/-** each. Trestles for do., **2 9** each.
Carriage extra.

LATEST TABLE GAMES.

Snap Shots.
Historical and Geographical.
Price **9d.**
Post **3d.**

Solitaire Boards and Marbles, in Box complete.
9d.
Post 3d.

An interesting game for Sunday Play.
Price **9d.**
Postage 3d.

Price **9d.**   Postage 3d.

The Game of
Aerial Contest or Flight.

The up-to-date Aeroplane Game, in whic all ncidents of a flight in an Aeroplane are thought out. A very amusing game for 2 to 6 players.

| Price | .. | .. | **4½d.** and | **9d.** |
| Postage | .. | .. | 3d. | 3d. |

Midget Golf.
In which all the special features of the outdoor game are introduced.   Price   **1/9** each.
Superior quality   **3/6**   Post 4d.
Do. with Metal Clubs, etc. **5 3**   ,,

British Empire. This Game has a decided educational basis, as it familiarises the players with the positions of the various British possessions and their products
Price   ..   **9d** and **1/9**

Trip to the Continent.—The Players start from London per rail by varying routes to the coast where steamers are used to ply the channel, the trains being requisitioned again a d the trip continued to Berlin passing through Paris and other towns *en route*. Views of the various towns visited are given on the board.
Price   **4½d.** and **9d.**   Post 3d.

A game full of fun and interest.   All the joys of a moto ride condensed into a game.
Price 4½d. 9'. **2/3** and **4/6**   Post 3d & 4d

Card House.—The Game which will never die
Price   ..   ..   **9d**   Post 3d.

Egg and Spoon.—A rollicking game. Nothing slow or tedious about this.   Fun all the time.   Price **9d.**   Postage 3d.

Planchette.   What does Planchette say?
Polished board with brass mounts, including pamphlet the game. It answers every question put by the player which have in many instances come perfectly true.
Price **9d** **1/4½** **1/9** **2/6** **3/6**   Postage 3d.

This is a board game of unusual interest and contains many novel features.   The trains call at stations, pick up and put down passengers. Flags have to be exhibited at various signal boxes to prevent collisions.
Price .. **4½d.** **9d.** **1/9**   Post 3d. and 4d.

An Instructive Game for Sunday Play.
Price   ..   **9d**
Post 2d.

LATEST GAMES.

Lotto or House.

No. 400.

4½d.   9d.

1/9 and 2/6

New Edition in polished box, superior fittings.

3/6

Post 3d. & 4d.

CUEPING

A NEW & FASCINATING GAME OF SKILL.

A capital game for winter evenings.
Complete with cue, plain and coloured posts, ball and rules in box.   Price **2/-**   Postage 4d.

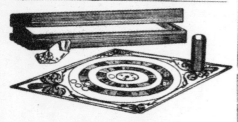

Four Corners.

An Ideal Game for Dull Evenings.

For 2 or 4 players.   Price **9d.**   Post 3d.

Blow Football.

Rare Fun for Evening Parties.

Price **4½d. 9d. 1/9 & 3/3**   With bellows **3/11**
Post 3d.   3d.   4d.   4d.   4d.

Word Making.   The old familiar Game.
Price **4½d. 9d. 1/3**   Postage 3d.

Extra large, **2/6**   Postage 4d.

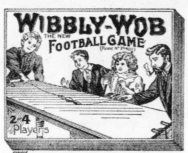

2-4 Players

**Gamage's Patent Game—
"Wibbly-Wob"
or Parlour Football.**

Every Footballer or lover of the Game should have one. It gives as much amusement to the lookers on as to the players.
Endless amusement combined with science.

"Wibbly-Wob." (Registered Name).

No. 0.   Special for 2 players **1/-**
 ,, 1.   For 2 Players **1/6**
 ,, 2.   For 4 Players **2/6**
Postage 3d.
Superior quality, wire goal nets.
Packed in strong box.

No. 3.   For 2 Players **5/-**
 ,, 4.   For 4 Players **6/-**
Extras— Strikers **6d.** each.   Balls **2d.** each.
Postage 3d.

THE NEW FOOTBALL GAME OF KICK

Prices :

9d.   1/9

3/6 & 7/3

Post 3d.,

4d. & 6d.

Kick.

Latest and Best of all Football Games, each one complete with metal figures which kick the ball.

MADE IN ENGLAND **THE NEW GAME OF** PATENTED
SOCKER
OR ASSOCIATION PARLOUR FOOTBALL

An Exciting Game of Skill played in accordance with the Rules issued by the Football Association Real Passing, Kicking, Dribbling, Throwing in and Goal Defending

1/- 3/- OR 2/6

Manufactured by D A Cº LONDON

Socker.   Price 9d. and 2/3
Larger size with full teams, **3/11** Post 3d. 4d. 5d.

Scramble Jack

Scramble Jack.

A Jolly Game for 4 players.

Complete with beans, pockets and gatherers.

Price .. **9d.**

Post 3d.

HALMA.

No. 1.   Board and Men for 4 players   ..   **9d.**
 ,, 2.   Leatherette ditto **1/4½**
 ,, 3.   Cloth-covered Board and box to
match **1/9**
 ,, 6.   Ditto **3/3**
Postage 3d.

All the Fun of the **MOTOR RIDE**

A Jolly Game.

The Great Game of Motor Tour or Motor Ride.

A grand Motoring Game full of exciting incidents.
Price **4½d. & 9d.**   Postage 3d.

THE NEW GAME OF **RETRIEVE**

One of the Novelties of the season. By a novel arrangement the dogs are made to go along the table and bring back a stick in their mouths.
Price **9d.** and **1/9**   Post 3d.

Stepping Stones.   (Registered.)

This is an amusing game which the spectators enjoy the most. It is difficult to balance a ball on a platter it is not easy to walk over stepping stones, but when both are attempted at the same time a steady hand as well as ready confidence and determination are needed. The game may be played in the drawing room or nursery or upon the lawn.

Price .. **5/-**   Carr. extra.

Latest Table Games.

NEW STANDARD INDOOR GAME.

A novel and interesting Railway Race Game.

Price **4½**d. **9**d. and **1/9**

Post 3d. and 4d.

"*BATTLE*"

EXCITING WAR GAME.

Played by 2 or 4 persons, by pieces representing Generals, Cavalry, Guns, Infantry and Ammunition, on a battlefield

| The Season's Craze. Endless combinations and problems. Supersedes Chess, Draughts and Cards. | **2/6** Or 2/10 post free | Military and Social Clubs and Cafes, wishing to be up-to-date, should immediately introduce it. —*Vide Daily Press* |

Holo. (Registered). Here is a game at once fast and furious. The players bend their energies and their backs to secure a goal. The excitement from start to finish is intense, as one cannot be certain till the very end that the game is lost or won. Price **3/3** Post 4d.

A novel and up-to-date game. For 2 or 4 players.
Price **9**d.   Post 3d.

An ingenious puzzle. **4½**d. Post 2d.

The Old Game of Tiddley Winks made very interesting with the Model of a Battleship.

The scoring being taken from the different part on which the shots land   Price .. **9**d. & **2/-**   Post 3d.

Aladdin.

A fascinating children's game, based on the old fairy tale and exquisitely carried out. Each player takes a magic lamp and the lucky one wins his way to fortune and marries the Princess.

Price.		Post
4½d.	..	3d.
9d.	..	3d.
1/9	..	4d.
3/6	..	5d.

Tapette.   A new and novel game of skill for 2 or 4 players.
Price **3/6** and **7/6**   Carriage paid.

This game consists of an egg box or "roost" in which there are a series of holes or "nests" a number of imitation eggs, and small spoons or "shovels." The game may be arranged for either two or more players, who, in the latter case, take sides. The players endeavour to pick up the eggs with their flat spoons and drop them into their respective nests—a task requiring considerable skill and creating endless amusement.

Price, for 2 or 4 players, **9**d. and **1/9**   Post 3d. and 4d.

E2 ..